WORLD IN CHANGE

W. E. Marsden
School of Education,
University of Liverpool

V. M. Marsden
Greenbank High School,
Southport

Maps and diagrams by Tim Smith, David Gardiner and Bill Wallace

Oliver & Boyd

Acknowledgements

The publishers thank the following for permission to reproduce photographs:

Aerial Photos International Inc., Boston: 11.3; Aerofilms: Plates 1.2, 4.7, 10.9, 16.5, 16.10, 16.16; Air Pollution Control Authority of Los Angeles: Plate 16.7; Australian Information Service: Plates 6.7, 6.8, 6.9, 6.10, 6.11, 6.12, 6.13; Barnaby's Picture Library: Plates 5.3, 5.5, 13.12, 14.9; J. Bathurst: Plate 5.6; R. G. C. Bathurst: Plate 2.9, 5.1, 10.1; BMW, Munich: Plate 13.6; Gunnar Bergbom: Plate 3.12; Braniff International: Plate 12.12; BBC Hulton Picture Library: Plates 3.9, 3.10, 7.5, 8.10, 11.1; British German Trade: Plate 13.5; British Petroleum: Plates 3.4, 3.5, 3.6; Camera Press: Plates 1.3; 5.2 (Daniel Blatt); 5.11, 5.12 (Werner Braun); 7.9 (Marcos Santilli); 7.10 (P. Villiers leMoy); 7.11 (Marcos Santilli); 8.7 (Paul Harrison); 8.13 (Freddie Mansfield); 11.8; J. Allan Cash: Plates 8.6, 9.4, 9.5; Central Office of Information (Crown copyright reserved): Plates 1.12, 1.13; Centre for World Development Education: Plate 15.10; Compix: Plates 6.2, 6.3, 7.6; Consulate General of FDR, Liverpool: Plate 13.11; Council for World Missions (John Crocker): Plate 15.16; Christian Aid: Plates 4.5, 6.4, 6.5 (Margaret Murray); 14.6, 15.6, 15.7 (Margaret Murray); 15.8, 15.9, 15.17, 16.13 (Margaret Murray); Dallas–Fort Worth Airport Authority: Plate 12.13; Danish Agricultural Producers: Plates 10.2, 10.3, 10.5; Danish Tourist Board: Plates 10.4, 12.3, 12.5; Desert Locust Survey: Plate 15.3; Fairchild Camera and Instrument Corporation: Plates 11.11, 11.12; S. Ferguson: Plate 8.9; FAO: Plates 15.2, 16.11, 16.12; Fox Photos: Plates 8.11, 8.12; R. Geipel: Plates 1.5, 16.20; Alan Hutchinson: Plate 6.1; Information and Documentation Centre for the Geography of the Netherlands: Plates 10.6 (Aero-photo, Nederland, Amsterdam); 10.7 (KLM Aerocarto, Schipol); 13.13 (Dienst Ruimtelijke Ordening, Amsterdam); 13.14 (Articapress, Haarlem); 13.15 (Bart Hofmeester, Rotterdam); 13.16 (Aerophoto, Schipol); International Defence and Aid Fund: Plates 2.7b (Tony McGrath), 14.10, 14.11, 14.12, 14.13; International Labour Office: Plates 2.5, 4.1; International Photobank: Plates 4.6, 9.6, 9.7, 16.14; Internationes, Bonn: Plates 12.6, 12.9; Japan Information Centre, London: Plates 8.14, 16.17; Keystone Press Agency: Plates 2.7a, 3.7, 3.8, 3.11, 5.4, 7.8, 8.3, 8.8, 12.10; Kuwait, Ministry of Information: Plates 5.8, 5.9, 5.10; LKAB, Sweden (Börje Rönnberg): Plate 3.13; Mansell Collection: Plates 11.9, 14.2, 15.13; Marion and Tony Morrison: Plates 4.2, 7.12, 7.13, 14.7; W. E. Marsden: Plates 2.2, 4.8, 4.9, 4.10, 13.4, 13.7, 13.8, 13.9; New Zealand High Commission: Plate 1.14; Novosti Press Agency: Plates 3.1, 3.14, 3.15, 10.11, 10.12, 10.13, 11.5, 11.6, 12.1, 12.2; H. Perry: Plate 16.3; R. J. Pipes: Plate 16.19; Popperfoto: Plates 1.4, 1.9, 1.10, 2.3, 2.6, 4.4, 7.1, 7.2, 7.3, 7.4, 8.1, 8.4, 8.5, 9.1, 9.2, 10.8, 11.4, 13.10, 14.5, 15.14, 16.2, 16.6; Port of Antwerp Promotion Association: Plates 13.1, 13.2, 13.3; Publifoto, Rome: Plate 12.11; Royal Norwegian Embassy: Plate 3.2; Save The Children: Plate 15.1; Society for Cultural Relations with the USSR: Plates 3.3, 11.7; Space Frontiers: Plate 1.7; Swiss National Tourist Office: Plates 12.4, 12.7, 12.8; Syndication International: Plates 10.10, 16.9; John Topham Picture Library: Plates 1.6, 8.2, 2.1, 11.2; UNESCO: Plate 5.13 (Daniel Franck): UNEP/Brüel and Kjael: Plate 16.8; UNICEF: Plates 14.8, 15.11; United Nations: Plates 4.3, 6.6, 7.7, 16.15; United Press International: Plate 2.4; US National Aeronautics and Space Administration: Plate 1.1; United States Travel Service: Plates 1.11, 9.3, 11.11, 12.14, 12.15, 16.18; T. Waltham: Plate 2.8; World Bank: Plate 15.15; World Health Organisation: Plates 5.7 (P. Almasy); 8.2, 14.1, 15.4, 15.5, 15.12, 16.1 (J. Mohr); 16.4; WHO/UNRWA: Plates 14.3, 14.4.

The publishers also thank all those who gave permission to reproduce extracts or tables from their publications (acknowledgement is given beneath each extract in the text). While every effort has been made to trace copyright owners, the publishers apologise for any omissions.

The author wishes to acknowledge the following sources which were used as a basis for some of the figures:

Earthquakes and Volcanoes, Scientific American Publication (Figs 1.1, 1.3, 1.4. 1.5); R. Geipel (Fig 1.6); F. Bullard *Volcanoes of the Earth*, University of Texas Press 1976 (Figs 1.7a, 1.11, 1.13); *National Geographic Magazine* January 1981 (Figs 1.8, 1.9, 1.10); *Geographical Journal* September 1963 (Fig 1.12); J. Dawson & D. Thomas *Man and his World*, Nelson 1975 (Fig 2.2); R. W. Steel 'The Third World: Geography in Practice' in *Geography* July 1974 (Fig 2.3); J. Beaujeau-Garnier *Geography of Population*, Longman (Fig 2.5); G. Trewartha *A Geography of Population: World Patterns*, Wiley 1969 (Fig 2.7); *The State of the World Atlas*, Map 3, Pan Books 1981 (Fig 2.8); E. Forsström 'Malmberget' Cultural Geography Seminar Paper, University of Stockholm (Fig. 3.9); P. Meusburger (Fig. 4.5); *BP Statistical Review* (Figs 5.9, 5.10); K. Atkinson in *Geography* July 1979 (Fig 5.13); M. Senior *Tropical Lands*, Longman 1979 (Fig 6.6); D. C. Harris in *Geography* July 1974 (Fig 7.4); *New Secondary Atlas for Malaysia and Singapore*, Collins-Longman 1981 (Fig 7.6); *Atlas of Japan*, International Society for Educational Information, Tokyo 1974 (Fig 8.7); *Dierke Weltatlas*, Westerman (Figs 8.9, 12.5, 13.4, 13.9, 14.15, 16.3, 16.5); *Wings Holiday Brochure* Summer 1981 (Fig 9.5: inset); T. Randle *Geographical Studies in Western Europe*, Oliver & Boyd 1979 (Fig 10.3); Information and Documentation Centre for the Geography of the Netherlands (IDG) *Bulletin 1977/78* (Fig 10.8); *World Atlas of Wine*, Mitchell Beazley 1971 (Fig 10.10); B. E. Price & E. Tweed *Geographical Studies in North America*, Oliver & Boyd 1979 (Figs 11.5, 16.4); W. Molle, *Regional Disparity and Economic Development in the European Community*, Saxon House, Farnborough 1980 (Fig 12.7); J. Salt & H. Clout *Migration in Post-war Europe*, Oxford University Press 1976 (Fig 12.8); R. E. G. Davis *Airlines of the United States Since 1914*, Putnam 1972 (Figs 12.11, 12.12, 12.14); Dallas–Fort Worth Airport Authority (Fig 12.15); Port of Antwerp Promotion Association (Fig 13.1); R. E. H. Mellor *The Two Germanies*, p. 191, by permission of Harper & Row Ltd (Fig 13.6); RCFP (Fig 13.7); IDG publication *Randstad Holland*, 1980 (Fig 13.11); IDG *Bulletin 1979/80* (Fig 13.12); C. Gibson *Population*, Basil Blackwell 1980 (Fig 14.3); J. Verduin & H. Verduin-Muller (Fig 14.4); World Bank's *World Development Report 1980* (Figs 14.5, 15.2, 15.4, 15.5); W. F. Hornby & M. Jones *An Introduction to Population Geography* (Fig 14.9); P. Lloyd *The 'Young Towns' of Lima*, Cambridge University Press 1980 (Fig 14.13); *World Bank Atlas* (Fig 15.1); J. Whittow *Disasters*, Pelican 1980 (Fig 15.6).

The cover photograph is by Christine Osborne and shows fisherfolk drawing nets on the beach in Fujairah (UAE). Behind is the sheikdom's first high-rise hotel.

Contents

Introduction

The underlying theme throughout this text is that of change and its impact on rural and urban environments in both developed and developing worlds. The aim is to achieve a balance between older and newer approaches to world study. The introductory chapters provide a physical and cultural framework. The following section, dealing with what we like to call 'hostile' environments, has a stronger physical basis, although throughout the book physical geography is used as a means to an end: the study of the interaction of human beings and their environments. At the same time, the physical basis is regarded as essential in providing a firmer foundation on which to build than in many 'world development' texts, and a framework for the economic, social and political case studies which follow. The chapters on the developed world switch to an emphasis on the impact of economic and political factors, and especially the influence of the two major systems, capitalism and communism. An important contention in the book is that political factors, as much as physical and economic, must have a role in any viable account of today's changing world, as must also a strong historical context. The developing world is again approached in a balanced way; it is seen as varied in character, differing markedly in degrees of economic well-being, and indissolubly connected with the developed world. Issues such as the North–South debate, pollution and use of world resources conclude the volume.

Each section is accompanied by sets of exercises, varied in style and designed to test graphicacy, application and problem-solving skills, as well as recall, recognition and comprehension. The text is lavishly illustrated with photographs, maps and diagrams, to which many of the exercises are attached, providing a large selection of data response items of a type increasingly being used in 'O' and CSE level examinations.

SECTION A: *Introduction*
1   The Physical Basis

THE CHANGING STRUCTURE OF THE WORLD

The Collision between India and Asia

Plate 1.1 is a photograph taken from the American Gemini XI spacecraft, flying at a height of almost 750 km above the Indian Ocean. It shows clearly the outline of Sri Lanka and India. The Himalayas are hardly noticeable in the background of the picture, where the earth's curvature forms the horizon.

It seems hard to believe that the earth's continents are in motion. But this is what scientists have recently confirmed. About 150 million years ago, a super-continent, since named *Gondwanaland*, existed in the southern hemisphere. From this, the present land masses of South America, Africa, India, Australia and Antarctica subsequently drifted away. Fig. 1.1 portrays India's northward drift. It has travelled about 7000 km over the last seventy million years: a rate of between 5 and 10 cm per annum.

Plate 1.1   Satellite photograph of India and Sri Lanka

About forty million years ago, India collided with Asia, and attached itself to it, and continued pushing against the crust of that continent. The line of collision is marked by the Himalayan mountains (Plate 1.2), the mightiest range on earth, with peaks rising over 8500 metres (m).

The Earth's Tectonic Plates

'Tectonic' is a term which refers to the structure of the earth's crust and the changes taking place within it. It is now known that the earth's crust is built up of a dozen or so moving plates, which make up its outer shell. These plates do not coincide with the land masses. Some are covered by great oceans, such as the Pacific. They are stable in the middle but unstable round the edges, where different types of movement occur:

(*a*) very slow movement, throwing up the great *fold mountain* ranges such as the Alps and Himalayas, and those surrounding the Pacific Ocean;

(*b*) sudden movement, causing *earthquakes* and *volcanic activity*.

Fold mountains, earthquakes and volcanoes are thus all associated with plate boundaries.

Fig. 1.1 India's northward drift (From Peter Molnar & Paul Tapponnier 'The Collision between India and Eurasia'.

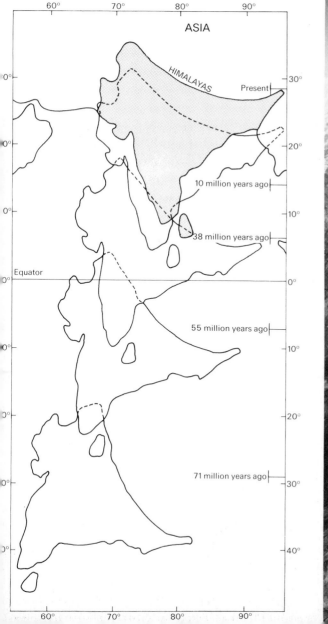

Plate 1.2 The Himalayas

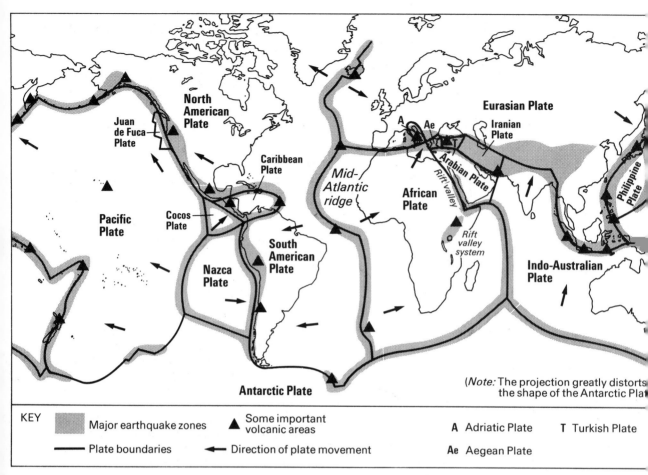

Fig. 1.2   The earth's tectonic plates

Continental Drift

The movement of the tectonic plates explains why continental drift has occurred. First of all, the plates are moving in different directions, as Fig. 1.2 indicates:

   (*a*) the African, Indo-Australian and Pacific Plates are pushing against the stable Eurasian (Europe + Asia) Plate;

   (*b*) the Nazca and South American Plates are colliding with each other;

   (*c*) the Pacific and North American Plates are slipping past each other at different rates;

   (*d*) the Eurasian and North American, and African and South American Plates, are moving apart.

   All these junction zones experience earthquake and volcanic activity and all, except (*d*), are associated with fold mountains. Notice (Fig. 1.2) how the Pacific Plate is almost completely encircled by volcanic and earthquake belts, the so-called circum-Pacific 'ring of fire'.

Geological Features Accompanying Tectonic Movement

Where plates are moving together, *compressional* features occur. Where plates are moving apart, *tensional* features result (Fig. 1.3).

COMPRESSIONAL FEATURES

While separate features can be identified, these often occur together. *Folding* is a form of distortion of the earth's crust, associated with fold mountain building. The enormous pressures occurring result in the crust breaking along *faults*. *Thrusting* takes place when the

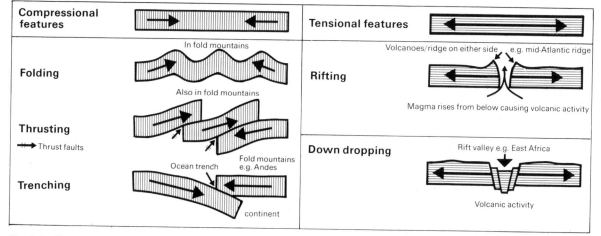

Fig. 1.3 Geological features accompanying tectonic movement

rocks ride over each other. Where one plate slides under another *trenching* occurs, with ocean trenches found where the margin of a continent and a tectonic plates coincide, as off the coast of South America.

TENSIONAL FEATURES

Where the Eurasian and North American and African and South American Plates have drawn apart, a huge series of *rifts* or breaks in the crust of the ocean floor have occurred. These have allowed magma to rise and create ridges on either side of the rift. The *mid-Atlantic ridge* has been produced in this way (Fig. 1.2). This lies mostly below the ocean surface, but in places volcanic activity has led to the formation of islands, such as Tristan da Cunha. Where rifting takes place, the land between the sides of the rift can drop between fault-lines to form a *rift valley*. The largest rift valley system is in East Africa, running north into the Red Sea (Fig. 1.2).

Exercises

1. With the help of an atlas and Fig. 1.2, make a list in two columns, one headed 'Areas liable to severe earthquakes' and the other 'Areas not liable to earthquakes'. Then place each of the following countries in its appropriate column: Alaska; Australia; Brazil; Chile; Finland; Guatemala; Italy; Morocco; northern Canada; New Zealand; Nigeria; Japan.
2. Describe what is meant by a tectonic plate. Explain why earthquake and volcanic activity are concentrated along the boundaries between plates. Give examples of different types of boundary.

EARTHQUAKES

The Guatemala Earthquake of 1976: An Eye-witness Account

The Guatemala earthquake of 4 February 1976 was triggered off by movement along the boundary between the North American and Caribbean Plates (Fig. 1.2). The physical magnitude of the shock was great, about 7.5 on the Richter Scale. Anything over 6 represents a very severe earthquake (see Table 1.1). 22 000 people died as a result of the Guatemalan earthquake. On the next page is a description of the experience by the famous explorer, Thor Heyerdahl, who was in Guatemala City on the night.

Table 1.1 Famous earthquakes of the twentieth century

Year	Area	Country/ state	Richter Magnitude	Number killed
1906	San Francisco	California	8.3	700
1908	Messina	S. Italy	7.5	120 000
1920	Gansu (Kansu)	NW China	8.6	180 000
1923	Tokyo	Japan	8.3	150 000
1960	Agadir	Morocco	5.9	14 000
1963	Skopje	Yugoslavia	6.0	1 200
1964	Anchorage	Alaska	8.6	130
1968	Dasht-e-Bayaz	Iran	7.4	11 600
1970	Chimbote	Peru	7.8	66 000
1971	San Fernando	California	6.5	65
1972	Managua	Nicaragua	6.2	5 000
1976	Guatemala City	Guatemala	7.5	22 000
1976	Friuli	N. Italy	6.5 nearly	1 000
1976	Tangshan	N. China	7.6 c.	650 000
1977	Bucharest	Romania	7.2	2 000

I was roused from my sleep at 3.05 a.m. by a faint tremor: 'an earthquake somewhere,' I thought. As the tremor grew, I told myself I must be dreaming. I could see nothing. But when the bed began shaking violently, I realised I was most definitely awake, and that if the shaking did not soon subside, the whole building might be seriously damaged. The jolting did not stop; it grew worse and worse.

Suddenly there was a tremendous roar, as though a lot of railway trains were rattling and rumbling through the darkness of the room. A fine cloud of plaster began to fall from the ceiling. The noise and jolting grew worse and I began to feel afraid. The whole building shook, my bed jumped up and down, and the noise was deafening; it was worse than a thousand thunderclaps – like being in a house struck by lightning. The bed danced about as if possessed and bits of brick and plaster rained down.

The outside wall yawned open and disappeared into the night (though I was unaware of it in the dark), and lathes and beams and great chunks of ceiling began to fall all about me. I turned over onto my stomach, prepared at any moment to be pitched face first into the void. When the first heavy pieces of masonry and woodwork landed across my legs, and the shaking and jolting and din were at their height, I thought the end of the world had come.

Gradually the tumult began to die down. The air was thick with dust, and I and my bed were buried in masonry and plaster. In inky blackness I fumbled about on the bedside table where I had a torch; the table was now deep in debris. I leapt out of bed, grabbed my shoes and tried to pull them on, but they were full of rubble. I snatched my clothes from a chair and the bag in which I kept my money and passport. Naked as I was, I picked my way to the door, which was gaping open, and made for the stairs.

. . .

The street was as black as everywhere else, not a glimmer of light in that vast city. Nearby walls had collapsed and I had to negotiate piles of rubble. . . . I could not see a soul in the blackness. There were fresh tremors at intervals, so I searched with my torch for somewhere in the middle of the street where there were no tall buildings threatening to collapse. . .

Another series of tremors . . . but none was as nerve-shattering as the first. The skyscrapers opposite my hotel suddenly began to disgorge a stream of people, some clutching lighted candles.

The quake's roar, intensified by the sound of thousands of falling walls and roofs, had now died away, and all I could hear was the incessant clamour of burglar alarms set off when doors and windows were ripped away . . . .
(from *The Sunday Times* 22 February 1976, by permission of Thor Heyerdahl)

The San Francisco Earthquake of 1906

The margins of crustal plates are marked by *faults*, and movement along these margins strains the rocks in the area. When this strain becomes greater than the friction which bonds the rocks together, a break takes place along the line of the fault. The rocks slip rapidly and rebound back into position. The energy released sets up waves which 'shake the ground'. The point of break on the fault is the focus or *hypocentre*, and the place above this at the surface is known as the *epicentre*. The shock waves travel out from the focus and decrease in intensity the further they go. Lines joining places where an equal intensity of shock is felt are known as *isoseismal lines* (Fig. 1.4).

The epicentre of the San Francisco earthquake was a few kilometres from the Golden Gate Bridge (Fig. 1.5), on the line of the San Andreas fault (see Fig. 1.10a), the fault along which the Pacific and North American Plates are slipping past each other. The break spread north and south along the fault. The earthquake struck San Francisco at 5.15 in the morning. Its aftermath is shown on Plate 1.3. Many buildings were demolished or severely damaged by the shock, and water and gas pipes severed. The extensive scale of the damage shown on the picture was largely caused by fires which raged the city centre for three days. Leaking gas caused the fires and, because of the broken water pipes, there was no water to put them out.

The Richter scale measures the actual physical magnitude of an earthquake shock. The Modified Mercalli scale (Table 1.2) registers the intensity of the shock as felt or noticed by people. Fig. 1.5 shows the isoseismal contours recorded after the San Francisco (1906) and San Fernando (1971) earthquakes. San Francisco was a much larger earthquake, but even in the San Fernando, the Modified Mercalli intensities of VII and more were registered over a small area, resulting, among other things, in the collapse of a motorway overpass. The damage in the San Francisco earthquake occurred over a much larger elongated zone, running along the San Andreas fault. The San Andreas fault remains in a high state of tension, and its release could create havoc in one or both of two of the richest cities on earth, San Francisco and Los Angeles.

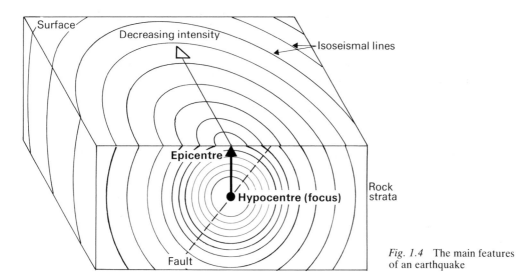

Surface

Decreasing intensity

Isoseismal lines

Epicentre

Hypocentre (focus)

Fault

Rock strata

Fig. 1.4 The main features of an earthquake

Table 1.2   Modified Mercalli intensity scale of earthquakes

I Not felt. Marginal and long-period effects of large earthquakes.

II Felt by persons at rest, on upper floors, or favourably placed.

III Felt indoors. Hanging objects swing. Vibration like passing of light trucks. Duration estimated. May not be recognized as an earthquake.

IV Hanging objects swing. Vibration like passing of heavy trucks, or sensation of a jolt like a heavy ball striking the walls. Standing motor cars rock. Windows, dishes, doors rattle. Glasses clink. Crockery clashes.

V Felt outdoors; direction estimated. Sleepers wakened. Liquids disturbed, some spilled. Small unstable objects displaced or upset. Doors swing, close, open. Shutters, pictures move. Pendulum clocks stop, start, change rate.

VI Felt by all. Many frightened and run outdoors. Persons walk unsteadily. Windows, dishes, glassware broken. Knickknacks, books, etc., off shelves. Pictures off walls. Furniture moved or overturned. Weak plaster and masonry D cracked. Small bells ring (church, school). Trees, bushes shaken visibly, or heard to rustle.

VII Difficult to stand. Noticed by drivers of motor cars. Hanging objects quiver. Furniture broken. Damage to masonry D, including cracks. Weak chimneys broken at roof line. Fall of plaster, loose bricks, stones, tiles, cornices, also unbraced parapets and architectural ornaments. Some cracks in masonry C. Waves on ponds; water turbid with mud. Small slides and caving in along sand or gravel banks. Large bells ring. Concrete irrigation ditches damaged.

VIII Steering of motor cars affected. Damage to masonry C; partial collapse. Some damage to masonry B; none to masonry A. Fall of stucco and some masonry walls. Twisting, fall of chimneys, factory stacks, monuments, towers, elevated tanks. Frame houses moved on foundations if not bolted down; loose panel walls thrown out. Decayed piling broken off. Branches broken from trees. Changes in flow or temperature of springs and wells. Cracks in wet ground and on steep slopes.

IX General panic. Masonry D destroyed; masonry C heavily damaged, sometimes with complete collapse; masonry B seriously damaged. General damage to foundations. Frame structures, if not bolted, shifted off foundations. Frames racked. Serious damage to reservoirs. Underground pipes broken. Conspicuous cracks in ground. In alluviated areas sand and mud ejected, earthquake fountains, sand craters.

X Most masonry and frame structures destroyed with their foundations. Some well-built wooden structures and bridges destroyed. Serious damage to dams, dikes, embankments. Large landslides. Water thrown on banks of canals, rivers, lakes, etc. Sand and mud shifted horizontally on beaches and flat land. Rails bent slightly.

XI Rails bent greatly. Underground pipelines completely out of service.

XII Damage nearly total. Large rock masses displaced. Lines of sight and level distorted. Objects thrown into the air.

MASONRY CATEGORIES

Masonry A. Good workmanship, mortar, and design; reinforced, especially laterally, and bound together by using steel, concrete, etc.; designed to resist lateral forces.

Masonry B. Good workmanship and mortar; reinforced, but not designed detail to resist lateral forces.

Masonry C. Ordinary workmanship and mortar; no extreme weaknesses like failing to tie in at corners, but neither reinforced nor designed against horizontal forces.

Masonry D. Weak materials, such as adobe; poor mortar; low standards of workmanship, weak horizontally.

(from M. Bradshaw *The Earth: Past, Present and Future*, Hodder & Stoughton 1980)

Plate 1.3 The San Francisco earthquake, 1906

Fig. 1.5 The San Francisco and San Fernando earthquakes

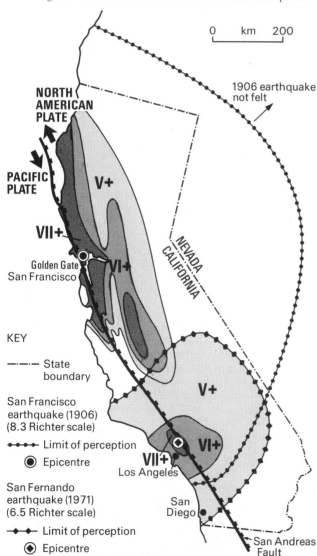

0   km   200

1906 earthquake
not felt

NORTH
AMERICAN
PLATE

PACIFIC
PLATE

V+

VII+

Golden Gate
San Francisco

VI+

NEVADA
CALIFORNIA

KEY

—·—·— State
boundary

San Francisco
earthquake (1906)
(8.3 Richter scale)

●–●–● Limit of perception

◉ Epicentre

V+

VI+

VII+
Los Angeles

San Francisco
earthquake (1971)

San Fernando
earthquake (1971)
(6.5 Richter scale)

◆–◆–◆ Limit of perception

◉ Epicentre

San
Diego

San Andreas
Fault

Roman numerals indicate Modified Mercalli scale (Table 1.2)

The Friuli Earthquake of 1976

In 1976 a disastrous earthquake struck the Friuli province in the Alpine area of Italy. This is the area of the boundary between the Adriatic and Eurasian Plates, where tension is continually caused by the northward push of the African Plate (Fig. 1.2). Forty-one out of 119 communities in the region were destroyed and forty-five others severely damaged (Fig. 1.6). The upland town of Gemona (Plate 1.4) was totally wrecked, with every building demolished or rendered too dangerous to use again.

Fig. 1.6 The Friuli earthquake, 1976

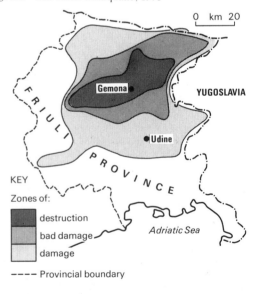

0   km   20

F R I U L I

Gemona

YUGOSLAVIA

Udine

P R O V I N C E

Adriatic Sea

KEY

Zones of:

destruction

bad damage

damage

—–—–— Provincial boundary

Plate 1.4 The devastation of Gemona (Friuli earthquake, 1976)

One of the factors that made this a worse disaster than it might have been was the structure of the houses, made up of large blocks of coarse masonry, poorly mortared together (category D on Table 1.2). The earthquake caused the walls to cave outwards. The narrow streets of the hill towns and villages were a death trap as people ran out of their houses when the tremors occurred. Nearly 1000 were killed, 2000 injured and thousands left homeless. 32 000 people were evacuated to resorts on the Adriatic coast (Fig. 1.6), where hotels and apartments were fortunately empty in the out-of-season period. Meanwhile. in Friuli province, prefabricated houses were built, often in monotonous lines, to form 'barraccopolises' or barrack towns. Plate 1.5 shows such a settlement, with the ruins of Gemona in the background of the picture. One year after the earthquake, over 65 000 people were still housed in prefabricated buildings.

Exercises

3. Refer to Tables 1.1 and 1.2.
   (*a*) Find out why the Chinese and Japanese earthquakes were accompanied by such an enormous loss of life. (Think of the magnitude of the shock, population density, building materials, etc.)
   (*b*) Why had the exceptionally strong Chilean and Alaskan earthquakes so little loss of life in comparison?
4. Refer to Table 1.2 and Fig. 1.5. What might you have felt or noticed had you been living in

   (*a*) San Francisco during the San Francisco earthquake;
   (*b*) Nevada during the San Francisco earthquake;
   (*c*) Los Angeles during the San Fernando earthquake;
   (*d*) San Diego during the San Fernando earthquake.
5. Refer to Plates 1.3 and 1.4. Describe and try to give reasons for the differences in the damage and problems caused by the San Francisco and Gemona earthquakes. What basic cause had they in common?

Plate 1.5 Barraccopolis near Gemona.

Plate 1.6 Mount St Helens before the 1980 eruption

VOLCANOES

Mount St Helens, 1980

Plate 1.6 shows Mount St Helens in the Cascade range of the north-western United States (Fig. 1.10*a*). Its perfect symmetrical shape rivalled that of Fujiyama in Japan. One American writer described it as 'a mountain in praise of mountains'. But its beauty was deceptive. In May 1980 it 'blew its top', in the most spectacular blast of the twentieth century (Plate 1.7), generating energy equivalent to about 500 atomic bombs.

Mount St Helens is an example of a *composite cone*, a type of volcano made up of layers of lava and volcanic ash, laid down in previous eruptions. In an eruption, molten material, *magma*, rises from the earth's interior (Fig. 1.7*a*). Lava and/or ash is ejected. The lava tends to flow slowly and cools in successive layers to form steep-sided cones. In this type of eruption it tends to be viscous (sticky), which is why it flows slowly, and when it solidifies it quickly plugs the vent. Both the volcanic pipe or vent, and side vents through which earlier magma emerged, may be stopped up by a plug of solidified magma. Later eruptions are often especially violent when this plug of older material has to be broken through.

Other types of lava are more fluid and flow more quickly. These form *shield volcanoes*, of more gentle slope (Fig. 1.7*b*), characteristic of Hawaii. In other cases, the magma rises not up a vent but along a fissure. As a result, the lava flows in a broad stream

Plate 1.7 The eruption of Mount St Helens in May 1980

14

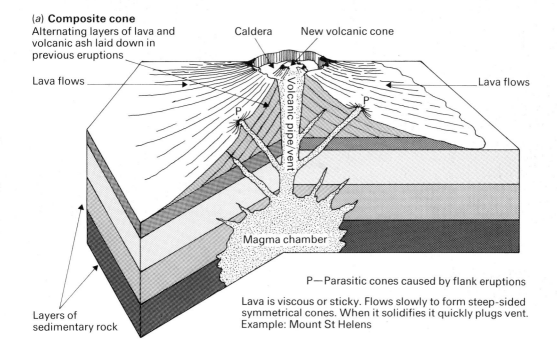

(a) Composite cone

Alternating layers of lava and volcanic ash laid down in previous eruptions

Caldera

New volcanic cone

Lava flows

Lava flows

Volcanic pipe/vent

P

P

Magma chamber

Layers of sedimentary rock

P—Parasitic cones caused by flank eruptions

Lava is viscous or sticky. Flows slowly to form steep-sided symmetrical cones. When it solidifies it quickly plugs vent. Example: Mount St Helens

(b) A shield volcano
Lava is more fluid and flows more quickly so spreads out to form gentle slopes. Example: Hawaii

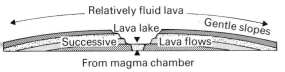

Relatively fluid lava

Lava lake

Gentle slopes

Successive

Lava flows

From magma chamber

Fig. 1.7 Different kinds of volcano

(c) Fissure eruptions
Magma rises up through fissure-crack rather than a vent so the lava flows in a broad stream over the landscape to form a plateau. Example: Iceland.
Fissure eruptions Newest Middle Oldest

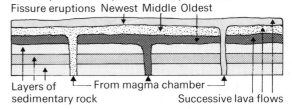

Layers of sedimentary rock

From magma chamber

Successive lava flows

over the landscape to form a plateau (Fig. 1.7c). *Fissure eruptions* of this type are found in Iceland.

To return to Mount St Helens: inactive since 1857, its perfect cone was damaged by explosions, forming craters, in March and April 1980 (Fig. 1.8a). Huge cracks appeared in the summit snowfield, ash and steam were ejected, and minor earthquakes indicated that molten rock was forcing its way upwards inside the mountain. By the end of April, a bulge had appeared on the north slope of the mountain (Fig. 1.8a). At 8.32.37 a.m. on 18 May, a force 5 earthquake 'broke the bulge', causing a huge landslide (Fig. 1.8b). Within fifteen more seconds, the north

slope of the mountain had burst asunder (Fig. 1.8c and Plate 1.7). The following were the consequences:
(1) the top 350 m of the mountain disintegrated (see Plate 1.10);
(2) a shock wave and hurricane force wind flattened trees, leaving them lying like matchsticks, pointing in the direction of the wind, swept away 250 km² of forest and caused a zone of destruction which extended for 25 km from the volcano (Fig. 1.9);
(3) the shock wave was followed by a towering wall of steam, gas, ash and pulverised rock debris, killing everything in its path, including over sixty people and untold numbers of wild-life;

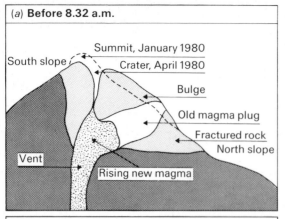

(a) **Before 8.32 a.m.**

South slope
Summit, January 1980
Crater, April 1980
Bulge
Old magma plug
Fractured rock
North slope
Vent
Rising new magma

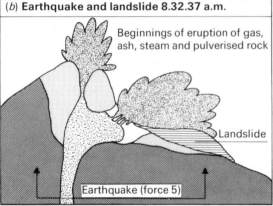

(b) **Earthquake and landslide 8.32.37 a.m.**

Beginnings of eruption of gas, ash, steam and pulverised rock
Landslide
Earthquake (force 5)

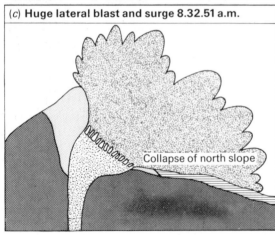

(c) **Huge lateral blast and surge 8.32.51 a.m.**

Collapse of north slope

Fig. 1.8 East–west section across Mount St Helens, 18 May 1980

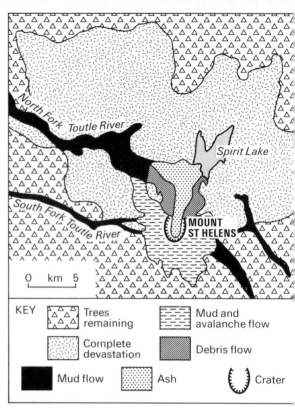

North Fork Toutle River
Spirit Lake
South Fork Toutle River
MOUNT ST HELENS

0   km   5

KEY

Trees remaining

Complete devastation

Mud flow

Mud and avalanche flow

Debris flow

Ash

Crater

Fig. 1.9 The destruction caused by the eruption of Mount St Helens

(4) the heat led to snow and ice melting, causing flash flooding and huge mud flows, which blocked lakes and valleys with trees, destroyed logging camps, such as that shown on Plate 1.8 on the North Fork Toutle River, roads and bridges, and reached 50 km from the mountain;

(5) a volcanic ash cloud rose high in the sky, and fine ash fell over the state of Washington for fifteen hours.

Day was turned to night, and the people of such towns as Yakima had to wear masks to avoid choking in the dusty air (Plate 1.9);

(6) finer ash was thrown high into the atmosphere, and was carried east; it crossed the USA in about three days, and circled the globe in about seventeen, causing spectacular sunsets;

(7) an attractive National Forest area was reduced to a grey, sulphurous wasteland;

(8) fears were expressed that Mount St Helens could go on erupting over a long period of time, and might signal renewed activity in the Cascades as a whole. In fact it erupted again on a smaller scale in July 1980, as Plate 1.10 illustrates, in a much smaller outburst. Notice the gaping northern slope of the volcano. Mount Hood (Fig. 1.10a) can be seen in the background.

Fig. 1.10a shows the series of volcanic peaks which form the Cascade range. They are related to crustal disturbance where a small ocean plate, the Juan de Fuca, is being drawn below the North American Plate as part of the trenching process discussed earlier (see Fig. 1.3). Magma chambers develop in the subduction zone (Fig. 1.10b) and it is these which feed the Cascade volcanoes.

16

Plate 1.8   The devastation of a logging camp caused by the eruption of Mount St Helens

Plate 1.9   Volcanic ash falling on the town of Yakima. Washington State, after the eruption of Mount St Helens

Plate 1.10   The eruption of Mount St Helens in July 1980

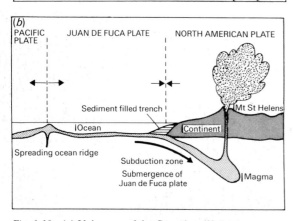

A much greater eruption than Mount St Helens must have occurred some 6500 years ago when the former Mount Mazama 'blew its top'. As a result, a massive crater or *caldera* was left (see Fig. 1.7*a*). When the vent was plugged, a caldera lake formed (Fig. 1.11*b*). Fig. 1.11*a* is an attempt to recreate the former outline of Mount Mazama and Fig. 1.11*b* shows its present form. The crater lake contains a small island, Wizard Island, the cone of a small later eruption (Plate 1.11). Crater Lake is now the location of a National Park.

Fig. 1.11   Mount Mazama and Crater Lake, Oregon

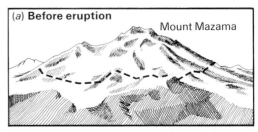

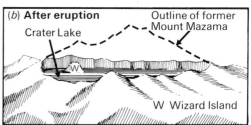

Plate 1.11   Crater Lake, Oregon

Fig. 1.10   (*a*) Volcanoes of the Cascades. (*b*) Section across Juan de Fuca plate and Mount St Helens

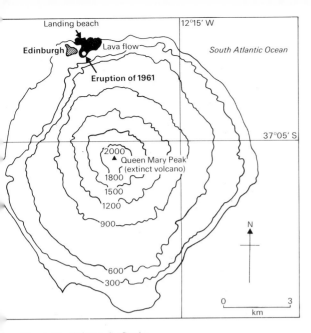

Fig. 1.12 Tristan da Cunha

Plate 1.12 Tristan da Cunha

Tristan da Cunha, 1961

Tristan da Cunha is a tiny remote island in the South Atlantic, made up of an ancient composite volcano of almost perfect conical shape. It rises 2000 m above sea level (Fig. 1.12), but no less than 6000 m from the mid-Atlantic ridge on which it stands (Fig. 1.2). The slope of the volcano is concave but is cut off round most of the island by steep cliffs (Plate 1.12). Many radial dykes (see Fig. 1.7*a*), occur on the slopes of the volcano, and it was from one of these that the 1961 eruption, an example of a *flank eruption*, occurred.

Cliffs do not reach the coast on the north-west side of the island and here the settlement, named Edinburgh, is located. On this low plateau-like area the 250 or so inhabitants depended for their living on fields of potatoes, and on the export of crayfish to South Africa. Plate 1.12 shows the site of Edinburgh on the level bench on the right of the photograph.

From August 1961 tremors were felt near the settlement, and early in October cracks appeared in the ground, followed by an incandescent glow. This was followed by the appearance of a cone of dark sticky lava, only 275 m east of Edinburgh. This spread to the coast (Fig. 1.12) and overwhelmed the crayfish factory and landing beach (Plate 1.13). In addition, dangerous rock falls occurred in the cliffs behind the settlement.

Although a minute eruption by world standards, it was a disaster for the local inhabitants, with their one export industry and their one landing beach destroyed. It was thought that the settlement might also be threatened, and the islanders were evacuated by ship, first to South Africa, and then to Britain. The volcanic activity quietened during December and had ceased altogether by March 1962.

On arrival in England, the Tristan da Cunhans were allotted homes in a former RAF base near Southampton. A school was opened for the children. None had previously seen a car, and they had to be taught how to cross roads. The 164 able-bodied men and women were found jobs, helping in factories or canteens or loading lorries. But the refugees very soon became homesick. When it was clear that the volcanic disturbances were over, an advance party left for home, in March 1963, to make the land and houses fit for re-settlement. There was need to repair tracks, and rebuild houses in the traditional style, using volcanic blocks for walls, smaller ones for ridge stones; scarce driftwood for doors and window frames, and local thatch for the roofing. These was also need to make good the landing beach and rebuild the crayfish factory. The rest of the islanders followed, only fourteen choosing to remain in Britain.

Plate 1.13 Lava flow from a flank eruption, Tristan da Cunha, 1961

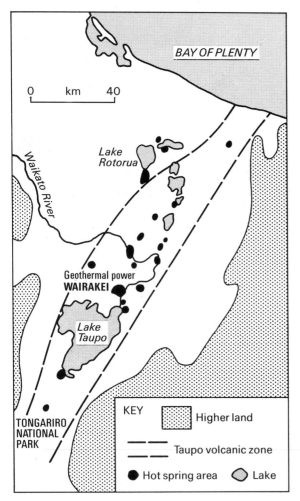

Fig. 1.13 Hot springs, North Island, New Zealand

KEY

- [shaded] Higher land
- – – – Taupo volcanic zone
- ● Hot spring area ◇ Lake

They are also a major tourist attraction. The Tongariro National Park (Fig. 1.13) is in this area, and includes an active volcano, Mount Ngauruhoe. The hot water, lying well below the surface, is also a source of *geothermal power*, and is tapped by wells which yield high-pressure steam. Plate 1.14 shows the steam production area of the Wairakei geothermal power project.

Plate 1.14 Wairakei geothermal power project, Auckland Province

The Geysers of North Island, New Zealand

Unlike earthquake activity, volcanic activity is not purely destructive. As we have just seen, volcanic rocks make tough building stones, while the lava and ash, which cause damage at first, eventually break down to form fertile soils, as on the slopes of Mount Etna in Sicily. Volcanic activity is also associated with the presence of hot ground water and geyser activity, to be found in Tuscany (Italy), Yellowstone Park (USA), Iceland, and North Island, New Zealand.

Geysers are hot springs from which columns of hot water and steam are discharged at regular intervals and with great force. The hot springs region of New Zealand is found in the volcanic district of North Island, centred on Lake Taupo (Fig. 1.13). The hot springs have long been seen as economically valuable. They were used by the Maori peoples, for example, for dipping flax, which was then made into garments.

Exercises

6. Make clear the differences between (*a*) composite, shield and fissure volcanoes; (*b*) magma and lava; (*c*) volcanic ash and lava; (*d*) a caldera and a parasitic cone. Use labelled diagrams to illustrate, where appropriate.
7. (*a*) Write your own version of the sequence of events on Fig. 1.8*a*, *b* and *c*.
   (*b*) With the help of Plates 1.6 to 1.10, and information in the text, summarise the effects of the Mount St Helens 1980 eruption.
8. (*a*) With the help of Fig. 1.12, draw a section southwest across the island through Queen Mary Peak. Label cliffs, steep slopes, and the site of the settlement.
   (*b*) On the basis of the photographs of Tristan da Cunha and information in the text, write a brief account of the landscape and people of the island.
   (*c*) Why did the people of Tristan da Cunha rank as refugees? Suggest reasons why they might well have found England a 'hostile environment'.

2 The Global Village

'THE SHRINKING WORLD': FROM OLDUVAI GORGE TO CAPE CANAVERAL

People have been on the move from the earliest times, to hunt, to fight, to explore, to trade, to move residence, to get to work, to visit friends, or to go on holiday. The motivation to move has changed over time. Few people travelled for leisure purposes before modern times, for example, and for few people today is hunting the main reason for travelling. One of the greatest changes in human history has been the increasing rate of travel (see Chapter 12).

Early Peoples

The first humans, characterised by the ability to walk upright (*homo erectus*), appear to have evolved in East Africa where, for example, in the Olduvai Gorge of Tanzania (Plate 2.1) and in Ethiopia (Fig. 2.1) remains have been found which date back over three million years. *Homo erectus* had evolved slowly into

Plate 2.1 Excavations in Olduvai Gorge, Tanzania

Fig. 2.1 The movements of early peoples

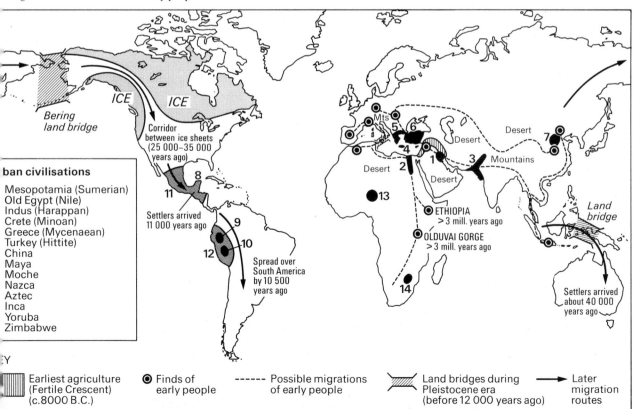

ban civilisations

Mesopotamia (Sumerian)
Old Egypt (Nile)
Indus (Harappan)
Crete (Minoan)
Greece (Mycenaean)
Turkey (Hittite)
China
Maya
Moche
Nazca
Aztec
Inca
Yoruba
Zimbabwe

Bering land bridge

Corridor between ice sheets (25 000–35 000 years ago)

Settlers arrived 11 000 years ago

Spread over South America by 10 500 years ago

Mts
Desert
Desert
Desert
Mountains
Desert
Land bridge

ETHIOPIA > 3 mill. years ago
OLDUVAI GORGE > 3 mill. years ago

Settlers arrived about 40 000 years ago

Earliest agriculture (Fertile Crescent) (c.8000 B.C.)

Finds of early people

Possible migrations of early people

Land bridges during Pleistocene era (before 12 000 years ago)

Later migration routes

modern man (*homo sapiens*) by about 50 000 years ago. *Homo sapiens* developed far more effective tools for hunting and other activities.

Human groups spread outwards from East Africa, following the easiest routes available, such as along valleys through mountain or desert regions. The earliest human remains found in Europe are about half a million years old. People reached Australia about 40 000 years ago. This was the time of the great ice ages, when the water taken up in the ice sheets lowered the sea's surface, creating *land bridges*. Fig. 2.1 shows land bridges between South-east Asia and Australia, and Asia and North America. The Bering land bridge, and a narrow ice-free corridor in northern Canada, allowed groups from Asia to move into North America and finally, about 10 500 years ago, South America. It therefore took human beings over 3 million years to spread over much of the world's surface.

The Agricultural Revolution

About 10 000 years ago (8000 B.C.), one of the great technological revolutions took place. People became *settled agriculturalists* and could therefore stay in the same place all the year round. Wild wheat and other grains and roots became farm products, and cattle, sheep and goats were domesticated. This revolution took place in the 'Fertile Crescent' of the Middle East (Fig. 2.1). By about 5500 years ago, the wheel, the plough, pottery and non-ferrous metal goods were in use. These developments allowed the first *urban revolution* to take place. Town growth characterised the civilisations of the Middle East: the Nile (early Egypt); Mesopotamia (the Sumerian civilisation); and the Indus (the Harappan civilisation) (Fig. 2.1). Later urban civilisations developed in the Mediterranean area and in China in the 2000 years before the birth of Christ, and in Latin America and Africa in the 1500 years after. These developments covered a period of about 12 000 years of human history, an enormous speeding up in the pace of change from the time that settled agriculture developed.

Trade and Exploration

From the classical civilisations of Greece and Rome and through the emergence of Christianity, a new culture spread over Europe. Overland trade contacts were established with Asian civilisations. What lay beyond the western ocean was unknown, however, until the great age of exploration, beginning in the late fifteenth century. Columbus crossed the Atlantic in 1492 in about 70 days. Nearly 100 years later, Drake circumnavigated the world, taking nearly three years to do so (1577–80).

The Industrial Revolution

The next great revolution in human history was based on the invention of the steam engine and the development of coal-based factory industry. The industrial revolution brought with it also a new urban revolution and a transport revolution, in which the development of canals and then railways made possible an improved flow of raw materials and finished manufactured products. Overseas trade was also speeded up by improved sailing ships and later steamships. By the late nineteenth century, ships were sailing from Europe to Australia in less than three months.

The Twentieth Century

Technological improvements have been even more marked in this century. In the first place it has been the age of the automobile and the aeroplane (see Chapter 12). To sail from Europe to Australia today takes nearly one month; to fly, about 36 hours. On land, the growth of motorway systems has in some cases more than halved the time it once took to travel between places. We have come to realise more and more that *time distance*, how long it takes to get from one place to another, is more important than spatial distance, how far apart the two places are on the ground.

Plate 2.2
Radio France, Paris

Plate 2.3 The launch of the space shuttle from Cape Canaveral, 1981

'Communication' means more than transport, however. People are now in much closer contact than even air travel can provide. This century has seen the rapid growth of radio (Plate 2.2) and telecommunications, the most effective ways of establishing communications and spreading ideas yet devised. Teleprinters allow identical copies of messages to be transmitted over the world in about four minutes. Earth satellites (see Plate 1.1) enable simultaneous transmission of television pictures over the world. Plate 2.3 shows the launching of the space shuttle from Cape Canaveral (Cape Kennedy) in 1981, heralding the start of what might become fairly routine space travel: a far cry from the human beginnings of Olduvai Gorge.

Exercises

1. Work out some of the routes followed in the spread of humankind up to about the time of the birth of Christ.
2. (*a*) What physical conditions have in the past assisted and hindered human development?
   (*b*) What technological developments in the last two hundred years have rapidly speeded up human development? State briefly the dangers that might result from them.

THE DIVERSITY OF HUMANKIND

Ethnic (Racial) Diversity

'Race' refers to descent from a common ancestor. In the course of human development from *homo erectus*, adaptation to different environments has produced considerable racial diversity. The world became a 'multi-racial' place at quite an early stage. Differences between ethnic groups occur in both physical and cultural characteristics. Three major 'races' have been distinguished (Fig.2.2):

Fig. 2.2 The major indigenous races of the world

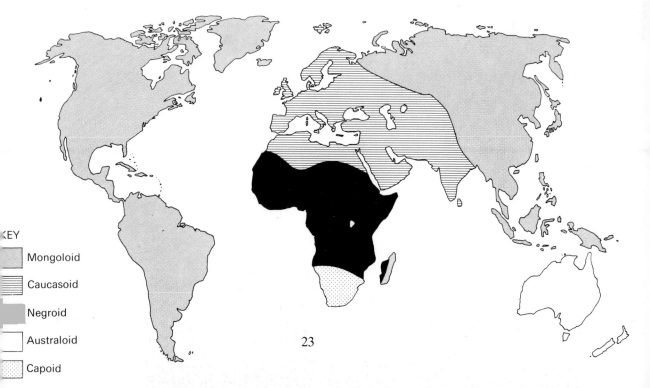

KEY

Mongoloid

Caucasoid

Negroid

Australoid

Capoid

23

(*a*) *the Caucasoid*, covering Europe, North Africa and South-west and South Asia;

(*b*) *the Mongoloid*, covering East and South-east Asia, and indigenous groups of the Americas (Amerindians); and

(*c*) *the Negroid*, basically in Africa south of the Sahara.

Two further sub-groups have also been distinguished, but are on a much smaller scale:

(*d*) *the Capoid*, Bushmen and Hottentots of South-west Africa, and

(*e*) *the Australoid*, or the Aborigines of Australia.

Plate 2.4 Tanzanian children, Darus Salaam

Plate 2.5 Indian children, Aurangabad

Plate 2.6 English Children, Disley, Cheshire

In physical appearance, these groups differ in height, skin colour, head shape and facial characteristics (eyes, nose and hair). But there are tremendous variations also *within* them, in physical characteristics and, even more, in ways of life. The children we see in Plates 2.4, 2.5 and 2.6, as they grow up, will, *within* each group, have different heights and weights, and different degrees of intelligence. The main difference *between* the groups will be that those children brought up in a 'developed' country (Plate 2.6), will have been offered much greater opportunities than those of the 'developing' world (Plates 2.4 and 2.5) (see Chapter 15).

Language Diversity

Equally, there is a great diversity of languages over the world. Language is vitally important, both as a means of communication and of handing down ideas from generation to generation. There are probably over 3500 languages in the world, but the age of exploration and colonisation resulted in a few becoming recognised as *world languages*, with English the most widespread. Plate 2.7a indicates the combined use of four different world languages in a frontier trouble spot, Berlin, where people were being warned that they are now leaving the American sector. Plate 2.7b is taken at the border of the Bantu 'homeland' of the Transkei in South Africa (see Chapter 14), showing a sign in two 'European' languages, English and Afrikaans (based on Dutch), and the local native African language.

Religious Diversity

Human beings have always found their world mysterious and frightening, and out of such feelings, and also a desire to explain what seems unexplainable, religions have developed. Tribal religions stretch back into the distant past, but the development of the great world religions follows the emergence of urban civilisations. Among the eastern religions, Hinduism is about 4000 years old and its offshoot, Buddhism, over 2500. The Chinese religions, Confucianism and Taoism, are of similar age to Buddhism. The Chinese religions, like Shintoism in Japan, stress the worship of nature, ancestors and emperors, as against the worship of deities (Gods) in Hinduism. Among the 'western', religions Judaism, going back to 1300 B.C., is the oldest, followed by Christianity (early A.D.) and Islam A.D. 630). All of these emerged in the Middle East,

Plate 2.7 Different languages in use: (*a*) at a frontier trouble spot in Berlin (*b*) at the border of the Bantu 'homeland' of the Transkei in South Africa

but have spread out over much larger areas. Western religions have been more effective 'colonisers' than eastern, readily crossing national and ethnic boundaries.

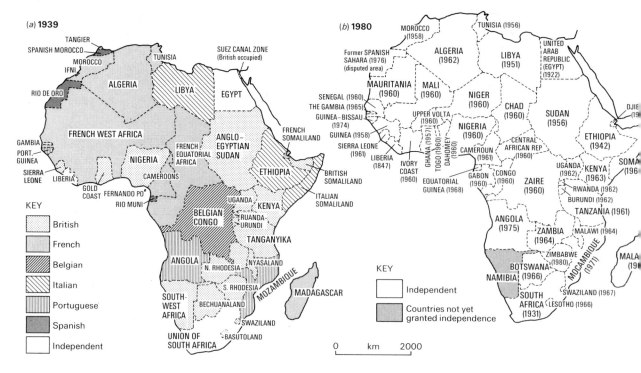

Fig. 2.3 Africa in (*a*) 1939 and (*b*) 1980.

Political Diversity

One of the most important aspects of human history has been the development of nation states. These too date back to the emergence of urban civilisation. Over time, some of the early city states became rich and powerful and established their rule over other states. As a result, empires developed, such as the Roman Empire in classical times, which spread over much of Europe, South-west Asia and North Africa. The age of exploration was accompanied by a new outburst of empire building, as was the period following the industrial revolution. The British Empire became the largest in the world. Since World War 2, the international trend has been towards de-colonisation, as can be seen by comparing the maps of Africa in 1939 and 1980 (Fig. 2.3*a* and *b*).

Over time, separate states have tended to group together, for mutual defence or trade, in alliances. Different groups have different interests. We can think today of the capitalist world and the communist world; the oil-rich Islamic countries; and of contrasts between rich and poor nations of the 'developed' and 'developing' worlds respectively. These divisions will be brought out in later sections of this book.

One of the most remarkable political developments of this century has been the spread of communism (Fig. 2.4). This is a political doctrine based on the writings of the nineteenth-century German philosopher, Karl Marx, advocating the abolition of private property, and a class war between working people (the proletariat) and the wealthy middle and upper classes. It represents therefore a conflict of views with those of capitalist societies.

Fig. 2.4 shows how communist governments have spread over the world since the first Marxist revolution, in Russia in 1917, which overthrew the Russian monarchy (the Tsars). After 1927, the new government 'nationalised' factories, mines, banks, trading companies and arms (see Chapters 10 and 11), and managed the whole means of production centrally, with the intent of serving the interests of the whole nation. As we shall see, the economic results have not been as favourable as the early pioneers would have hoped. Just as the Russian Revolution followed World War 1, so the chaos following World War 2 provided the opportunity for other communist take-overs, in Eastern Europe, China, and North Korea and North Vietnam. While communism is much less well established in other parts of the world, it has widespread influence, and has often provided the political philosophy and financial support for guerrilla movements in the developing world.

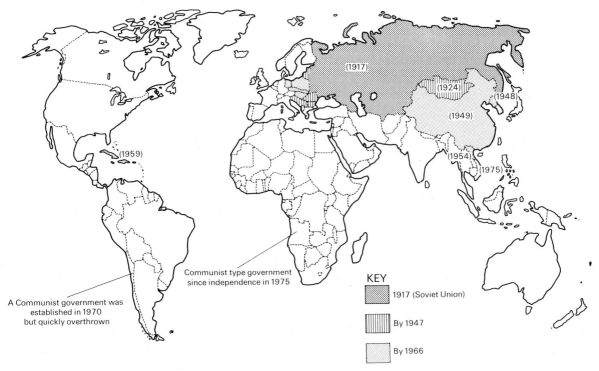

Communist type government
since independence in 1975

A Communist government was
established in 1970
but quickly overthrown

KEY

1917 (Soviet Union)

By 1947

By 1966

Fig. 2.4 The spread of communism

Diversity and Conflict

Unfortunately, diversity has normally been associated with suspicion and conflict, rather than the capacity to live happily with differences.

Thus colonisation has been accompanied by the need or desire to dominate others, and has usually been associated with repression, cruelty, economic exploitation, and even mass killing. Much of the oppression during human history has resulted from religious, political and economic differences. It has often had a racist basis. The argument is that different ethnic groups are racially pure and distinct (which is not true); that some races are superior to others (an opinion rather than a fact); and that this gives races which see themselves as superior the right to dominate others, as a means of improving the human race as a whole. This was the doctrine of fascism in the inter-war period, which resulted in the murder of millions of Jews. It remains the basis of the apartheid system in South Africa (see Chapter 14).

The problem has been made more complex over the last two hundred years by the increasing ease of communication, and the mixing of ethnic, political and religious minorities in the same society. The USA was thus almost from the start a multi-racial society, with the deportation of slaves from West Africa in the eighteenth and early nineteenth centuries, and the in-flux of various peoples from Europe in the nineteenth and twentieth centuries, and from the Caribbean and Mexico in the twentieth (see Chapter 14). One of the great social problems of the time is the great differences in economic and social opportunity in the world's cities, particularly between whites and coloured groups, illustrated here in the differences between the spacious affluence of the Beverly Hills suburb of Los Angeles (Plate 2.8) and the crowded tenements of Manhattan, New York, mixed in with towering offices, noisy streets and parking lots (Plate 2.9). The variations in opportunity shown in this comparison are, however, small compared with differences between the rich and poor worlds (see Chapter 15).

Exercises

3. Refer to Fig. 2.3*a* and *b*.
   (*a*) Which were the most influential colonising countries in Africa in 1939 in terms of (i) extent and (ii) number of territories colonised?
   (*b*) (i) describe the sequence of granting independence among the different European colonisers.
   (ii) Find out where there remains either internal conflict or conflict between adjoining states in Africa, following de-colonisation.
4. Refer to Plates 2.8 and 2.9.
   (*a*) Describe the differences in the intensity of the use of the land and show how these indicate variations in social and economic opportunity.
   (*b*) How have these differences arisen?

Plate 2.8 Beverly Hills residences, Los Angeles

Plate 2.9 New York: offices and tenements in Manhattan

POPULATION DISTRIBUTION AND DENSITY

The way people are distributed over the globe is also very varied, and gives rise to differing densities of population. *Distribution* refers to the way in which people are *dispersed* or spread out over space. This can be mapped, often in the form of a dot distribution map, with each dot representing a certain number of people, as shown in the maps of the Americas, East Asia and Australasia in Fig. 2.5. *Density* refers to the

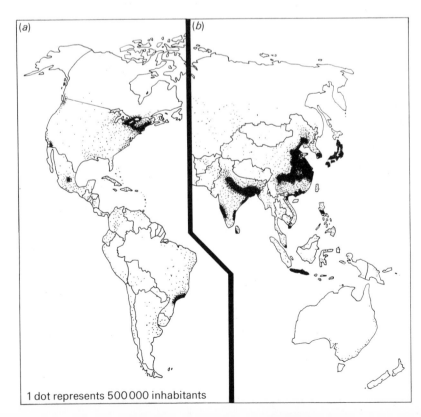

1 dot represents 500 000 inhabitants

Fig. 2.5 Population distribution: (*a*) the Americas, (*b*) East Asia and Australasia

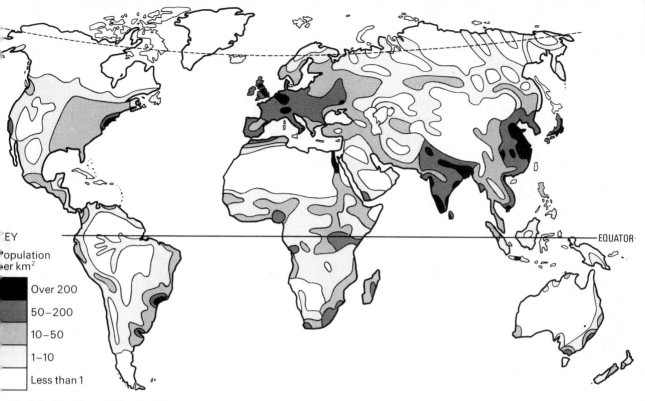

KEY

Population per km²

⬛	Over 200
▨	50–200
▧	10–50
▢	1–10
⬜	Less than 1

EQUATOR

Fig. 2.6 World population density

ratio of the number of people in an area to the amount of space in that area, and is usually expressed as numbers per square kilometre. Population maps showing density of population usually use a different type of shading for each general ratio, as shown on Fig. 2.6, where the most densely peopled areas have over 200 per square kilometre ($200/km^2$), and the most sparsely populated less than one.

Fig. 2.6 shows how population density varies over the world, ranging from over $200/km^2$ in industrialised areas of the western world, and in the alluvial lowlands of the oriental world; to less than $1/km^2$ in such

Table 2.1 Reasons for differing density

High density	Examples	Low density	Examples
(1) Areas of *low elevation* (e.g. plains)	Ganges valley, India; Kanto Plain, Japan; Low Countries	(1) Areas of *high elevation*; jagged relief	Andes; Himalayas; Rockies
(2) Areas of *moderate climate* with *adequate rain* (or irrigation)	Western Europe; China and Japan; much of the USA; Bangladesh; India	(2) Areas of *extreme climate*, especially very cold or very dry	Tundra of northern Alaska, Canada and the USSR; hot deserts
(3) Areas of *thick fertile* (*alluvial or loam*) *soils*	Corn Belt of the USA; Low Countries; eastern England; Ganges and Yellow River (China) plains	(3) Areas of *thin, rocky, acid* soils	Hot deserts; mountain areas; coniferous forests
(4) Areas of *open woodland or grassland*	Temperate deciduous forest and grassland areas, e.g. Western Europe; Corn Belt; Pampas	(4) Areas of *impenetrable vegetation*	Parts of hot wet equatorial forest such as Amazon Basin; mountains of New Guinea; mangrove/swamp areas
(5) *Coastal areas* with ease of access	Coasts of South America, Australia and Japan	(5) *Areas of the interior* with poor access	Central Asia; central areas of southern continents
(6) Areas of *rich economic resources* (but note, where physical environment is poor, these may be limited in extent (e.g. Siberia))	Coalfields of Western Europe; the USA; goldfields of South Africa	(6) Areas of *few economic resources*	Southern Chile/Patagonia; Afghanistan; Sahel countries

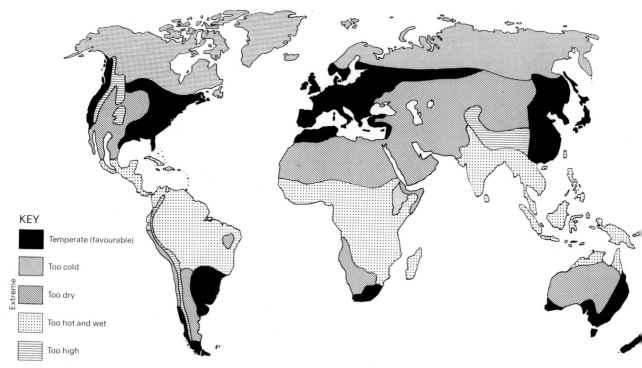

KEY

■ Temperate (favourable)

▨ Too cold

▧ Too dry

⬚ Too hot and wet

▤ Too high

Extreme

Fig. 2.7 Limitations on population density

areas as the cold and hot deserts and the forests of Amazonia. Table 2.1. and Fig. 2.7 summarise some of the basic reasons for differing population densities. It is noticeable that population densities are lower in areas of extreme climate, whether of cold, heat or drought, in areas of steep slopes and bare rock, as in mountainous regions, or in areas of general remoteness. Such environments are sometimes called 'hostile' by westerners, though there are people in each who have adapted skilfully to difficult conditions. These different environments and the different population densities that result are fundamental geographical divisions which make up the chapters of the following section of this book.

Apart from physical features, other factors which influence population density are the presence of economic resources, and degree of development. The amount of population a country has is in its turn an important influence on development. Some countries are seriously over-populated while others suffer from a lack of people. Fig. 2.8 shows a way of expressing this by drawing each country, not according to its actual area, but according to its size of population, and not worrying too much about the shape. We can see that China, for example, is much larger than the USSR in terms of population but has a much smaller area (see Fig. 2.4). This is an important fact of political geogra-

phy, producing tension between these neighbouring states of the communist world. For Asiatic Russia has huge open spaces, and the Soviet government fears that China may have designs on this area to help to relieve the massive problem of having a population of approximately 1000 million people. We shall find later (Chapters 14 and 15) that population and poverty and politics are closely associated as world problems.

Exercises

5. Refer to Figs. 2.5, 2.6 and 2.8.
   (a) Why are some parts of Fig. 2.5 shaded solid black?.
   (b) Describe similarities and differences in the distribution of population in (i) the USA and China; (ii) Canada and Australia.
   (c) What are the advantages and disadvantages of the different methods of showing population on these maps?
6. Refer to Figs. 2.6 and 2.7.
   (a) Name areas in which higher population densities (i) are, and (ii) are not, related to hot wet conditions.
   (b) Have all dry areas low population densities? If there are exceptions name them and give reasons why they are so.

Fig. 2.8 (*opposite*) World 'map' showing countries' share of world population, 1977

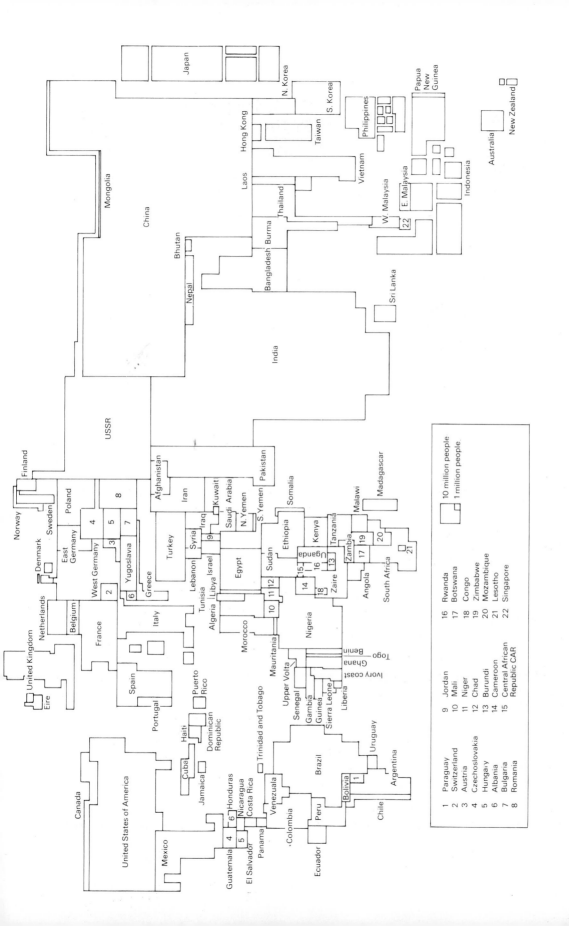

Japan

N. Korea

S. Korea

Papua New Guinea

Hong Kong

Taiwan

Philippines

Mongolia

China

Laos

Vietnam

W. Malaysia

E. Malaysia

Australia

New Zealand

Thailand

Indonesia

Bhutan

Bangladesh Burma

Nepal

Sri Lanka

22

India

USSR

Finland

Norway

Afghanistan

Sweden

Pakistan

Poland

Iran

Denmark

4

8

East Germany

5

Kuwait

Saudi Arabia

N. Yemen

S. Yemen

Somalia

West Germany

3

7

Turkey

Syria

Iraq

9

Netherlands

2

Yugoslavia

Greece

Lebanon Israel

Egypt

Sudan

Ethiopia

Kenya

Tanzania

Madagascar

Malawi

United Kingdom

Belgium

6

Libya

Sudan

16

Zambia

19

20

Eire

France

Italy

Tunisia

Algeria

11 12

14

Uganda 13

Zaire

17

21

Spain

Morocco

10

Nigeria

18

Angola

South Africa

Portugal

Mauritania

Benin

Togo

Ghana

Ivory coast

Canada

Haiti

Dominican Republic

Upper Volta

Senegal

Gambia

Guinea

Sierra Leone

Liberia

United States of America

Cuba

Jamaica

Trinidad and Tobago

Brazil

Uruguay

Puerto Rico

Venezuela

Mexico

Honduras

Nicaragua

Costa Rica

Panama

Colombia

Bolivia

1

Argentina

Guatemala

4

6

Peru

Chile

El Salvador

5

Ecuador

10 million people

1 million people

1	Paraguay	9	Jordan	16	Rwanda
2	Switzerland	10	Mali	17	Botswana
3	Austria	11	Niger	18	Congo
4	Czechoslovakia	12	Chad	19	Zimbabwe
5	Hungary	13	Burundi	20	Mozambique
6	Albania	14	Cameroon	21	Lesotho
7	Bulgaria	15	Central African	22	Singapore
8	Romania		Republic CAR		

SECTION B: Sparsely Populated Regions
3   Tundra and Taiga: the Cold Regions

LOCATION

The cold northern lands form a vast stretch of country across the north of North America, Scandinavia and the northern USSR (Fig. 3.1), a circum-polar region (see Fig. 3.5) marked by different land and seascapes:

(1) the northern polar seas, with the North Pole itself part of a frozen sea area, with northern sea routes on the continental margins kept open only by ice-breakers (Plate 3.1);

(2) the western margins of continents, as on the south coast of Alaska and the coast of Norway, with ice-free waters as the result of the presence of warm ocean currents, such as the North Atlantic Drift (see Fig. 3.8);

(3) permanent ice, as in Greenland, some islands off northern Canada, and parts of the Norwegian highlands (matched in the southern hemisphere by most of the continent of Antarctica);

(4) the *tundra*, mostly well to the north of 60° N, but found further south in mountainous areas;

(5) the northern boreal or coniferous forest (called the *taiga* in the USSR), north of 60° N on the western sides of continents, but extending as far south as 50° N on the eastern sides, and in mountainous areas. Just as the tundra grades into the taiga without a sharp break in the north, so the taiga becomes mixed with deciduous trees on its southern margin.

Fig. 3.1   Tundra and taiga: location

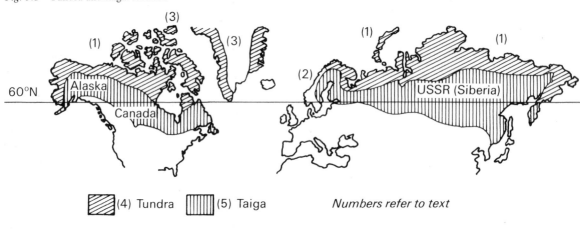

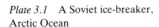 (4) Tundra   (5) Taiga   *Numbers refer to text*

Plate 3.1   A Soviet ice-breaker, Arctic Ocean

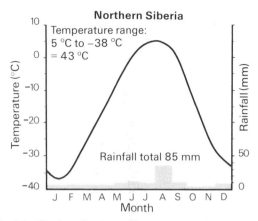

Fig. 3.2   Tundra: climate graph

PHYSICAL FEATURES OF THE TUNDRA

Climate (Fig. 3.2)

TEMPERATURE

The tundra climate is marked by average summer temperatures of under 10 °C. No other areas, except polar and high mountain areas, are so low. The coldest month averages below −20 °C and often below −30°C, giving annual ranges of temperature of over 25 degrees. Despite the long hours of daylight in summer, the sun is always low in the sky and this lack of strong, direct insolation keeps the temperatures low. The short hours of daylight in winter mean that the sun's rays are ineffective, and it is therefore always very cold in this season.

RAINFALL

Conditions are usually dry, with less than 300 mm per annum and in some areas under 100 mm (see Fig. 3.2). Tundra regions are cold deserts. Rain falls mainly between June and September. Precipitation falls as snow in winter but this is usually light, although strong winds cause blizzards and drifting.

Precipitation is low because tundra regions are dominated by high pressure, and dry descending air. In summer, however, some depressions penetrate, giving rainfall. But cold air can hold little water vapour, and rain, when it comes, often falls as drizzle.

These 'average' conditions do not, however, convey adequately the extremes of weather experienced, nor their impact on people's activities. Thus winter extremes on the north slope of Alaska and in northern Siberia can plunge below −50 °C. In summer, temperatures can occasionally soar to over 30 °C. The land is frozen in winter but, in summer, surface areas melt to form a quagmire. Mosquitoes can make life unpleasant. There is almost complete darkness for over two months and in mid-summer almost continuous daylight. Offshore ice breaks up in summer to allow not more than six weeks clear navigation, but icebreakers can be used to extend the season (Plate 3.1). Planes land on skis in winter and on floats on lakes and rivers in summer.

Vegetation

Tundra vegetation is composed mainly of dwarf species growing close to the ground, often in a cushion-like form. Cotton grass, mosses and lichens are common plants. In general, plants are similar in appearance giving an unvaried landscape (see Plate 3.3). Dwarf willow and birch trees can be found in sheltered places. Tundra vegetation is of no commercial use to people, but is important for reindeer (northern Scandinavia and Siberia) (Plate 3.2) and caribou (North America) grazing.

Plate 3.2   A reindeer herd in the tundra of northern Norway

Plants are closely adapted to their harsh environment. They have a long dormant period during the cold dark winter, but grow rapidly in the summer when there is continuous daylight. They grow closely together and are cushion-shaped to avoid strong winds, which increase transpiration at times when the soil is too cold for the plant to take up water through the roots. Most plants have shallow roots because the soil is permanently frozen at a shallow depth. Only a few centimetres thaw out in the summer.

Permafrost

One of the most characteristic features affecting tundra soils is *permafrost*, which means soil that is permanently frozen. In northern Alaska the permafrost zone extends to over 600 m in depth. Thawing of the surface layer in summer, in the presence of moisture, results in waterlogging, as the permafrost below forms an impermeable layer, preventing downward drainage.

The permafrost makes building of all kinds difficult. Occupied buildings allow heat to escape downwards, causing melting of the permafrost, even in winter. Unless the subsoil is insulated, subsidence can occur. Houses are therefore built on piles; water and sewage pipes are insulated and laid on the surface; while roads have to be constructed on beds of gravel to prevent subsidence through thawing of the permafrost.

PHYSICAL FEATURES OF THE TAIGA (NORTHERN CONIFEROUS FOREST)

Climate (Table 3.1)

TEMPERATURE

A major feature distinguishing the taiga climate from the tundra is that summer temperatures rise higher, to over 15 °C. Winter months are nearly as cold as those of the tundra, with temperatures falling below 20 °C. Conditions are less cold near western coasts. Like the tundra region, the taiga has long hours of summer sunlight, but its more southerly latitude gives it stronger insolation and higher summer temperatures. As in the tundra, the low angle of the sun and short hours of sunlight in winter mean very cold temperatures in that season. As the taiga is an area of high pressure in winter, clear skies occur, causing loss of heat by radiation, thus making conditions even colder.

RAINFALL

The annual rainfall totals are normally low, in the region of 300 mm per annum, and always under 500 mm. There is a summer maximum of rainfall. Precipitation in winter falls as snow, but is low in amount, though blizzard conditions can occur in strong winds near the northern margins where trees are sparse.

Table 3.1 Temperature and rainfall figures for a station in the taiga

	J	F	M	A	M	J	J	A	S	O	N	D	
Temperature (°C)	−18	−16	−13	−3	11	19	22	19	14	4	−7	−15	Range 40
Rainfall (mm)	20	9	10	20	32	39	50	38	36	27	15	14	Total 310

Plate 3.3 A logging camp in the Siberian taiga

As in tundra areas, the high pressure conditions in winter mean cold descending air and therefore little precipitation. Some areas are in rain shadows (see Fig. 8.4), such as those behind the Rocky mountains of North America and the Scandinavian highlands in Europe, which cut off moist westerly winds. But much of the coniferous forest belt is in any case very far from west coasts, and few depressions from the west get through. Convectional heat in summer and the few depressions which penetrate give summer rainfall.

Vegetation (Plate 3.3)

The characteristic vegetation forms are tall tapering evergreen trees with needle-like leaves. Among the most common trees are fir, pine, spruce and larch, with a few deciduous trees such as birch in the more southerly areas. There are relatively few different species, however, and many trees occur in stands of one species. There is little undergrowth because fallen pine needles and lack of sunlight prevent the growth of ground plants.

The trees are adapted to climate and soils in various ways. Different trees prefer different types of soil. Thus pine trees thrive on sandy and spruce on more clayey soils. In general, coniferous trees do well on the infertile *podsol* soils of the taiga region. Such soils can be identified by an ashy grey layer near the surface, from which mineral nutrients have been washed downwards. The pine needles provide little organic matter for the surface layers.

Trees suffer from drought in winter, because the ground is cold and water is not taken up by the roots, while strong winds increase transpiration in exposed areas. Trees have shallow roots to keep above the permafrost layer, where this occurs. The conical shape of the trees (Plate 3.3) and the needle-like leaves help to withstand falling snow and strong winds. Evergreen trees can start their growth as soon as the temperature rises in the spring, and therefore need a shorter growing season than deciduous.

Exercises

1 (a) Refer to Table 3.1 and, using the figures it provides, draw a climatic graph similar to that in Fig. 3.2.
(b) Describe similarities and differences in tundra and taiga climates.
(c) Give reasons for these similarities and differences.
2 Refer to Plates 3.2 and 3.3.
(a) Describe the physical conditions shown on the two photographs.
(b) Give reasons for the differences which exist between tundra and taiga vegetation.

THE HUMAN RESPONSE: TRADITIONAL ADAPTATION TO THE TUNDRA ENVIRONMENT

Nomadic Hunters and Herders

These include the *Eskimoes (Inuit)* of northern Alaska and Canada, who traditionally fished, hunted seals and, on the land, hunted caribou, an animal closely related to the reindeer. In northern Siberia, tribes such as the *Yukaghir* also hunted and fished, and herded reindeer. Many Inuit people now live in permanent settlements, while most of the Yukaghir are settled on collective farms in northern parts of Soviet Asia. In northern Scandinavia (Fig. 3.3), the *Lapps* were also traditionally a reindeer-herding people (Plate 3.2).

Some Lapps were entirely dependent on semi-domesticated reindeer for food and clothing, while those at the coast also fished. In winter they lived in wooden huts and tents in sheltered interior valleys, following the herd as it searched for moss under the snow. In summer, the herds moved north to the summer pastures near the Arctic coast (Fig. 3.3). Reindeer meat and skins, and traditional clothing, were exchanged for paraffin, salt, tobacco and beverages.

There have been many changes in this century, with Norwegian, Swedish and Finnish governments (whose

Fig. 3.3 Lappland: grazing areas

35

countries are overlapped by Lapp territory) providing timber for permanent huts, boarding schools for children, stoves, and other conveniences. Probably only about 10 000 of a total of 40 000 Lapps are still concerned with reindeer herding. Many now work as lumberjacks or as farm employees in the coniferous forest to the south. Lappland is increasingly attracting tourists to its wild scenery, the phenomenon of the 'midnight sun', and the Lapp people themselves, some of whom now dress in traditional costume purely for the benefit of the visitors.

THE HUMAN RESPONSE: MODERN DEVELOPMENTS IN THE TUNDRA

The Exploitation of the Oil Reserves of the North Alaska Slope (Fig. 3.4)

DEVELOPMENT

The Prudhoe Bay oilfield on the north Alaska slope is one of the most important discoveries of the last twenty years (Plate 3.4). Oil and gas were found there in 1967, but the location is remote, and the natural means of sending out the oil, by sea, is blocked for most of the year by Arctic ice. It was not until 1977 that a 1300 km pipeline to the ice-free Pacific port of Valdez (Fig. 3.4 and Plate 3.5) was completed. From here, tankers now take the oil to the west-coast ports of the USA and via the Panama Canal to the Gulf coast, a major refining area. The Prudhoe Bay oilfield is of

Plate 3.4   Prudhoe Bay operations centre, Alaska

enormous importance to the United States, providing about one-third of its oil and 12% of its natural gas reserves. It helps the country's balance of payments and also its political position, by reducing its dependence on oil from the unstable Middle East area.

The field is also of great importance to the state of Alaska, as it employs over 2000 people, and up to 5000 when new developments are taking place. The oilfields and gas fields bring huge revenues to the state. Britain also benefits indirectly, in that British Petroleum has a 53% stake in the Sohio Oil Company, which is one of the two companies working the Prudhoe Bay field. Many of the workers on this cold and remote field 'commute' by air from Fairbanks and Anchorage (Fig. 3.4), the two largest Alaskan towns, working 12 hours a day for eight days in every fourteen.

Fig. 3.4   Exploitation of oil in Alaska

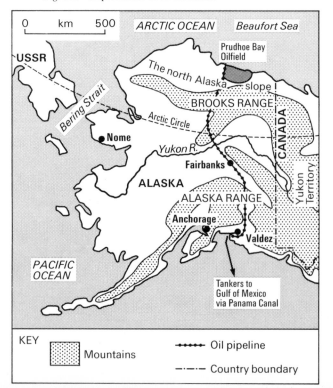

Plate 3.5   Valdez: the Alaska pipeline terminal

Plate 3.6 The Alaska pipeline near Brooks Range

PROBLEMS

(1) The oil drilling, extraction and pumping have to take place under appalling weather conditions, with freezing cold (Plate 3.4), blizzards, and hazardous conditions under foot.

(2) Permafrost makes it necessary to place buildings on piles (Plate 3.4), and pipelines taking out the oil have also to be raised above ground level (Plate 3.6).

(3) The 1300 km pipeline has not only to cross permafrost areas, but great fold mountain ranges, such as the Brooks Range (Plate 3.6) and the Alaska Range (Fig. 3.4).

(4) The remoteness of the field makes it difficult to bring in supplies. While there is a road to the field, this is not always open, and heavy equipment has in any case to be transported by sea, open only for six weeks in the year. Personnel, perishables, and high-value cargo come in by air.

(5) The pipeline also crosses a major earthquake belt on the edge of the Pacific plate in the Anchorage area (see Chapter 1). An earthquake splitting the pipeline could cause havoc, although the oil companies state that the pipeline is built to bend rather than break, even in a devastating earthquake such as the one which hit Anchorage in 1964.

(6) The populations of Alaskan towns have soared with the influx of oil and ancillary workers. Fairbanks has grown from 16 000 in 1974 to 27 000 in 1975, creating great housing problems.

(7) The pipeline crosses traditional caribou trails and environmentalists fear that it may disturb the delicate balance between these animals and their grazing grounds.

(8) The oilfield has caused general disturbance of a wilderness environment. One of the reasons for the delay in the exploitation of Alaskan oil was the activity of conservationist pressure groups, who used their political skills to block government permission to the oil companies to exploit the field. They were given support for their case by the mess produced on the north slope by the oil companies in the early stages of oil exploitation, when thousands of tons of gravel were removed from streams and beaches to serve as foundation material for roads, airstrips, drilling rigs and buildings.

However, the overwhelming national economic case for developing the fields overcame the conservationist arguments, although stringent conditions for exploiting the oil were laid down by the United States government. The Prudhoe Bay area has now been declared a game reserve and is closed to hunting.

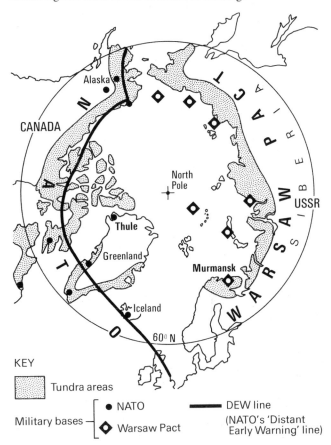

KEY

Tundra areas

Military bases —
● NATO
◇ Warsaw Pact

━━━ DEW line
(NATO's 'Distant Early Warning' line)

Fig. 3.5 The political geography of the polar north

The Political Geography of the Circum-Polar North

We do not always realise, because we are so used to using atlas maps, that continents almost completely surround the north polar ocean (Fig. 3.5), with only one substantial break, between Greenland and Norway. The Bering Strait is a shallow and narrow 90 km

gap between the USSR and the USA. It is also not always appreciated that the circum-polar north is strategically important, with the North Atlantic Treaty Organisation (NATO) powers (most of those of North America and Western Europe) facing those of the Warsaw Pact (the USSR and its East European satellite countries) (see Fig. 2.4).

Fig. 3.5 shows the north polar ocean dotted with military bases of these two political blocs, such as Thule (NATO) in northern Greenland, and Murmansk in the USSR. Nuclear submarines follow a secret and sinister existence in the unfrozen waters below the ice-packs, and indeed such submarines have surfaced at the North Pole. NATO's 'Distant Early Warning' (DEW) line crosses Alaska (one of its stations being shown in Plate 3.7), northern Canada, Greenland, Iceland, and then moves south into Britain (Fylingdales Moor in Yorkshire).

Plate 3.8 Bonanza Creek, Klondike, as it is today

Exercises

3. Describe differences in the natural conditions on Plates 3.4, 3.5, and 3.6. In what ways have these posed problems for oil exploitation?
4. Debate either in class or in an essay the pros and cons of the case for the exploitation of oil and natural gas in Arctic Alaska.
5. Write an account of the disadvantages and advantages of being an oil worker in an environment such as that of Alaska.
6. Refer to an atlas map of the latitudes above the Arctic Circle which is not centred on the North Pole. Compare this with Fig. 3.5, and indicate the differences in the ways the tundra regions surrounding the north polar ocean are shown.

THE NORTHERN CONIFEROUS FORESTS: MODERN DEVELOPMENTS

The northern coniferous forests offer more opportunities for development than the tundra, though much of the area is equally remote and sparsely populated. Various economic resources are exploited, including fur-bearing animals and forestry (renewable resources) and minerals and energy sources (non-renewable).

Mining in Yukon Territory, Canada

THE 'GOLD RUSH': THE RISE AND FALL OF DAWSON CITY

Plate 3.8 shows a desolate scene near Dawson City (Fig. 3.6), in what is today a very sparsely populated part of Canada. Yet in the 1890s this small valley of Bonanza Creek, a tributary of the Klondike River, was alive with activity, with 17 000 mining 'claims' along its banks. It was the time of the Klondike 'gold rush'. Gold was found in 1896 and by 1899 Dawson

Fig. 3.6 Yukon Territory: the 'gold rush' and modern mining

Map labels:

To Inuvik
Clinton Creek (Asbestos)
Dawson City (Gold)
Klondike River
Elsa (Silver, lead, zinc, cadmium)
Mayo
64° N
CANADA
YUKON TERRITORY
Yukon River
Faro (Lead, zinc, silver)
To Fairbanks
Carmacks (Coal)
ALASKA HIGHWAY
Kluane Lake (Nickel, copper, platinum, gold)
Whitehorse (Copper)
ST ELIAS MOUNTAINS
Carcross
To Edmonton
60° N
Chilkoot Pass
Bennett
Dyea
White Pass
BRITISH COLUMBIA
Skagway
COASTAL RANGE
Juneau
PACIFIC OCEAN

0   km   150

Railway
Road
Country boundary
State boundary

City, only about 4000 found gold at all, and only a few hundred 'made it rich'. The Klondike was a very inaccessible area. While it only took two weeks, by rail and steamer, to get from New York to the small ports of Skagway or Dyea (Fig. 3.6), the next 50 km could take three months. Why was this the case?

But of the 100 000 who set out to find gold in the Klondike, about 30 000 to 40 000 reached Dawson City, only about 4000 found gold at all, and only a few hundred 'made it rich'. The Klondike was a very inaccessible area. While it only took two weeks, by rail and steamer, to get from New York to the small ports of Skagway or Dyea (Fig. 3.6), the next 50 km could take three months. Why was this the case?

As Fig. 3.6 indicates, the route inland from the coast was blocked by high mountain ranges, crossed by two passes, the Chilkoot Pass and the White Pass. The Chilkoot was the more dramatic although the White

Pass, later to be used by the railway (Table 3.2), was equally arduous. The Canadian government insisted that the prospectors should take enough food to last a year. In addition they had to carry prospecting and mining equipment, tents and winter clothing, cooking utensils, and boat-building equipment. This had all to be carried, requiring many ascents, over the dreaded Chilkoot Pass, known as 'the icy steps to hell'. Winter was the best season, as steps could be cut in the ice

Plate 3.9 Dawson City during the gold rush, 1898

and snow. In summer it was a barren and almost impassable rocky slide. Plate 3.10 shows the camp at the foot of the Pass, and the continuous trail of prospectors climbing to the top.

Once they were at the top with all their equipment, the prospectors spent the rest of winter in a tented city on Lake Lindeman (near Bennett on Fig. 3.6), building boats for sailing down the Yukon to the Klondike, when the ice melted. When this occurred, the next hazard was to get through the treacherous waters of

Table 3.2 White Pass and Yukon Railway timetable, 1982 (Thomas Cook Overseas Timetable)

WHITEHORSE – SKAGWAY   WPY

O.W. U.S.$ 1 cl.	PEX 1 T	2	2	MEX 1 T		282	0.914 m.		1	PEX 1 T	1	MEX 1 T
		ⒶS	T		km				ⒶS		T	
0.00	....	0800	0945	1945	0	dep.	**Whitehorse** .....arr.	1530	....	1700	0330
	....		1145		69	dep.	Carcross..........dep.			1505	
49.00	....	1230	1350	2355	96	dep.	Bennett* ....dep.	1220	....	1350	2355
	1110		1430		117	dep.	Fraser ....dep.		1035	1150	
60.00	1245	1530	1615	0330	179	arr.	**Skagway**........dep.	0800	0900	1000	1945

Steam Excursion trains will operate Whitehorse–Skagway on June 7, July 5, Aug. 1, 30, returning on June 21, July 19, Aug. 16, Sept. 22. ⓡ.
1/2— ⓟ and car-carriers (ⓡ) for motor vehicles).   S—Oct. 1–May 31.
*—   1 hour stop at Bennett for complimentary ✕.   T—June 1–Sept. 30.
WPY— White Pass and Yukon Railroad.

Plate 3.10 Chilkoot Pass during the Klondike gold rush

Miles Canyon, with rapids such as the Whitehorse (Fig. 3.7). Once past here, the prospectors could expect to reach Dawson City in about two weeks, there to find a 'claim' and build a log cabin near the diggings. But the gold was soon worked out.

By 1899 the 'gold rush' was over. Dawson City's population plunged from nearly 30 000 to 9000 in 1901 and 800 by 1931. It is not quite a ghost town today, as many former mining boom towns of this period are. It is now a summer tourist centre, with visitors following, in more comfortable circumstances, the route of the 'klondikers', and panning for gold in the streams round Dawson.

Plate 3.11 Whitehorse, capital of Yukon Territory

WHITEHORSE: CAPITAL OF YUKON TERRITORY (Plate 3.11)

Like Dawson City, Whitehorse developed as a result of the 'gold rush' but, unlike it, Whitehorse has prospered and has taken over from Dawson its status as provincial capital of Yukon territory. It now has nearly 16 000 people, about two-thirds of the population of this sparsely populated province. The reason it has prospered is that it became an important communications node and *break of bulk* point.

Its *site* (Fig. 3.7) is just north of the Whitehorse rapids. As these were a hazard to the flimsy boats of the prospectors a wooden tramway was built to bypass them, and at the end of this tramway a settlement developed. The most important stimulus, however, came with the opening of the White Pass and Yukon railway in 1900, which connected Whitehorse with Skagway at the coast. It still runs today (Table 3.2). Whitehorse therefore became a break of bulk point between railway and river traffic.

Another important event was the construction of the Alaska Highway, for strategic reasons, during World War 2. This passed through Whitehorse, making another break of bulk point with the railway. Since then, other types of mineral wealth have been exploited in the Yukon, as labelled on Fig. 3.6, and an improved road network has developed, centred on Whitehorse. From here the ores can be carried by the railway for export via Skagway.

Iron Mining in Northern Sweden

Like the Yukon, northern Sweden is rich in mineral wealth. It has high-grade reserves of iron ore, over 60% pure, centred on Gällivare–Malmberget and Kiruna (Fig. 3.8).

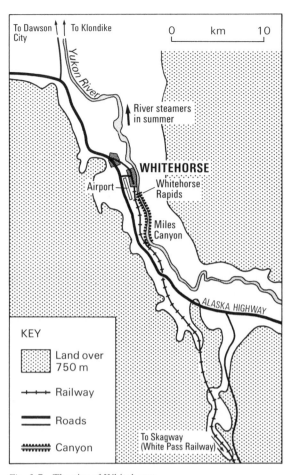

Fig. 3.7 The site of Whitehorse

Fig. 3.8 Northern Sweden: iron mining

EARLY DEVELOPMENT AT GÄLLIVARE–MALMBERGET

Fig. 3.9 (*a–d*) shows stages in the growth of iron mining at Gällivare–Malmberget. The inaccessible situation, far from the coast, at first prevented any substantial growth. In the mid-nineteenth century, iron ore was taken by road to iron foundries on the Gulf of Bothnia round about Lulea (Figs. 3.8, 3.9*a*).

THE COMING OF THE RAILWAY

A railway linked Gällivare and Lulea in the late 1880s and led to the rapid expansion of iron mining at Malmberget. An early shanty town developed to house the influx of workers (Fig. 3.9*b*). The mining at this time was open-cast. Exploitation of the much larger ore deposit at Kiruna (Fig. 3.8) began in the 1890s. The greatest stimulus was the completion of the railway link between Lulea and Narvik. Narvik has the great benefit of being an ice-free port, while Lulea is open for only five months of the year.

TWENTIETH-CENTURY DEVELOPMENT

Since about the time of World War 1, open-cast mining has been supplanted by underground mining (Fig. 3.9*c*). Malmberget has continued to be the main mining centre, and can be seen in the background of Plate 3.12. Gällivare, in the middle ground, is the main regional centre (Fig. 3.9 *b* and *c*), on the Lulea – Narvik railway. The railway and the mines in the area are supplied with power from hydro-electric power (HEP) stations at Porjus and Harspranget on the River Lule (Fig. 3.8).

TODAY

(1) In recent times, fully integrated steelworks have been developed at Lulea and at Mo-i-Rana (Norway) (Fig. 3.8), based on the high-grade ores of Kiruna and Malmberget. Most of the ore is still exported, however, particularly to Belgium, West Germany and Poland.

(2) The underground mining has become increasingly highly mechanised, as is shown on Plate 3.13.

(3) Much of the ore is now concentrated into a purer form before leaving the mining area, making it more economic to transport. This is done by *pelletisation* (Fig. 3.9*d*), involving rolling powdered ore into pellets of iron.

(4) Export is increasingly by bulk ore carriers. Narvik can take vessels of 235 000 tonnes and Lulea vessels of 66 000 tonnes.

(a) Before railway (c. 1880)

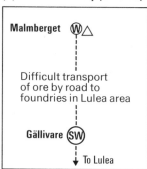

Malmberget Ⓦ △

Difficult transport
of ore by road to
foundries in Lulea area

Gällivare ⓈⓌ

↓ To Lulea

(b) Railway arrives 1880s

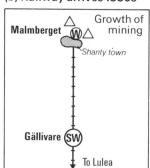

Malmberget △ Growth of
Ⓦ △ mining

Shanty town

Gällivare ⓈⓌ

↓ To Lulea

Fig. 3.9 Stages in the growth of
Gällivare–Malmberget

PROBLEMS

It has been necessary to pay high wages and provide
good amenities to attract workers to these remote and
climatically harsh areas of northern Sweden. Developments at Kiruna, Malmberget and Lulea have been
subsidised by the government, to make Sweden self-
sufficient in steel production, and to provide employment in the north.

(c) 1911–1960 period

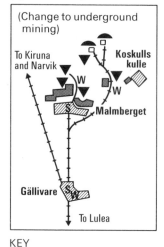

(Change to underground
mining)

To Kiruna
and Narvik

Koskulls
kulle

W

W

S

Malmberget

Gällivare ⓈⓌ

↓ To Lulea

(d) 1970s

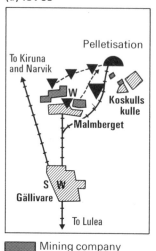

Pelletisation

To Kiruna
and Narvik

W

Koskulls
kulle

Malmberget

S W
Gällivare

↓ To Lulea

Plate 3.13 Underground iron mining at Malmberget

KEY

△ Open-cast ⎫
▼ Underground ⎬ Iron
mining

◗ Small ⎫
● Large ⎬ Processing
plants

▨ Mining company
dwellings

▨ Urban growth:
private housing

S Services (e.g. shopping)
W Work places

Plate 3.12 Gällivare–Malmberget in northern Sweden

World recession in the 1970s has caused a declining demand for steel and therefore for iron ore. Kiruna sent out only 13 million tonnes in 1978 (capacity 23 million) and Malmberget 5 million (capacity 7 million). This has caused a decline of employment in areas almost entirely dependent on the iron industry. The Gällivare area had over 1000 unemployed in 1978 and is trying to provide a more balanced employment structure. But the remoteness of the area and lack of local markets makes it difficult to attract industry.

Forestry in Siberia

There are many different 'images of Siberia', as the following quotation shows. In the western world, it is imagined as a land of

> ice and snow; seventy degrees of frost; endless forests, known as taiga; treacherous marshes and barren steppes, called tundra – a region which no man would enter of his own free will and which the Russian Tsars and Stalin therefore used as a vast concentration camp. Millions of deportees were sent to Siberia and they were followed by millions of prisoners during the first and second world wars . . . Others, who had fared a little better there, painted a picture of a thinly populated, poverty-stricken, backward region, remote from European civilization . . . [P]oets and writers . . . who did not have to live there as prisoners were full of praise for the hospitality of the Siberians and fell in love with the countryside – the dark cedars and silver birches of the taiga, even with the Siberian winter, whose cold climate is dry and whose white nights are utterly still . . . The Soviet press has for a number of years been painting yet another picture of Siberia . . . of pipelines and transmission grids, of power stations and of mines, of new cities and railway lines. Siberia . . . is regarded by the Soviet state as a huge reservoir of raw materials.

(from H. Portisch *I Saw Siberia,* Harrap 1972)

The major resource of the taiga is *softwood timber.* three-quarters of the Soviet forests are of spruce, pine, fir or larch and the large stands of the same tree make exploitation easier. As softwood, the timber is readily sawn. Many species have little resin, which makes the wood suitable for pulp and paper. The wood is also used for the construction and furniture industries, and as cellulose for plastics. Sawdust and trimmings are made into chipboard. As Fig. 3.10 indicates, the USSR is the world's largest softwood timber producer, though it comes behind the USA and Canada in wood

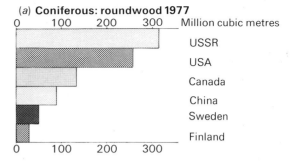

(a) **Coniferous: roundwood 1977**

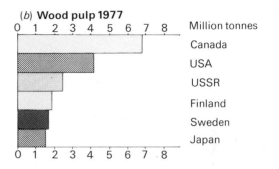

(b) **Wood pulp 1977**

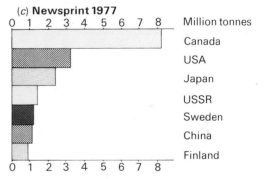

(c) **Newsprint 1977**

Fig. 3.10 World production of timber and timber products, 1977

pulp production, and behind these and Japan in newsprint.

Three main types of development can be identified in the Siberian timber industry.

(1) The *logging areas* (Plate 3.3) support small settlements of log cabins, with access by forest roads to the timber felling points and to the saw-mills, often near rivers or railways.

(2) Huge *timber combines,* making the range of products listed above, are centred on towns such as Bratsk and Krasnoyarsk, taking advantage of the great hydro-electric power stations on the Angara and Yenisei rivers (Fig. 3.11).

43

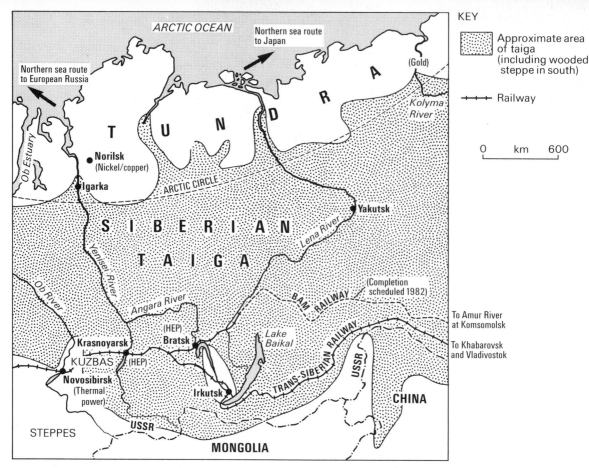

Fig. 3.11 Central Siberian taiga

(3) *Marketing* the timber and timber products is a major problem. While 80% of Russia's timber is in Siberia, two-thirds of the manufacturing of timber products is in the European part of the country. There are two main ways of exporting timber and wood products out of Siberia.

(*a*) The Trans-Siberian Railway, in the case of the southern parts of the taiga (Fig. 3.11), is an important west–east line of transport, taking the goods to industrialised areas of Siberia and European Russia. It is fed by a number of tributary railways, such as the one shown on Plate 3.14, running along the upper Yenisei river. The BAM railway (Fig. 3.11) is opening up new areas of the forest for exploitation.

(*b*) Timber is also floated down north-flowing rivers, such as the Yenisei, to exporting ports, of which the largest is Igarka (Plate 3.15), which grew from a population of less than fifty in 1927 to 20 000 in 1939. Here the timber is stacked in huge yards waiting for ships of up to 10 000 tonnes to take away the timber to Japan or European Russia. Ice-breakers (Plate 3.1) enable the northern sea route to be kept open for about 4½ months every year.

Exercises

7. Describe the scenes on Plates 3.9 and 3.10. Try to fit these into a fuller account of the 'gold rush' and its geography.
8. (*a*) In what ways do the urban landscapes of Dawson City (Plate 3.9) and Whitehorse (Plate 3.11) differ?
   (*b*) With reference to Fig. 3.6, indicate the differences in the sites and situations of the two towns.
   (*c*) Why did Dawson City's population rise and fall rapidly, and that of Whitehorse grow more steadily?
9. With the help of Fig. 3.9 and other information in the text, describe and explain the stages in the growth of the towns of Gällivare and Malmberget.
10. With the help of Figs. 3.6 and 3.8, and Plates 3.11 and 3.12, compare the situations and landscape settings of Whitehorse and Gällivare.
11. Refer to Fig. 3.12.
   (*a*) State three different types of location at which timber/timber products industries are to be found in eastern Canada.
   (*b*) Outline the advantages for the development of these industries.
   (*c*) Compare and contrast the development of these industries in eastern Canada and Siberia, under the headings: raw materials, power supplies, transport and markets.

Plate 3.14   Rail transport of timber in the upper Yenisei valley

Plate 3.15   Igarka: timber port

Fig. 3.12   Eastern Canada: coniferous forests and associated industries

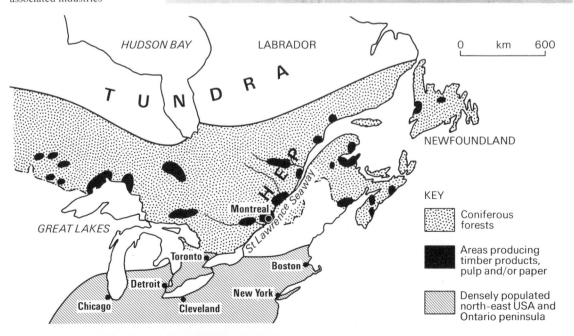

HUDSON BAY   LABRADOR

0   km   600

T U N D R A

NEWFOUNDLAND

GREAT LAKES

H.E.P.

Montreal

St Lawrence Seaway

Toronto

Detroit

Boston

Chicago   Cleveland

New York

KEY

Coniferous forests

Areas producing timber products, pulp and/or paper

Densely populated north-east USA and Ontario peninsula

4 Mountain Regions: the Andes and Alps

THE ANDES OF PERU AND BOLIVIA

Introduction: Altitude and Human Adaptation

> One of the first things a visitor to the high Andes notices is that the stocky inhabitants of these mountain slopes have tremendous barrel-shaped chests. And they have lungs to match. Furthermore the small pockets, or alveoli, which line the lungs and give added lung capacity are, in these people, always opened wide. This lets the greatest possible amount of blood flow through the delicate lung tissues and thus pick up all possible oxygen that is breathed in.
>
> (from L.J. & Margery Milne *The Mountains*, Time-Life International 1973)

These are just some of the physiological adaptations that allow the Indian peoples of the Andes to adjust to high altitudes. They have more blood and, in addition, richer thicker blood than lowlanders. They also need larger hearts to allow this more viscous blood to be pumped round their bodies. Their bodies are squat and compact (see Plate 4.3) so that the blood does not have to be pumped so far.

Lowland people are in trouble above about 3000 m, where the oxygen available is only two-thirds of that at sea level. At 6000 m it is about 40% and at 9000 m about 25%. Above 3000 m *soroche* or mountain sickness may occur. Read the following account of an American traveller on the railway from Lima into the Peruvian mountains, which reaches a height of over 4500 m:

> It begins as dizziness and a slight headache. I had been standing by the door inhaling the cool air ... Feeling wobbly, I sat down, and if the train had not been full I would have lain across the seat. After an hour I was perspiring and, although I had not stirred from my seat, I was short of breath ... I stood unsteadily and made for the rear of the train, where I found a Peruvian in a smock filling balloons from a tank of oxygen. He handed these out to distressed looking passengers who gratefully gulped from them. I took my place in the queue and discovered that a few whiffs of oxygen made my head clear and helped my breathing ...
>
> (from Paul Theroux *The Old Patagonian Express*, Hamish Hamilton 1979)

Altitudinal Zonation and Agriculture

In mountain areas, there are pronounced changes of climate, vegetation and types of agriculture with altitude. Temperature, like atmospheric pressure, drops with height (Fig. 4.1). As the northern Andes are in equatorial latitudes, there is little seasonal range of temperature. Thus in the lowland forests of the

Fig. 4.1 Altitudinal zones of the high Andes

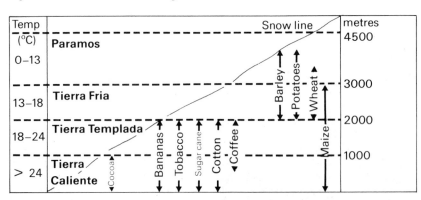

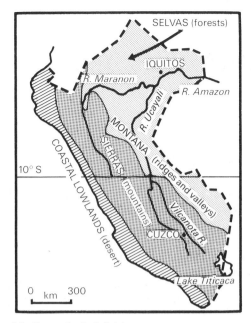

Fig. 4.2 Peru: physical divisions

Amazon (selvas) (Fig. 4.2), the range is from 27 °C to 28 °C, while at Quito, 2850 m in height, every month in the year averages 12 or 13 °C. At 4500 m, the average is around 0 °C.

In the northern Andes (Colombia, Ecuador and northern Peru), distinct altitudinal zones have been recognised, varying with temperature (Fig. 4.1):

TIERRA CALIENTE (hot zone)

This extends to a height of about 1000 m. The natural vegetation of the zone is equatorial forest, but where this has been cleared, commercial crops of sugar cane, cocoa, bananas, coconuts and rice can be grown. Owing to a cool offshore current, much of the Peruvian coast is a desert (see Chapter 5). But the presence of rivers running down to the Pacific from the mountains allows irrigated commercial crops of sugar, cotton and rice.

Plate 4.1 An Indian woman tending a potato field in the Andes

TIERRA TEMPLADA (temperate zone)

From heights of 1000 to 2000 m a less luxuriant tropical rain forest is found, as in the Montana region of Peru (Fig. 4.2). Again the forest has been cleared in many areas for plantation crops such as coffee and cotton. Maize is grown as a subsistence crop in all altitudinal zones up to nearly 3000 m (Fig. 4.1).

TIERRA FRIA (cold zone)

This is a wet and cloudy zone from about 2000 to 3000 m high, with temperatures ranging from 13 °C higher up to 18 °C lower down. Here there is a shift from predominantly cash crop to predominantly subsistence agriculture. Plate 4.1, of an Indian woman working a potato patch on the poor soils of this zone, illustrates the backward state of peasant agriculture in the high Andes.

The jagged relief, with rocky peaks and steep-sided valleys of the sierras (Fig. 4.2, Plate 4.2), makes for a variety of conditions for farming. Plate 4.2 is a photograph of valley of the Vilcanota, one of the many rivers of the sierras which feeds into the Amazon system. Fig. 4.3 is a plan of a small *hacienda*, or estate, in this valley. The owner of the estate cultivates only 24 of the 142 hectares. But this is mostly the better quality irrigated lands on the flood plain of the river, where

Fig. 4.3 A generalised diagram of a hacienda in the Vilcanota valley, Peru

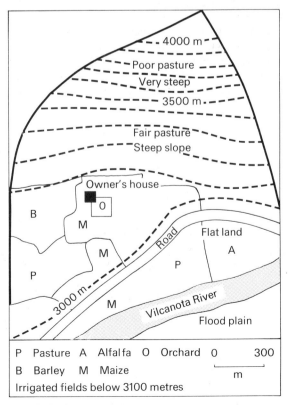

Plate 4.2   Vilcanota valley, Peru

maize, alfalfa and a little fruit is grown. A small herd of cattle is fed the alfalfa and also grazes on the flood plain and lower slopes.

The peasant families who live and work on the estate are left with the unirrigated slopes, and on their tiny plots they cultivate wheat, maize, barley, potatoes and other roots, and some vegetables, mostly for their own use, but with some sold at local markets. Animals are grazed on the poorer pastures of the steep slopes, even above 3500 m. Here the pasture is stiff and dry,

and really part of the next zone, the Paramos.

PARAMOS

In this zone, sheep rearing is characteristic, but there are also animals peculiar to the Andes that are made use of. One is the llama, a domesticated beast of burden. There are also the alpaca (semi-domesticated) and vicuna (wild). All of these provide hair or wool for clothing.

48

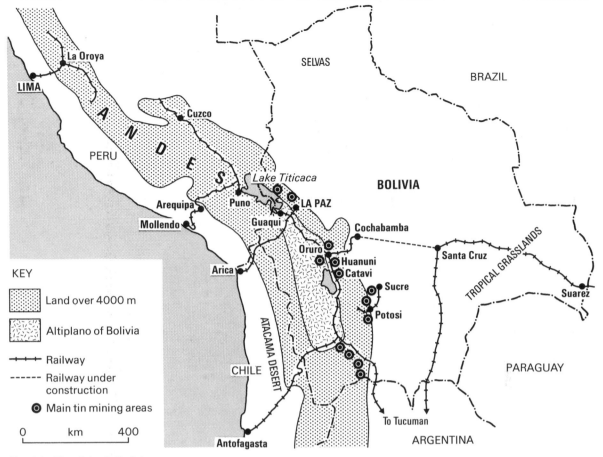

Fig. 4.4 Tin mining in Bolivia

KEY

- ░ Land over 4000 m
- ⠂ Altiplano of Bolivia
- ┼┼┼ Railway
- – – – Railway under construction
- ◉ Main tin mining areas

0 km 400

Tin Mining in Bolivia

DEVELOPMENT

The tin mines of Bolivia (Fig. 4.4) are the highest in the world. They are found in the eastern cordillera of the Andes, overlooking the Bolivian plateau (altiplano) at heights of 4000 to 5000 m. Plate 4.3 shows Indian women employed as labourers at a mine at 4500 m. Tin is widespread in its occurrence and is by far the most important export of Bolivia.

Plate 4.4 A remote tin mine in Bolivia

te 4.3 The high-level Andes: workers at a tin mine in Bolivia

(1) The tin ore is usually of low grade, with less than 2% of tin content. What is more, the grade is declining as the best veins have been exploited. Production is declining. Bolivia extracted 45 000 tonnes in 1929, 35 400 in 1950, and only 16 400 in 1978, when it was the world's eighth largest producer.

(2) The mines are found in difficult and inaccessible mountain areas (Plate 4.4). High costs are involved in building roads and branch railways to transport the ores. Buildings and housing for workers have to be constructed in difficult terrain. Local water supplies and fuel for processing the tin ore, and timber for mine props, have all to be brought in.

(3) Exporting the ore is a problem because Bolivia is a large and land-locked country (Fig. 4.4). As the tin ore is of such low grade, it has to be concentrated. This process raises the percentage of tin to about 60% pure. Oruro and Potosi have concentrators, and there is a smelter making pure tin at Vinto, near Oruro. These all help to lower transport costs. The most accessible ports for export are Antofagasta and Arica in Chile.

(4) The largest mines, at Huanuni and Catavi near Oruro, have the least bad working conditions. In many of the smaller mines, such as that on Plate 4.4, the miners work under primitive and stifling conditions, and suffer seriously from silicosis, acquired by breathing in dust in the mines. As Plate 4.5 illustrates, the miners and their families live in monotonous, barrack-like terraces. Their families 'scavenge' tin by digging in the waste-heaps deposited after the ore has been concentrated.

(5) Another major problem is the fluctuation in world tin prices. One journalist expressed the problem in this way: 'When the world price of tin rises, the West complains. But for the men and women who scavenge for the metal in Bolivia, a higher world price can mean the luxury of an egg or a joint of scraggy llama meat...'

(6) Bolivia also suffers from having to compete with low-cost tin from South-east Asia and from Malaysia in particular (see Chapter 8). As a result of inaccessible location and the low grade of the ore, Bolivia is a high-cost producer.

Exercises

1. With the help of tracing paper, draw an annotated sketch of Plate 4.2, labelling: the Vilcanota River; flood plain; steep forested slopes; cleared slopes; bare rock slopes. Try to work out which land is used by (a) hacienda owners; (b) peasant farmers.
2. Compare the contrast the climate, vegetation and agricultural activities of the four altitudinal zones of the northern Andes.
3. With the help of Plates 4.3, 4.4, and 4.5, and information in the text:
   (a) describe the landscape of the Bolivian tin mining region;
   (b) outline the physical, economic and social problems associated with this mining.

AN ALPINE REGION: THE VORARLBERG MOUNTAINS OF AUSTRIA

The provinces of the Tyrol and Vorarlberg in Austria are in the heart of Alpine Europe, surrounded by the Bavarian, Swiss and Italian Alps. In the western part

Plate 4.5 A tin mining settlement in Bolivia

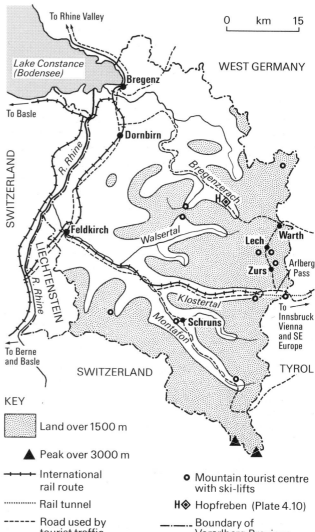

Fig. 4.5 Alpine Europe: the Vorarlberg Province of Austria

of the Vorarlberg lies the industrialised Rhine valley, which is quite densely populated (Fig. 4.5). Further east, apart from the more important valleys in which tourist resorts are found, the population becomes sparser with increasing height and remoteness.

Altitudinal Zonation in the Alps

As in the Andes, there is an altitudinal zonation of vegetation and land use, as Fig. 4.6 shows. Above the grassland of the valley floor there is often discontinuous deciduous woodland quickly followed by mixed forest, then coniferous trees, up to 1500 m. Forests tend to cling to the steep slopes of the U-shaped glaciated valleys, but if not too steep the slopes are often cleared for pasture. Above the steep slopes the land levels out to form high-level benches or 'alps'. These formed the valley floors before glacial erosion took place. Here there are high level pastures, with Alpine plants and dwarf trees. This zone is succeeded at about 2000 m by bare rock, with permanent snow above 2500 m. Something of this pattern can be recognised on the photograph of the Lauterbrunnen valley in Switzerland (Plate 4.6).

The Alpine region experiences heavy winter snowfalls. There is a great deal of difference between summer and winter conditions. Roads are often impassable in winter. In the Vorarlberg, it is often difficult to keep the major west–east route over the Arlberg Pass into the Tyrol open. Thus a road tunnel has been built parallel to the rail tunnel (Fig. 4.5).

KEY

▨	Land over 1500 m
▲	Peak over 3000 m
+++	International rail route
....	Rail tunnel
-----	Road used by tourist traffic
⊙	Mountain tourist centre with ski-lifts
H◈	Hopfreben (Plate 4.10)
–·–·–	Boundary of Vorarlberg Province

Fig. 4.6 Altitudinal zones of an Alpine region

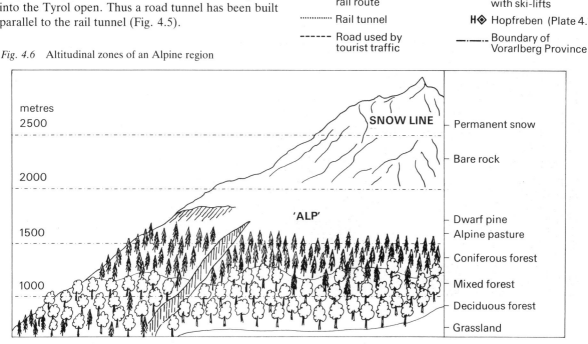

Plate 4.6 Lauterbrunnen valley, Switzerland

Plate 4.7 An avalanche in Switzerland

Avalanches

In spring *avalanches* are a major hazard (Plate 4.7), sometimes blocking roads, which have to be kept closed, even when not covered with snow, because of this danger. Plate 4.8 illustrates expensive avalanche protection on the road from the Arlberg Pass to the important resort of Lech (Plate 4.9).

An avalanche is a sudden fall of snow and/or ice, often mingled with soil, pebbles and boulders, which rushes down the mountainside, destroying everything in its path. Avalanches usually occur on slopes steeper than 22°, and often happen after a rapid heavy snowfall. 'Loosening' of the snow in spring can take place as a result of strong sunshine (affecting south-facing slopes in particular), heavy rainfall, or the onset of the föhn, a warm wind from the south. In certain years, conditions occur together to trigger off large numbers of avalanches. In the Vorarlberg in 1954 there were 125 deaths as a result of avalanches. In some cases deaths are caused by thoughtlessness, through skiers ignoring hazard signs, for example. But occasionally a severe avalanche can overwhelm a whole village.

Plate 4.8 Avalanche protection near the Arlberg Pass

Plate 4.9 Lech, Vorarlberg resort

Almwirtschaft (Transhumance)

To make full use of the farmland on the valley floor and on the 'alps' (see Plate 4.6), the traditional form of farming involves a seasonal movement of animals (particularly cattle) up the mountains, known as *transhumance*. In Austria, the system is termed *almwirtschaft*, meaning simply the economic use of the Alpine pastures. Although rarely found today in its pure form, it is practised in a modified way in such Vorarlberg valleys as the Walsertal and upper part of the Bregenzerach (Fig. 4.5).

In winter, the people live in their permanent homes in the valleys, with animals relying on fodder which is collected from the valley pastures in summer then dried and stored in lofts. In the Bregenzerach valley, in May to late July, and in September and October, families live temporarily in 'middle-level' settlements,

such as the one shown on Plate 4.10 at Hopfreben, which was not being used when the photograph was taken (in late March). Then in late July and through August and early September, cowherds move up to high-level pastures with their herds, living in more primitive wooden chalets. Traditionally the cows' milk was made into butter and cheese, but now it can in some cases be sent down into the valley by cable car, or even by 'milk pipelines'. Today, cooperative butter and cheese factories process the milk. In some areas, the cattle are now left in the valleys through the summer, and hay that is collected from the Alpine pastures is transported down for winter feed. The construction of cable cars and roads for the tourist industry has made a lot of difference to the farming economy.

53

Plate 4.10 Almwirtschaft: temporary homes at Hopfreben in the Vorarlberg

Tourism in the Vorarlberg

Plate 4.9 is a photograph of Lech, one of many resorts in the Vorarlberg which has grown rapidly with the post-war boom in tourism. So important is tourism to the Vorarlberg and the neighbouring Tyrol province, that lavish expenditure has been made on providing winter roads, such as the one shown in Plate 4.8 and the Arlberg tunnel. The area has many advantages for tourism, in common with the whole Alpine region

(1) The glorious winter scenery of snow-capped peaks and forested slopes is almost equally attractive in the summer season after the snow melts.

(2) There are extensive ski-slopes of varying degrees of difficulty, linked with a range of facilities such as ski-schools, ice rinks, cable cars, indoor swimming pools and a range of hotels and guest-houses, catering for both expensive and cheaper package holidays. Lech has 6000 beds for tourists and twenty cable car and ski-tow lines.

(3) Nearness to international road and rail routes, in this case the Arlberg Pass, makes this an accessible region, especially in summer.

(4) Equally important is the presence, to the north, of the most affluent countries in Europe: West Germany, Scandinavia and the Low Countries, from which most of the tourists who visit the Vorarlberg come.

Exercises

4. With the help of Figs. 4.1 and 4.6 outline the differences between the altitudinal zonation of vegetation and farming in the Andes and the Alps, and explain why these are so striking.

5. With the help of tracing paper, draw an annotated sketch of the Lauterbrunnen valley (Plate 4.6), similar to that of the Vilcanota valley in exercise 1. What are the main differences in the physical and human landscapes of the two valleys?

6. Since the war, the population of mountain areas in the Alpine region has decreased, while that of major valleys has increased. Give reasons for these changes.

7. What features on Plates 4.6 to 4.9 suggest these are areas liable to the avalanche hazard? Outline different ways in which steps are taken to avoid the hazard.

8. With the help of route maps and/or railway time-tables, work out ways in which you could travel to Lech for a winter sports holiday.

5 Hot Deserts

PHYSICAL FEATURES

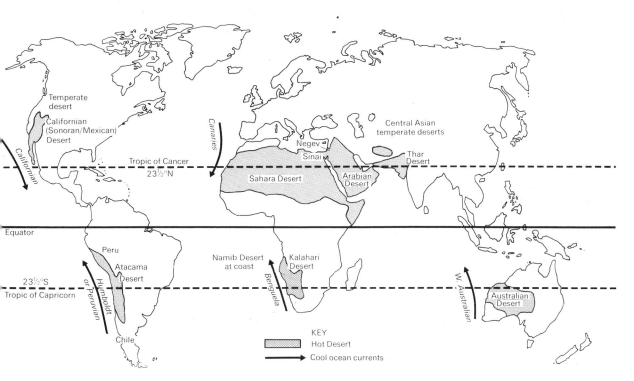

Fig. 5.1 Hot deserts: location

Climate

As the following advice to tourists and business people going out to the Middle East suggests, hot deserts, like high mountains, are difficult for strangers to adapt to:

> Summers can be extremely harsh. Between May and October the average maximum shade temperature is around 38 °C. In July temperatures in the shade can go up to 50 °C or even higher.

> In intense heat, dehydration is likely, and can be avoided by drinking plenty of liquids. You should drink at least two litres of water plus an extra litre for every 10 °C in every twenty-four hours. So at 20 °C you should drink four litres and at 30 °C five litres per day.

CHARACTERISTICS

Interior deserts

Here we are considering only hot deserts (Fig. 5.1) and not the interior deserts of the temperate zone: in central Asia, for example. The hottest months in the interiors of hot deserts average 30–35 °C (Fig. 5.2a). There are considerable diurnal ranges (between day and night), with exceptionally hot days, rising to over 45 °C. The coolest months average 12–16 °C, and at this season night-time temperatures can be very cold, even below freezing point. The other main characteristic of the climate is lack of rainfall: always under

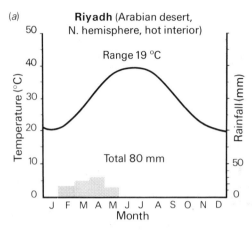

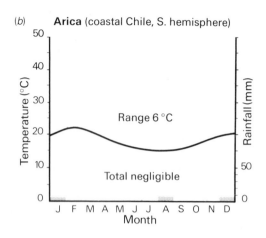

Fig. 5.2 Hot deserts: climatic graphs

250 mm, often under 100 mm and sometimes less than 50 mm per annum (Fig. 5.2a). The rainfall is extremely uncertain in its incidence, and when it falls may do so in torrential downpours.

Coastal deserts

While the Saharan–Arabian, Australian, and Sonoran (USA) Deserts stretch well into the interior, others are confined to the coasts, as in the Namib, Atacama and Lower Californian (Mexico) Deserts. In the coastal deserts, annual temperature ranges are lower than in the interior, with less hot summers (16–21 °C) and slightly warmer winters (over 15 °C) (Fig. 5.2b). The coastal deserts are even drier than the interior. Rain almost never falls in parts of the Atacama Desert, where the town of Iquique once went fourteen years without it.

FACTORS AFFECTING CLIMATE

Interior deserts

The extremely high summer temperatures result from the fact that the hot deserts are located in the tropics (Fig. 5.1) where the sun is vertically overhead in June (Tropic of Cancer) and December (Tropic of Capricorn). The sun gives intense heat at this high angle. Cloudless skies mean long spells of hot sunshine. On the other hand, clear skies also cause rapid radiation of heat after dark giving cold nights, and a high diurnal range of temperature.

These tropical latitudes are also centres of high pressure, from which winds blow outwards, from land to sea (offshore winds). Thus there are no onshore winds to carry in rain from the sea, and the desert interiors are far from the sea in any case. The occasional

summer downpours are caused by convection, where warm air rises, cools, condenses to form clouds which in desert regions occasionally give rain.

Coastal deserts

It seems strange that the coastal deserts are even drier than the interior. This is because of the cool offshore currents which wash their shores (Fig. 5.1). Winds blowing from the sea are cooled, which reduces their capacity to hold moisture. On reaching the land, they are rapidly warmed, becoming drier. These west coast deserts, however, mostly experience south-easterly winds, which are offshore, and blow off a dry interior. The Atacama Desert is in the rain shadow of the Andes, and the Kalahari in the rain shadow of the Drakensburg mountains of South Africa. The cool currents do, however, produce coastal fogs and these result in markedly cooler summers than in the hot interior deserts.

Adaptation of Vegetation to Climate

Some areas of hot deserts, such as moving sands and salt pans, have little or no vegetation. In other areas, desert vegetation growth can be surprisingly rich, although usually in scattered rather than continuous patterns. This is because plants have evolved many ways of getting to grips with drought, making maximum use of whatever water is available. Various types of plant can be found:

Ephemeral, drought evading plants, which have seeds which remain dry and apparently lifeless for long periods, but spring suddenly into life when the rains come, resulting in a 'blossoming of the desert'.

Perennial, drought resisting plants, of two main kinds.

(1) *Phreatophytes*, which have long tap roots penetrating down to the water table. Phreatophytes tend to grow near channels or springs. The date palm is an example, as is the sagebrush of the USA, shown in the foreground of Plate 5.1. This also has an extensive network of shallow rootlets, enabling it to absorb occasional rain.

(2) *Xerophytes* resist drought in various ways. Among the xerophytes are *succulents* such as the cactus (Plate 5.1), storing up water in barrel-like trunks and swollen branches. Other xerophytes have tough, shiny, leathery leaves, reducing transpiration further by means of the dense hairs which cover their surfaces. Others have an astonishingly extensive root network as well. Some plants need no rain at all, existing entirely on the water vapour in the desert atmosphere at night.

Plate 5.1　Desert vegetation in Arizona, USA

The Landforms of Hot Deserts

TYPES OF DESERT SURFACE

As a result of erosion, transportation and deposition, mainly by the agency of the *wind*, three types of desert surface are produced: rocky desert (the *hammada* of the Sahara); stony desert (the *reg* or *serir* of the Sahara); and sandy desert (the *erg* of the Sahara).

Plate 5.2 shows a rocky desert wilderness with a stony (reg) surface in the foreground, in the Sinai Desert, part of the world's most extensive hot desert, stretching from the west coast of the Sahara to the Thar Desert of Rajasthan in India (Fig. 5.1).

Plate 5.2　Wadi Natzb, in the rocky desert of the Sinai Peninsula

Plate 5.3 Sand desert, Tunisia

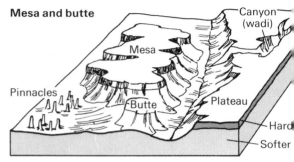

Fig. 5.3 A mesa and butte

Mesa and butte

Canyon (wadi) · Mesa · Pinnacles · Butte · Plateau · Hard · Softer

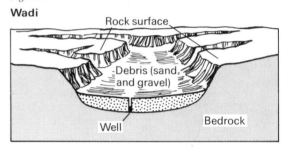

Fig. 5.4 A wadi

Wadi

Rock surface · Debris (sand and gravel) · Well · Bedrock

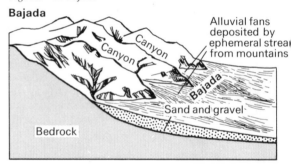

Fig. 5.5 A bajada

Bajada

Alluvial fans deposited by ephemeral stream from mountains · Canyon · Canyon · Bajada · Sand and gravel · Bedrock

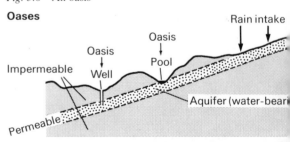

Fig. 5.6 An oasis

Oases

Rain intake · Oasis · Pool · Oasis · Well · Impermeable · Aquifer (water-bearing) · Permeable

In contrast, Plate 5.3 is a photograph of a true sandy desert, a 'sea of sand' (erg), in the Tunisian part of the Sahara.

PROCESSES AND LANDFORMS

(1) The wind, provided with 'tools' in the shape of coarse particles of sand, can be an important agent of erosion Where tough bands of horizontally bedded sedimentary rocks overlie weaker ones, wind erosion can cause undercutting. The upper parts collapse, leaving a steep cliff. This process and the flat top caused by the horizontal bedding produce a table-shaped upland called a *mesa*. A detached part of a mesa is termed a *butte*, which can be further broken down into isolated rock *pinnacles* (Fig. 5.3).

(2) In rocky deserts, the occasional rainfall, falling briefly but torrentially, causes *flash floods*. These, laden with loose debris and sand, erode out deep ravines or *wadis*, which can be narrow and canyon-like, or much wider and on a bigger scale (Fig. 5.4 and Plate 5.2). When the floodwaters reach the gentler slopes at the edge of the desert uplands, they dry up quickly and material is deposited, in some cases as an alluvial fan. A series of coalescing alluvial fans forms a *bajada*, a continuous apron at the edge of the uplands (Fig. 5.5). Here alluvium may overlie sand and gravel.

Unless a wadi is nourished from headwaters in an area of heavier rainfall, the streams which occupy it will be short-lived. Wadis are irregular features with floors containing rock basins which may be infilled with silt and pebbles (Plate 5.2). The river channels shift frequently. The building of dams to form reservoirs for irrigation is hazardous as they silt up very quickly. But even where wadis are dry, water usually lies near enough to the surface to be reached by wells. Often chains of *oases* result, and wadis may therefore become important trade routes. Oases occur where the permeable water-bearing layer (aquifer) reaches or comes near to the surface (Fig. 5.6), which may happen in wadis. The aquifer will usually originate in a region of higher rainfall, giving a water intake area.

Plate 5.4 Shibam, South Yemen

Plate 5.4 is a photograph of a large oasis settlement, Shibam, in the Wadi Hadhramaut of the South Yemen (Fig. 5.7). Shibam is built on a low mound which forms a *dry-point* site on a valley floor which can be flooded. In the background are the steep slopes of the uplands of the Hadhramaut, crossed by an intricate series of tributary canyons (Fig. 5.7).

(3) The desert sands are blown into different forms of dunes. The erg of the Sahara is a true 'sea of sand' (Plate 5.3). A similar region of the Arabian Desert is

Fig. 5.7 Wadi Hadhramaut, South Yemen

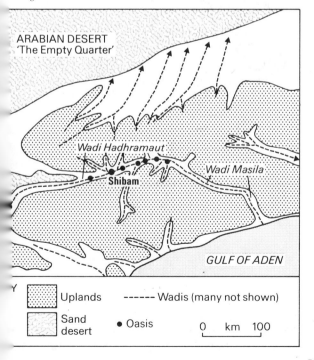

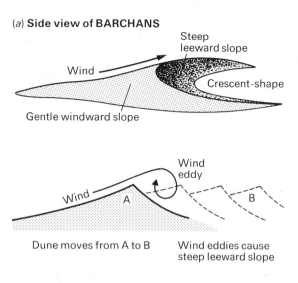

(a) **Side view of BARCHANS**

Dune moves from A to B   Wind eddies cause steep leeward slope

(b) **Plan of parallel SEIFS**

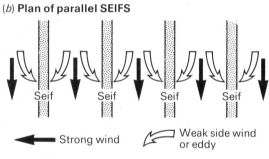

Fig. 5.8 *(a)* Barchans (side view) and *(b)* a plan of parallel seifs

known as the 'empty quarter' (Fig. 5.7). Sometimes the sand is shaped into crescent-like dunes or *barchans* (Fig.5.8a), which move forward in the direction of the prevailing wind. Sometimes the dunes are arranged in long lines, known as *seif* dunes (Fig. 5.8b), running parallel to the prevailing wind, but blown into shape also by weak side winds. Seif dunes can reach 200 m and more in height, and create problems for desert camel trains having to traverse their soft steep slopes when travelling in a direction at right angles to them. As has already been noted, the main desert agent of erosion and deposition is the wind, and when strong winds blow, *sandstorms* are another hazard for the traveller.

(4) Sometimes depressions are formed in desert areas, either through down-faulting, or removal of sand by the wind. These may go down to the water table. If so, *playa lakes* are formed. Owing to the high levels of evaporation, these often dry out and become salt pans or mud flats. Examples are the Great Salt Lake in Utah (USA) and Lake Eyre in Australia.

Plate 5.5 Bedouin nomads near Dhahran, Saudi Arabia

THE HUMAN RESPONSE: TRADITIONAL ADAPTATION

Nomadic Pastoralism: the Bedouin of the Arabian Peninsula

The Bedouin are nomadic pastoralists who wander the desert with herds of camels, sheep and goats (Plate 5.5). They are forced to move in search of pasture for their animals, and have regular lines of movement related to the availability of water.

The camel is the most valued resource (Plate 5.6). Its milk, flesh, hide and hair are all made use of. But above all it is a beast of burden, superbly adapted to desert conditions. Its height keeps its head above the normal level of wind-blown sand, while its hump, made up of fat, functions as a store of food and water. Its broad soft-soled feet are adapted to walking through sand. It also has slit-like nostrils, three eyelids, and small hair-covered ears, all useful protection against sand and duststorms.

Plate 5.6 'Camel Park' North Yemen

The nomads exchange their produce from animals for the food produced in oases, such as grain and dates. They are not only herdsmen but also traders (Plate 5.6). In the south part of the Arabian peninsula, for example, a whole network of caravan routes developed for the spice trade, in frankincense and myrrh, organised by merchants in the towns of the region. Shibam (Plate 5.4) was on one such route.

The traditional way of life is under attack, as Saudi Arabia and adjoining states have become rich through oil extraction. Oil pipelines cross the traditional lines of Bedouin movement. Notice the refinery in the background of Plate 5.5, in the Dhahran region in the east of Saudi Arabia. Oil development also provides employment opportunities, drawing Bedouin into sedentary occupations, as do irrigation developments and measures to control animal disease. These all encourage settled agriculture and discourage nomadism.

Traditional Irrigation: Oasis Agriculture

The presence of oases provides an opportunity, through irrigation, to engage in settled agriculture, produce fruit, vegetables, grains and, above all, the date palm, as in the date gardens of Shibam (Plate 5.4).

Fig. 2.6 shows the Nile valley of Egypt as a strip of very dense population in the middle of a sparsely peopled wilderness. This is because the Nile valley is one long oasis. Nourished by rainfall in the mountains of East Africa, it never dries up. Its annual floods deposit fertile silts, on which crops of maize, sugar cane, cotton, fruits and vegetables are grown. *Traditional methods of irrigation* involve lifting water out of the Nile, and transferring it to irrigation channels, through mechanisms such as the *sakia*, shown on Plate 5.7.

Plate 5.7 Traditional irrigation: a sakia by the White Nile, Su

Older methods have been overtaken by *perennial irrigation*, which is available all the year round as a result of the construction of dams and reservoirs, such as the Aswan Dam on the Nile. Increased production of crops is made possible. But problems have also followed. Reservoirs tend to silt up, lessening the volume of water available for irrigation. More seriously, bringing too much water to the farmland can cause waterlogging and, where evaporation is great, also a high level of salinity (salt content) in the soil, which can be poisonous to plants.

Exercises

1. Refer to Figs.5.1 and 5.2. Describe the distribution and climatic characteristics of the world's hot deserts, explaining why they are so hot and dry.
2. What impact does the desert climate have on
    (a) vegetation; (b) animal life;
    (c) traditional human activities.
3. Outline the main differences between the desert landscapes shown on Plates 5.2 and 5.3
4. Compare the ways of life of desert nomads and oasis dwellers, showing how they depend on each other.

5. (a) Outline the differences between traditional and perennial methods of irrigation, and the advantages and disadvantages of each.
    (b) With the help of an atlas, draw a sketch map of the Nile basin, labelling the main dams and towns, and indicating the climatic zones the river crosses.

THE HUMAN RESPONSE: MODERN DEVELOPMENTS

Oil in the Persian Gulf: Kuwait

The states around the Persian Gulf (Fig. 5.9) form the most important oil producing area in the world today. Although the USA and USSR are major producers, much less of their oil enters world trade. Fig. 5.10 illustrates the great significance of the oil trade route which leaves the Persian Gulf, and supplies the advanced industrialised countries of Western Europe, the USA and Japan with what is now the most important form of energy. The major oil-producing states of the Middle East are Libya and, round the Persian Gulf, Iraq, Iran, Bahrain, the United Arab Emirates, Saudi Arabia and Kuwait.

Fig. 5.9 World oil production and consumption, 1969 and 1979

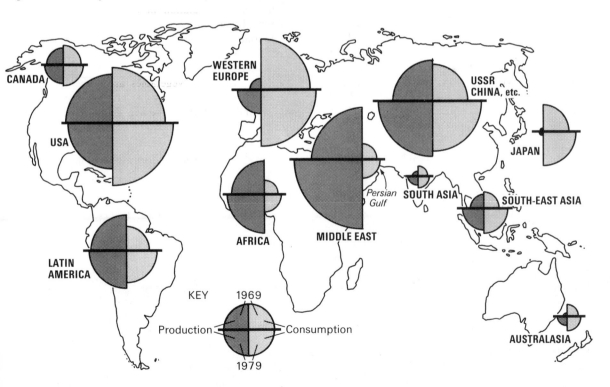

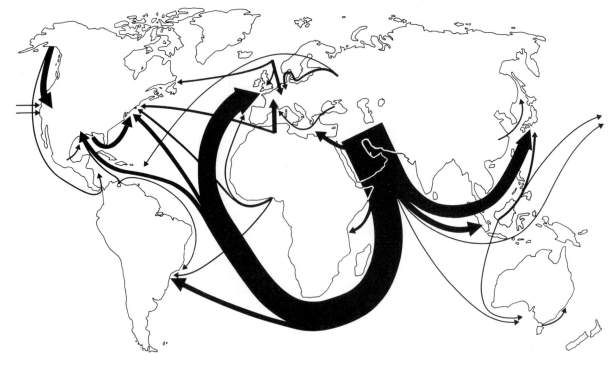

Fig. 5.10 Main oil movements by sea, 1979

Fig. 5.11 Kuwait

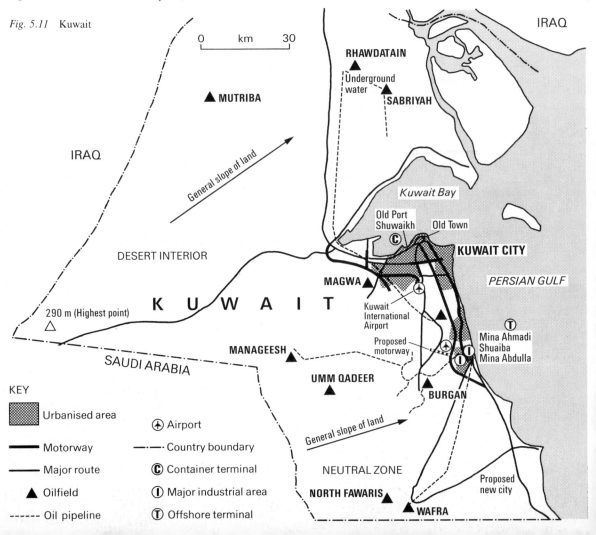

IRAQ

0 km 30

RHAWDATAIN

Underground
water

SABRIYAH

MUTRIBA

IRAQ

General slope of land

Kuwait Bay

Old Port
Shuwaikh

Old Town

KUWAIT CITY

DESERT INTERIOR

PERSIAN GULF

MAGWA

Kuwait
International
Airport

Proposed
motorway

Mina Ahmadi
Shuaiba
Mina Abdulla

K U W A I T

290 m (Highest point)
△

MANAGEESH

UMM QADEER

SAUDI ARABIA

BURGAN

General slope of land

KEY

Urbanised area

Airport

Motorway

Country boundary

Major route

Container terminal

Oilfield

Major industrial area

Oil pipeline

Offshore terminal

NEUTRAL ZONE

Proposed
new city

NORTH FAWARIS

WAFRA

Kuwait illustrates well the boom that has resulted from the rapid exploitation of the oil resources in the post-war period. Its population rose from about 200 000 in 1957 to 1.4 million in 1980. Its gross domestic product (GDP) is the highest in the world, $11 307 per head, as against $8665 in the USA and $4377 in Britain. 85% of government income and 93% of export earnings come from oil.

ADVANTAGES OF KUWAIT OIL

(1) As in most other Middle East oilfields, the oil-bearing sandstones are thick and gently folded and easy to exploit.

(2) The reserves are huge, with a life of about 100 years: the Burgan field (Fig. 5.11) is the second largest in the world, and much of Kuwait's territory is underlain by oil.

(3) The oil is under strong pressure, and at the surface it travels under gravity down gentle easterly slopes, through open country, to the coastal terminals.

(4) The distances involved are small: from well to terminal is often less than 25 km.

The only internal problem is that the oil is high in sulphur content and an expensive desulphurisation plant is required at the refineries.

THE IMPACT OF OIL ON KUWAIT

Apart from the massive growth in national income and population, a most striking development has been the need to bring in immigrant labour, mostly Jordanian and Palestinian, with also considerable numbers from Iraq, Iran, Egypt, India and Pakistan. 54% of the population and 70% of the work-force consists of non-Kuwaitis. They make up 90% of the work-force in manufacturing and 95% in the huge construction industry, building refineries, factories, offices, houses and roads, and making Kuwait one of the most urbanised states in the world. Notice on Plate 5.8 not only the high density, modern, central area development, but also the large number of cars around. Kuwaiti nationals are provided with interest-free loans for housing, and Plate 5.9 shows the sort of houses lived in by people with *limited* income. The immigrant labour, however, lives in much poorer conditions in desert townships on the fringe of the city.

Plate 5.8 Kuwait city

Plate 5.9   Housing for low-income Kuwaiti nationals

Plate 5.10   Shuaiba port, Kuwait

Kuwait oil is nationalised and full use is made of the oil revenues. A major industrial zone has been established in the south-east (Fig. 5.11), away from the capital city, near the oil terminals at Shuaiba (Plate 5.10) and Mina Abdulla. Here are located oil refineries, desulphurisation plants, petro-chemical industries (producing plastics, fertilisers, insecticides and solvents), and factories producing a wide range of constructional materials.

In a rapidly growing state in a desert area, water supply is a problem. Underground reserves are found in the Rhawdatain oilfield (Fig. 5.11), but the state must depend largely on sea-water distillation plants. These are too expensive for most countries but essential in Kuwait. Oil revenues have also been spent on a modern road system, important in a small country which now has half a million vehicles. The government also guarantees employment, provides free education and medical care, and subsidises energy, for Kuwaiti nationals.

Like other oil states, Kuwait has benefited from the vast increase in oil prices from the early 1970s. In the longer term, however, this has led to declining consumption in importing countries, and the early 1980s have seen an oil glut, with the oil states finding it difficult to sell all they want. With vast funds committed to internal development, this is causing problems.

Developing the Negev Desert of Israel

The state of Israel came into being in 1948 to provide a homeland for the Jewish people, millions of whom had been murdered by Nazi Germany in the 'holocaust' of the 1930s and early 1940s. The new state was not recognised by surrounding Arab countries, and large numbers of Palestinian Arabs were displaced (see Chapter 14). Israel continues to exist in a state of conflict with its neighbours and this has sometimes broken out into open war. Israel's population grew rapidly from 1.4 million in 1951 to 3.9 million in 1980. In 1948 the Jewish population was just over 700 000; by 1978 it was 3.1 million. There is still a considerable Arab minority in the population.

At the time Israel was founded, the Negev (Fig. 5.12) was largely an unpopulated desert, used by Bedouin nomadic pastoralists. The flood of Jewish immigrants led to great pressure on the more fertile Mediterranean coastal plain of Israel to the north (see inset to Fig. 5.12). For this reason and for strategic purposes, the Israeli government decided to develop the Negev as much as possible. Between 1948 and 1967 its share of the Jewish population of Israel increased from 0.2 to 5.8%.

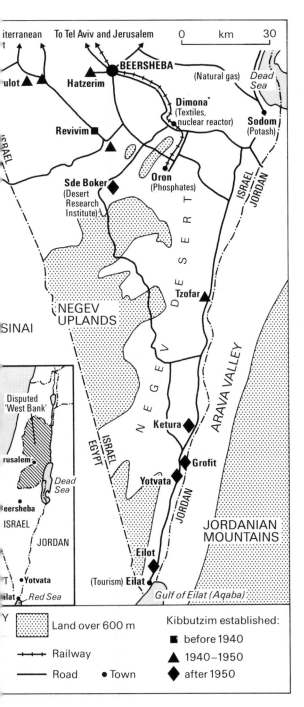

Fig. 5.12 The settlement of the Negev Desert

Map labels:
iterranean
To Tel Aviv and Jerusalem
0 km 30
BEERSHEBA
(Natural gas)
Dead Sea
ulot
Hatzerim
Dimona (Textiles, nuclear reactor)
Revivim
Sodom (Potash)
Sde Boker (Desert Research Institute)
Oron (Phosphates)
ISRAEL
ISRAEL / JORDAN
Tzofar
NEGEV UPLANDS
SINAI
NEGEV DESERT
ARAVA VALLEY
Disputed 'West Bank'
rusalem
Dead Sea
eersheba
ISRAEL
JORDAN
ISRAEL / EGYPT
JORDAN
Ketura
Grofit
Yotvata
JORDANIAN MOUNTAINS
Eilot
Yotvata
ilat
Red Sea
(Tourism) Eilat
Gulf of Eilat (Aqaba)

Land over 600 m

Railway
Road
Town

Kibbutzim established:
■ before 1940
▲ 1940–1950
◆ after 1950

Like Kuwait, Israel is predominantly an urban country. While the kibbutz principle is one the best-known features of Israeli settlement, the rural percentage of the population is small. The kibbutzim have an importance out of all proportion to their numbers, however. First started in 1910, they have been of great significance to Zionism, the movement to find a Jewish homeland. They have

(*a*) symbolised the ideals of national ownership of land, mutual assistance and a moneyless society;

(*b*) allowed the pioneering of difficult areas, such as marshland and desert;

(*c*) produced many of Israel's famous soldiers and politicians;

(*d*) been of great strategic importance, being used for defensive purposes near the frontiers with Arab states. Many have started as *nahal* or military settlements.

Not all cooperative settlements are of the kibbutz type. The *moshavim* are cooperative villages in which the farmers have small-holdings, of equal size and quality of land. There are worked under private initiative, with cooperation in the purchase of seeds, fertilisers and equipment, and in the sale of produce.

The *kibbutzim*, on the other hand, are true collective farms, in which all are expected to work together for the common good. Tasks are assigned to members, whether on the farm, in the canteen, the laundry, or the local factory. No wages or salaries are given, but food, clothing and accommodation are all found. The only cash handed out is for holidays or buying presents. Children are reared together in kindergartens and creches. Income is provided by the collective sale of agricultural produce, and some by non-agricultural enterprises such as manufacturing goods and providing tourist accommodation. Living quarters are separated from the farm and any industrial buildings. In the centre of the living areas are the communal buildings, such as the dining hall and concert hall, children's dormitories and classrooms.

Yotvata Kibbutz

Most of the kibbutzim are in the more fertile, better watered northern parts of Israel, but a number have been established, mostly since 1950, in the Negev (Fig. 5.12). They are located mostly in the Beersheba area, or the Arava valley, and have been designed

65

Fig. 5.13   Trickle irrigation in the Negev. Dark patches indicate wetted areas

Plate 5.11   Yotvata kibbutz, Arava valley

Plate 5.12   Eilat: holiday resort

both to help to open up the Negev and, in the case of those on the Jordan border, some of which began as *nahal* settlements, for defence as well. In both these areas, water from wells or springs is available.

Plate 5.11 shows the setting of Yotvata, with the Jordanian highlands in the background and a barbed wire fence in the foreground, illustrating its frontier position. The dry ground surface is shown, in a desert area which averages less than 50 mm of rain per annum, and experiences temperatures of over 40 °C in summer. Yotvata has the advantage of being sited over an underground water supply, although the water is salty and a desalination plant is needed.

Irrigation is needed in order to grow crops. These have usually been watered by sprinklers, but this method wastes 45% of the water in evaporation, an unacceptable percentage in so dry an area. *Trickle irrigation* (Fig. 5.13) was introduced into Israel at Yotvata. It is expensive to set up, and involves laying plastic pipes along rows of plants, allowing water to drip through holes into the roots. This avoids loss by evaporation, especially when it takes place by night. Chemical fertiliser can also be dissolved in the water to feed the plants. The crops grown include tomatoes and flowers, together with beet, and alfalfa for the dairy herd. There are also date groves and fruit orchards. The key 'industrial' plant is the dairy, not only producing milk and yoghurt, but also buying in concentrated orange juice and processing it into sachets. These are much in demand in a hot desert area and are sold in the kibbutz 'milk bar', located on the road to the holiday resort of Eilat.

Eilat (Plate 5.12) on the Gulf of Aqaba (called Gulf of Eilat by the Israelis) has grown to be an important coastal resort. It has spectacular desert mountain scenery behind and varied beaches and cliffs at the coast. There is almost continuous sunshine which attracts visitors throughout the year. The completion of the road from Beersheba after the war made Eilat's growth possible, and it is planned to connect it by railway also (Fig. 5.12). The hotels of Eilat provide a market for the milk, yoghurt, vegetables, tomatoes, fruit and orange juice of Yotvata. Kibbutz Eilot, just outside Eilat, has a laundry which does the washing for Eilat hotels. The combined impact of the growth of kibbutzim, the tourist industry, and its strategic importance, have made the Arava valley a minor growth point in the Negev.

The main growth area of the Negev, however, is on its northern edge, centred on Beersheba, which has grown considerably in importance since Israel was established. From a population of 5000 in 1948, it had grown to 70 000 by 1967.

Site
Beersheba is sited in a narrow gap in chalk hills, at the confluence of the Nahal Be'er Sheva and a tributary stream (Fig. 5.14). Its main advantage was the presence of good supplies of underground water which could be tapped by wells.

Situation
Beersheba has a classic market-town situation: between uplands and coastal plain; between desert and fertile lowlands; and an economy of nomadic pastoralism and settled agriculture. It was also on the main route between the southern end of the Dead Sea and the Mediterranean Sea, through a gap in the uplands (Fig. 5.12). By the end of World War 2 it was still a small market centre for the local Bedouin population: a frontier town on the 'edge of civilisation', with the wilderness beyond.

Functions
After the foundation of Israel, Beersheba was first used as a military base. It then grew rapidly as a result of the exploitation of resources of the Negev, as roads were built south into the desert. These allowed the development of, for example, the phosphate deposits of Oron. A railway reached the town in 1956, by which time it was an important route centre.

While not an important manufacturing town, Beersheba is the service centre for a region with major extractive industries, both phosphates and natural gas. Dimona is a new town with textile manufacturing and a nuclear station, many of whose employees live in Beersheba. Beersheba has become an important residential centre. Plate 5.13 shows one of its early new housing estates, with irrigated trees being planted to break up the arid monotony. Such estates, and the many tertiary activities such as offices, have been a boost to the construction industry in the region.

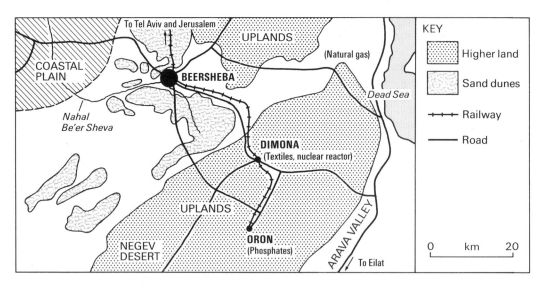

Fig. 5.14 Beersheba (Be'er Sheva): a desert town

Plate 5.13 Beersheba: the modern city under construction

Exercises

6. Compare the sites, situations, urban landscapes and ways of life of the people, of Shibam and Kuwait.

7. Refer to Fig.5.9.

(*a*) Outline major changes in oil production and consumption between 1969 and 1979.

(*b*) Describe and explain the distribution of major consumers.

(*c*) With the help also of Fig. 5.10, outline how the pattern of production and consumption is reflected in the main lines of trade in oil.

8. Compare the irrigation techniques used in the Arava valley with those of the Nile valley.

9. Compare and contrast the locations and functions of Eilat and Beersheba.

6 Tropical Grasslands (Savanna)

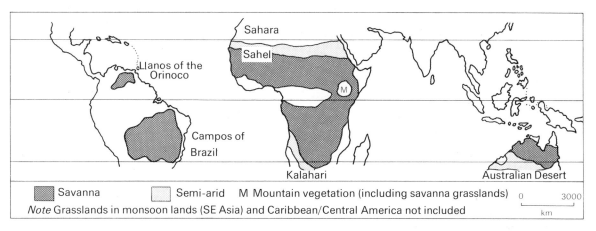

Fig. 6.1 Tropical grasslands (savanna): location

The tropical grasslands (savanna) extend approximately from 5 ° to 20 ° both north and south of the equator, in South America, northern Australia and especially in Africa (Fig. 6.1). In East Africa the grasslands cross the equator, for here the land is much higher and altitudinally above the equatorial forest zone. The savanna grasslands are a transition zone between equatorial forest and desert.

PHYSICAL FEATURES

Climate

The savanna region experiences considerable seasonal variations in temperature and rainfall (Fig. 6.2*a*, *b*).

TEMPERATURE

Summer temperatures average 26–30 °C, and winter 21–24 °C, giving an annual range of from 3 °C to 9 °C. In the summer season, the sun is vertically overhead and a high degree of insolation occurs, giving hot conditions. In the winter season, the sun is overhead in the opposite hemisphere, but remains quite high in the sky, and conditions remain very warm. The length of daylight varies more than at the equator, giving a higher range of temperature than in equatorial latitudes.

Fig. 6.2 Tropical grasslands: climatic graphs

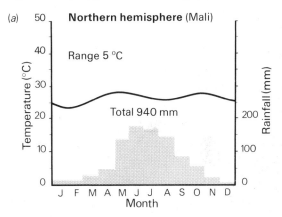

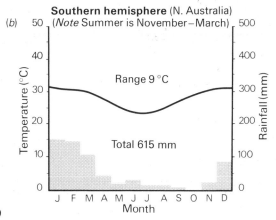

This varies from an annual average of about 1500 mm at the equatorial forest margin to about 600 mm towards the desert margin. Here the rainfall is unreliable, the rainy season shorter, and rainfall totals are much lower. Rain falls mainly in summer, mostly during the hot afternoons.

The rainy season occurs when the equatorial low-pressure belt moves polewards during the summer. This contains *the inter-tropical front*, a zone of convergence of air masses, causing rising air, condensation and rainfall (Fig. 6.3). At this time winds are drawn towards the front from sea to land (onshore winds) and are therefore moist. Additionally, there is convection rain in the hot afternoons.

In winter, however, the tropical high-pressure belt moves towards the equator. Under high-pressure conditions air descends and becomes drier. At this season winds are blowing from land to sea (offshore winds), and these are warm and dry.

West Africa (Fig. 6.3) provides a very good example of these processes in operation in a climatic transition zone in which, as one moves polewards, the amount of rainfall decreases, the reliability of the rainfall decreases, the length of the rainy season decreases, and summer heat increases.

The Sahel (Fig. 6.3) is very much at the desert margin and, owing to a series of droughts between 1968 and 1974, during which period the inter-tropical front did not reach this far north, it became almost true desert. This hot region, which normally averages modest rainfall totals of from 250 mm to 750 mm per annum (see inset on Fig. 6.3), saw the desert marching south. Drought is always normal in the Sahel in the winter season, when the hot dusty wind from the Sahara, the *harmattan*, blows, causing great discomfort (Plate 6.1).

Vegetation

Savanna vegetation follows fairly closely the climatic transition between equatorial forest and desert. Near the equatorial forest margin, patches of woodland still persist, mixed with tall coarse grass (elephant grass), providing a continuous cover over the soil. The true savanna is a parkland landscape of open grassland with occasional trees, such as the characteristically flat-topped acacia shown on Plate 6.2. Towards the desert margin, the grass becomes shorter, wiry and tussocky, with bare soil between the clumps. There are thornier acacia trees, with small leaves to reduce transpiration,

Fig. 6.3 Drought in the Sahel

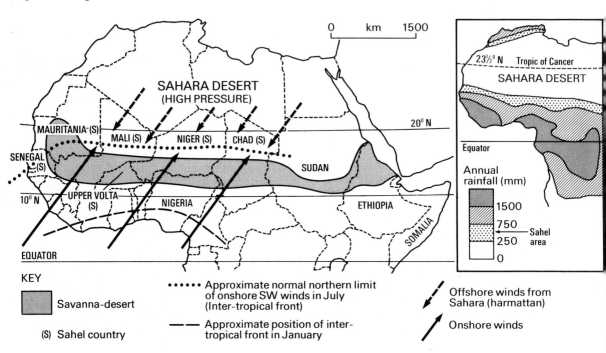

KEY

Savanna-desert

(S) Sahel country

•••••• Approximate normal northern limit of onshore SW winds in July (Inter-tropical front)

——— Approximate position of inter-tropical front in January

Offshore winds from Sahara (harmattan)

Onshore winds

Plate 6.1   A dust-storm in the Sahel

and the barrel-trunked baobab tree, with deep roots tapping soil water, and the capacity to store water inside the trunk. All of these features are illustrated on Plate 6.3.

In the hot season there is vigorous growth, but in the dry season grasses wither and deciduous trees shed their leaves. Ground water conditions are important as well as rainfall, and patches of rain forest replace grassland near rivers. When drought conditions occur,

herds of animals seek pasture and the vegetation is further degraded by over-grazing. This occurs particularly round water holes, where all the grass can be stripped, causing *desertification* (Plate 6.4).

Plate 6.3   A baobab tree, Tanzania

Plate 6.2   Savanna grassland and wildlife in Kenya

71

Plate 6.4 The dry edge of the savanna: a water hole in the Sahel

TRADITIONAL ADAPTATION IN THE SAVANNA REGION OF WEST AFRICA

Types of Agriculture

Three main types of agriculture reflect the transition of climate and vegetation in West Africa (Fig. 6.4):

(1) *Nomadic pastoralism* is still practised by groups such as the Fulani. It is found mainly in areas with less than 600 mm of rainfall per annum, and generally north of the Niger River. In the short summer rain season the pastoralists move north in search of water and pastures, while in the long dry season they move south again. This is a form of *transhumance*.

(2) *Mixed pastoral/agricultural subsistence farming* is becoming more important at the expense of pure nomadic pastoralism, however. Only about 8% of the Fulani population of northern Nigeria (Fig. 6.4) are still purely pastoralists, for example. Under the mixed economy, transhumance is practised on a more limited scale near the homestead, made possible by the richer vegetation of more southerly areas. The main crops grown are millet and guinea corn (sorghum). Guinea corn, requiring over 750 mm of rain, is found to the south of the millet growing area.

Fig. 6.4 Agricultural regions of West Africa

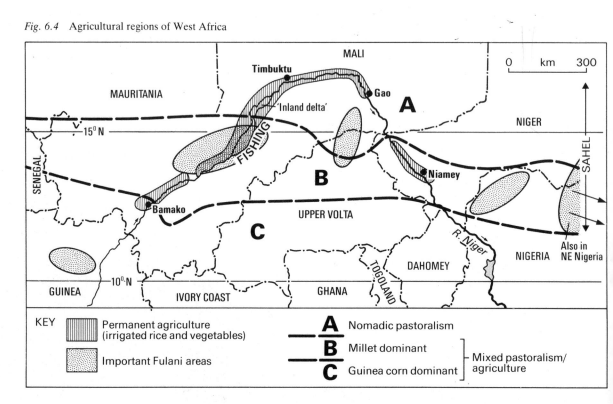

(3) *Permanent agriculture* depends on the flooding of the Niger or on irrigation. In these areas, rice can be planted on the damp clayey plains. Near towns such as Niamey and Bamako (Fig. 6.4) vegetables are grown. Fishing in the 'inland delta' area between Bamako and Timbuktu (Fig. 6.4) increases the protein content in the diet. These towns are ancient market centres, exchanging the produce of the settled agriculturalists of the south for that of the nomadic peoples to the north, and also for the salt of the Sahara region, brought by nomadic traders.

THE GREAT SAHEL DROUGHT 1968–74

Although the peoples of the Sahel countries have long been used to normal drought conditions, they were unable to adapt to the unprecedented series of droughts between 1968 and 1974 when the Sahara Desert extended south. The six countries of the Sahel (Fig. 6.3) have a combined population of about twenty-five million, and are among the poorest countries on earth (see Chapter 15). The impact of the droughts was disastrous. In one year alone, 1973, it was estimated that 100 000 people died from famine, and untold numbers of animals perished. Plate 6.5 shows the drought-ravaged landscape. People had to walk much further to find water, and many had to leave their homes to try to find food. As the vegetation dried out, hungry animals scoured the region (Plate 6.6) for whatever herbage remained. Round water holes, the vegetation was completely destroyed by the converging animals,

and the land became a dust bowl (Plate 6.4).

The problem was worst for the nomadic pastoral groups whose animals had died. They were forced into camps on the outskirts of towns such as Timbuktu and Gao in Mali (Fig. 6.4) and Dakar in Senegal. In 1973–4, the refugee camps of Mali contained 43 000 nomads depending on food handouts, and 28 000 camped in local rice-growing areas. The settled agriculturalists were at first less badly hit, but as crops ran out, about 24 000 settled agriculturalists in Mali also sought aid.

Since 1974 the droughts have receded, and increased overseas aid has improved the situation. Various solutions have also been tried, but some of them create further problems.

(1) Vaccination of cattle has improved their health, but has meant an increase in numbers, causing further over-grazing and destruction of vegetation.
(2) Money has also been spent on making concreted wells (see Plate 15.7), which conserve water and make it less liable to contamination. But the more cattle that can use a well, the worse the problem of over-grazing near it.
(3) The heavy summer rainstorms of the region lead to rapid run-off and evaporation. One means of retaining the water is by holding it back in earth dams; cultivation can then take place downstream from the dam, using irrigation water. The presence of a water supply, however, encourages nomadic pastoralists to settle by it, once more causing over-grazing.

Plate 6.5 Drought in the Sahel

Plate 6.6   Emaciated cattle in the Sahel drought of 1973

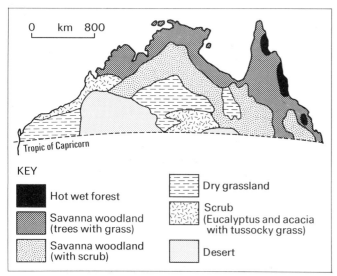

Fig. 6.5   Tropical Australia: vegetation

Fig. 6.6   Tropical Australia: cattle ranching

Exercises

1. (a) Explain what is meant by a 'climatic transition', illustrating from the case of the savanna region of West Africa.
   (b) Show how Plates 6.2, 6.3 and 6.4 reflect a transition in vegetation types. Indicate how this is related to the climate.
   (c) Explain why rainfall is so unreliable in the Sahel region.
2. (a) Outline the distribution of different farming activities on Fig. 6.4, and show how these are related to climate and vegetation.
   (b) Describe the impact of the great drought of the 1968–74 period on the landscape and people of the Sahel countries.
   (c) Explain why they had to seek foreign aid and outline the problems this in turn has caused.

MODERN DEVELOPMENTS IN TROPICAL AUSTRALIA

Commercial Beef Ranching

Fig. 6.5 suggests a more complicated pattern of vegetation in northern Australia than in West Africa. It is basically a savanna region, however, ranging from eucalyptus woodland with plenty of grass, to very sparse, scrubby grassland. The range is thus from desert in the central interior to small areas of hot wet forest on the Queensland coast. The region has a true savanna climate with rains brought in summer (November–April) by onshore north-westerly winds, while the winter drought is associated with offshore south-east winds from the interior desert. The November–April period is very hot and the May–October very warm (Fig. 6.2b).

Fig. 6.6 shows the distribution of cattle rearing and fattening areas in Australia; rearing is found in savanna areas with rainfalls of from 400 mm to 1000 mm per annum.

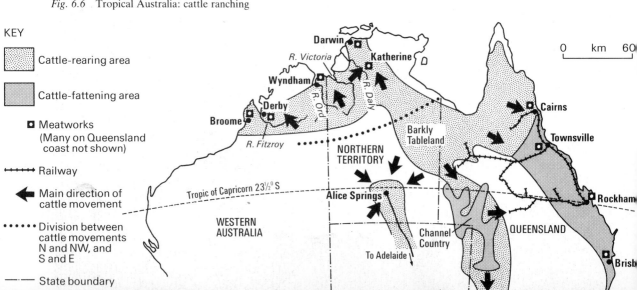

ADVANTAGES FOR BEEF RANCHING

(1) There are vast expanses of grassland, not readily usable for any other form of farming. The properties of land used for beef ranching are huge, of several thousand square kilometres, with a central homestead. They are found particularly on the more favoured grasslands of the Barkly Tableland and the valleys running to the north-west coast (Fig. 6.6). Plate 6.7 shows the Victoria Downs Station on the Ord River.

(2) During the wet season the creeks and water holes fill up, and the grass grows to produce good grazing, although the food value of the grasses is of variable quality.

(3) During the dry season, the ranchers have access to underground sources of water, usually from wells sunk into *artesian basins*, found in the north of Western Australia and the west of Queensland. In the latter (Fig. 6.7), rain falling on the Eastern Highlands seeps

Plate 6.7   Victoria Downs cattle station, Ord River valley

Fig. 6.7   Great artesian basin

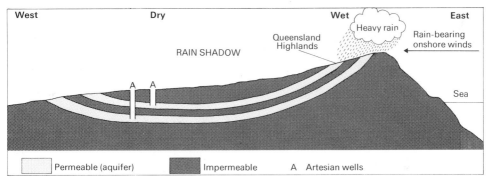

Plate 6.8   The Channel country

into the permeable water-bearing layer (aquifer) and moves downslope, to be tapped in the dry interior. The average depth of the wells is 400–500 m. True artesian water rises under its own pressure, but water can also be pumped out (sub-artesian).

(4) A potential problem is finding stockhands to engage in the difficult and lonely job of mustering the cattle on the 'open range', where there are few fences. This is done once or twice a year. The indigenous people of this area, the aboriginals, are often used as stockhands.

(5) Certain areas are suitable for fattening cattle, which lose weight after their long drive from the rearing areas. Such areas need to be near rail-heads or the meatworks themselves. As Fig. 6.6 shows, the fattening areas include eastern Queensland and the Channel country. The latter, shown on Plate 6.8, consists of the alluvial soils of a former huge delta, which floods after the summer rains and leaves rich pasture. Another fattening area is in the Ord River valley, where irrigation water helps to produce better grassland and nourishing fodder crops.

(6) European cattle, particularly shorthorns, have been crossed with Indian Brahmin cattle to produce strains able to flourish in the tropical conditions.

(7) There is a large demand for beef in the affluent towns and cities of more southern parts of Australia, and 80% of the output is consumed at home. Most of the rest is exported to the USA and Japan.

PROBLEMS FOR BEEF RANCHING

(1) European breeds tend to suffer under tropical conditions from pneumonia, cattle tick and buffalo fly. Inter-breeding with Indian cattle, has, however, made them more adaptable.

(2) The main problem is undoubtedly *drought*, for even in the wet season the rains are not reliable, for the same sort of reasons as in West Africa. By the end of the dry season also, there is usually severe water shortage, and the pastures are generally poor.

(3) *Inaccessibility* of the cattle-rearing areas from markets means that cattle have to be driven 'on the hoof' from areas such as the Barkly Tableland to the Queensland rail-heads (Fig. 6.6) and Alice Springs (Plate 6.9). Others are taken by road, as to the meatworks at Wyndham and Katherine in the north. Meatworks are also to be found in east coast towns, reached by the railways from the interior.

In being driven over long distances, the cattle lose weight and therefore value. The northern meatworks are vital to the beef industry of Northern Territory and Western Australia. The opening of the meatworks at Katherine doubled the price per head for stock.

Plate 6.9 A rail-head near Alice Springs

Plate 6.10 Weipa on the remote Queensland coast

Mining in Northern Australia (Table 6.1)

RESERVES

In the last twenty years, remote areas of northern Australia have been opened up by the discovery and exploitation of valuable mineral deposits. On the northern coast of Queensland at Weipa (Plate 6.10) and at Gove in Northern Territory are some of the world's largest bauxite deposits. Manganese is produced in the iron ore region of Western Australia and on Groote Eylandt off the Northern Territory coast; while major

Table 6.1 Mining in northern Australia: world ranking (1978)

	Bauxite	Iron ore	Manganese	Uranium*
(1)	**Australia**	USSR	USSR	USA
(2)	Guinea	**Australia**	South Africa	South Africa
(3)	Jamaica	USA	Gabon	Canada
(4)	USSR	Brazil	Brazil	France
(5)	Surinam	China	**Australia**	Niger
(6)	Guyana	Canada	India	**Australia**

* Major recent discoveries in the Alligator Rivers district of Northern Territory will undoubtedly lift Australia's ranking as they are developed.

Fig. 6.8 Mineral deposits of tropical Australia

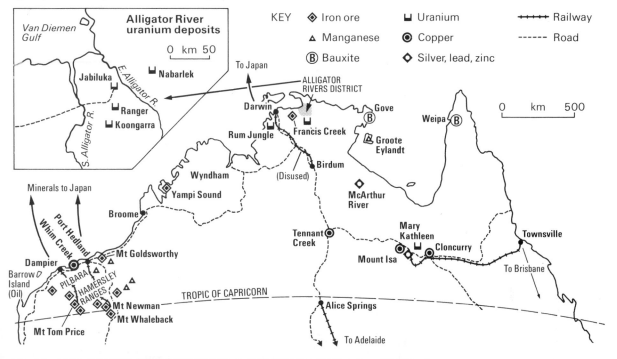

Plate 6.11 Open-cast iron mining at Mount Whaleback

reserves of uranium are being exploited at Rum Jungle and are about to be exploited in the Alligator Rivers district (Fig. 6.8). Reserves here and in other parts of Australia make it the world's third largest producer of lead and zinc, sixth largest of silver, and tenth largest of copper. With a few exceptions, such as Mount Isa in Queensland, the reserves have been recently developed, are extensive, and have a long life in front of them.

IRON MINING

Opportunities

Fig. 6.8 shows the location of massive deposits of iron ore in the Hamersley Ranges of Western Australia, at Mount Tom Price, Mount Newman and Mount Whaleback, and at Mount Goldsworthy near the coast. The great advantages are the high grade of the ores, which have an iron content of over 60%, the vastness of the deposits, and the fact that they can be mined by open-cast methods, as at Mount Whaleback (Plate 6.11), an iron mountain over 5 km long and 1 km wide, covering 568 hectares.

Plate 6.12   The railway from Mount Goldsworthy to Port Hedland

Plate 6.13 An iron ore terminal at Dampier

Railways have been built to carry the ores to iron terminals at Dampier (for Mount Tom Price) and Port Hedland (for Mount Newman, Mount Whaleback and Mount Goldsworthy). Plate 6.12 shows a long train carrying ore from Mount Goldsworthy. At the coast, deep water terminals are found at Dampier and Port Hedland which take huge bulk carriers. Plate 6.13 shows the stock piles of iron and loading piers at Dampier, together with a pelletisation plant which raises the iron content to 90% purity and makes it more economic to export. Most of the ore, together with manganese, is sent to Japan, which is not much further away by sea than the steel-making centres of the south and east of Australia.

Problems

The ore is bulky and costly to transport, and the railways and processing facilities needed to do this have had to be constructed at enormous expense in a remote region. To open Mount Tom Price cost 60 million Australian dollars ($A) for the mine; $A 63 million for the railway; $A 19 million for rolling stock and $A 83 million for building the port at Dampier. Apart from this there is the difficulty of shipping in materials for construction.

This is one of the hottest regions in the world. Marble Bar, on the road to Port Hedland, has recorded temperatures of 32 °C and over on 151 consecutive days, and the average January temperature is over 40 °C. To attract employees, high wages have to be paid, perhaps 25% above the national average. At Mount Newman in 1970 there were fewer than 600 workers, but these were of 47 different nationalities. Expensive air-conditioned residential facilities have also had to be built for employees.

THE VALUE OF MINING TO THE AUSTRALIAN ECONOMY

(1) The exploitation of the mineral reserves of the north has helped to open up a remote 'outback' tropical region (see Plates 6.10 and 6.12), and has brought a lot of new employment, not only in the mining, but also in ancillary services (see Plate 6.13).
(2) New trading patterns have been opened up. Australia's links with Britain and Western Europe declined in the 1960s and 1970s, but have increased vastly across the Pacific with Japan in particular, and also the USA. By 1970, Japan was taking 70% of Australia's iron ore exports.
(3) The mining companies contribute large amounts of royalties to state budgets. Thus in 1970 Western Australia received over $A 20 million in royalties.

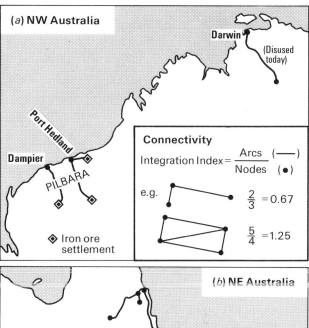

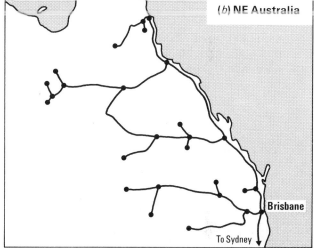

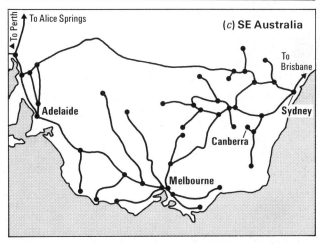

Fig. 6.9   The railways of Australia

79

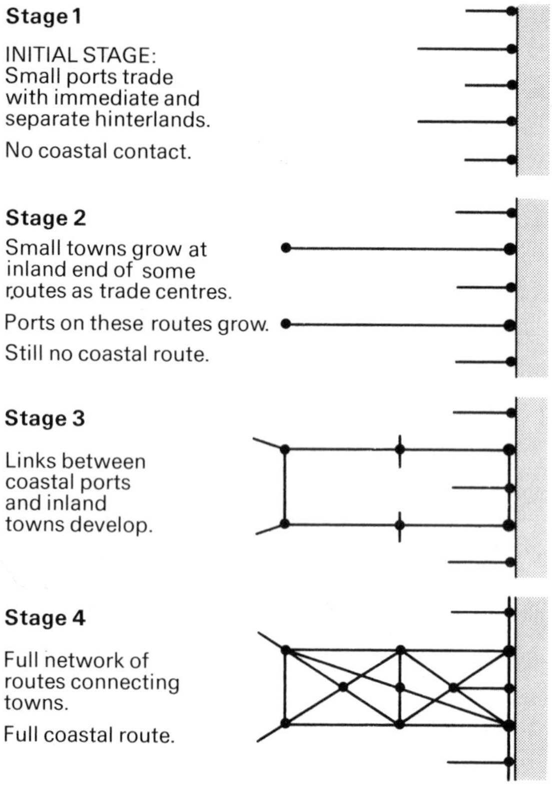

Stage 1

INITIAL STAGE:
Small ports trade
with immediate and
separate hinterlands.

No coastal contact.

Stage 2

Small towns grow at
inland end of some
routes as trade centres.

Ports on these routes grow.

Still no coastal route.

Stage 3

Links between
coastal ports
and inland
towns develop.

Stage 4

Full network of
routes connecting
towns.

Full coastal route.

Fig. 6.10 The theoretical development of a transport network

Exercises

5. Outline the differences between cattle farming in the Sahel countries and in northern Australia.
6. (a) Compare and contrast iron ore production in northern Australia and northern Sweden (Chapter 3).
   (b) Why do you think a steel plant has *not* been set up at Dampier or Port Hedland, while one has at Lulea?
7. Fig. 6.9 *a,b,* and *c* show maps of the railway networks of three corners of Australia. The inset shows a theoretical way of comparing these networks with regard to their degree of development. It indicates that the *connectivity* (degree of connection) can be worked out through an *integration index*, dividing *arcs* (in this case railways) by *nodes* (settlements)
   (a) Work out the integration index for (i) Port Hedland (ii) Dampier and Darwin (iii) north-east Australia as a whole* (iv) south-east Australia as a whole.*
   (*Count as a single arc each of the lines marked as arrows to Sydney, Brisbane, Perth and Alice Springs.)
   (b) What do the indices tell you about the degree of connection of railways in these three quadrants of Australia?
   (c) These maps show only railways. With the help of Fig. 6.8 indicate the impact of roads on the connectivity index of the north-western quadrant.
8. Fig. 6.10 indicates a theoretical model of the development of a rail network.
   (a) Describe in your own words what the model shows, at each stage of development.
   (b) What stage of development does (i) north-west Australia, (ii) north-east Australia, (iii) south-east Australia, most nearly fit?
   (c) Does the road network of north-west Australia (Fig. 6.8) make any difference to your choice? If so, what?
   (d) Why is the Pilbara region at an early 'stage of development'?
   (Note that the railways were built much later than those of other parts of Australia.)
9. With the help of a recent atlas, draw a map of the countries of West Africa from Senegal round to Nigeria, together with the railway systems and the major towns they connect. Work out the 'stage of development' of at least four different countries.

7 Equatorial Forests

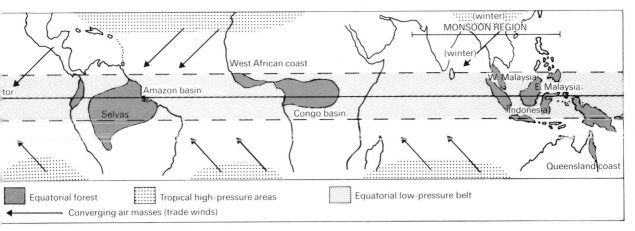

Fig. 7.1 Equatorial forests: location

The equatorial (hot, wet) forest zone (Fig. 7.1) is, as the name suggests, confined to latitudes up to 10° from the equator. In many areas it then shades into savanna woodland (Chapter 6), but in South-east Asia tropical evergreen forest extends into the monsoon regions (Chapter 8).

PHYSICAL FEATURES

Climate

The following is a description of normal afternoon weather in the equatorial forest region, in this case the jungles of West Malaysia:

> Then, away at the eastern end of the valley the clouds banked together and became dark and swollen. They moved slowly and heavily in the sky and in the jungle there was no movement. Only the heat and the stillness and the silence of the midday. And the bank of clouds came surging up the valley, blanketing the hilltops, and from afar came the grumbling of thunder and the noise of the rain in the trees like soldiers marching. Suddenly a soft wind came, gently, moving the tall grasses, whispering through the tops of the high trees.   . . .
>
> The noise of the rain came first, moving swiftly along the valley, and then big drops of rain spattered into the dust making a speckled pattern on the dried earth of the track across the clearing. It hissed on the bare rocks and then the clouds were upon us and the rain was coming from above, forcefully, pounding down into the parched earth; running in little rivers between the cracks in the boulders, splashing in puddles, seeping down deep into the dried grass; cascading in tiny waterfalls from the ends of branches; spouting from lengths of creeper; dripping in crystals from the tips of the leaves; bubbling and gurgling as it rushed in small torrents through the roots of the trees. The air became brighter and the sultriness of the day vanished.
>
> (from J.Slimmimg *Temiar Jungle: a Malayan Journey*, John Murray 1958)

81

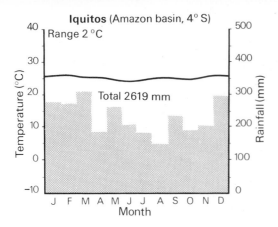

Fig. 7.2   Equatorial forests: climatic graph

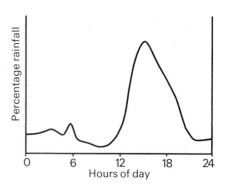

Fig. 7.3   Daily rainfall at Kuala Lumpur

TEMPERATURE

Temperatures are more or less uniform through the year, averaging about 25 °C. There is little range of temperature between seasons, at most 2 or 3 °C (Fig. 7.2). Altitude makes a considerable difference to the temperature level (see Chapter 4).

The high and even temperatures result from the fact that the sun at mid-day is always high in the sky. Length of daylight varies little through the seasons, giving a constant level of insolation. Temperatures are slightly higher at the equinoxes (March in northern hemisphere and September in southern hemisphere) when the sun is vertically overhead at the equator, and slightly lower at the solstices (June in northern hemisphere and December in southern hemisphere), when the sun is overhead at the tropics.

RAINFALL

Heavy rainfall is experienced at all seasons, totalling at least 1800 mm per annum, and usually over 2000 mm (Fig. 7.2). There is no distinguishable wet or dry season, but there are sometimes slight peaks at the equinoxes. As the previous extract indicated, rainfall is normally received every day in heavy outbursts during the afternoon. Fig. 7.3 illustrates the high percentage of rainfall received after mid-day in the West Malaysian capital, Kuala Lumpur.

The heavy and regular rainfall results from the constant presence of the equatorial low pressure belt, drawing in air masses from the tropical high pressure zones (Fig. 7.1). When this converging air meets, it rises, causing condensation and rainfall. Intense heat from the sun, and transpiration from the forests give high humidity daily. Rising convection currents lead to towering cumulus clouds and heavy afternoon rain. Thunderstorms are common in these conditions.

As Fig. 7.1 suggests, there are complications in South-east Asia, where the equatorial region becomes mixed with the monsoon region (Chapter 8). Here there is a seasonal reversal of wind direction. In West Malaysia, for example, south-west winds dominate from June to September and north-east from November to February. The season of heaviest rainfall thus varies more here than in other equatorial areas. Every month has rain, but the west coast has most rain in the 'summer' monsoon period, and the east during the 'winter' monsoon. The west side is, however, drier as it is protected by Sumatra from the full force of the south-west monsoon. The heaviest rainfall is in the eastern highlands, where it rises over 3500 mm per annum (Fig. 7.11).

Vegetation

CHARACTERISTICS

Plate 7.1 is an aerial view of the dense equatorial forest of the Cameroon Highlands of the Malayan peninsula. Plate 7.2 is an interior view of this tangled luxuriant forest. Both photographs indicate how difficult the forest is to penetrate without modern technology. The forest is characterised by a vast number of species, dominated by evergreen trees.

The following are usually present:

(a) a layered growth of forest with, at the top, tall *emergents* growing out above the general level (Fig. 7.4);

(b) below this a middle layer of tall trees growing close together, with the crowns forming a continuous canopy in places;

(c) below this a lower layer of smaller trees forming additional leaf canopies;

Plate 7.1 Equatorial forest in Malaysia

(*d*) little undergrowth, except near rivers and clearings, where direct sunlight can get through;

(*e*) rope-like plants called *lianas*, growing from the shaded ground and reaching light in the higher canopies by climbing the larger trees;

(*f*) plants growing *on* the trees, between branches and trunks, called *epiphytes;*

(*g*) parasitic plants which feed on the sap of the tree, eventually killing it;

(*h*) strong buttressed roots;

(*i*) at the coast or by rivers, *mangrove trees*, rising above mudbanks on stilt-like roots.

Plate 7.2 Inside the equatorial forest

Fig. 7.4 Equatorial rain forest

The constant heat and moisture encourage continuous and luxuriant growth. Trees are therefore *evergreen*, with new leaves growing as old leaves fall, at irregular intervals. Leaves are generally thick and leathery, so as to be able to stand strong sunlight. They often have a downward 'drip-tip', to enable them to get rid of rainwater and dry relatively quickly. Plants are so crowded that there is a constant struggle to survive in competition with other plants. It must be emphasised that the equatorial forest tends to 'feed on itself'. Very little of its organic matter is passed through to the soil, for example, which is why equatorial soils are infertile.

The large trees develop spreading buttresses to enable their weight to be distributed over the moist ground. The mangrove tree has a complicated root system, with stilt roots, which anchors the plant to its muddy environment.

TRADITIONAL ADAPTATION: WEST MALAYSIA (MALAYAN PENINSULA)

Hunting and Gathering

Hunting and gathering peoples are found in all the equatorial forest areas, although their numbers are very rapidly decreasing. They collect leaves, shoots, berries, nuts, fruits and tubers. They hunt small forest mammals and birds, using blow-pipes or bows with the darts or arrows tipped with poison, Alternatively they set traps. Fishing in the rivers is also practised.

Shifting Cultivation

This is a widespread activity, found not only in equatorial but also other tropical forests. It is practised by the majority of the indigenous tribes of Malaysia, where it is known as *ladang* cultivation. It is a system of agricultural adaptation to infertile tropical soils:

(*a*) a clearing (ladang) is made in the forest by *slash and burn* methods, cutting down and burning the felled tress, the ash of which helps to fertilise the soil for a short period;

(*b*) crops such as hill padi (rice), maize, bananas and tapioca are planted;

(*c*) these are not tended, but merely harvested when ready;

(*d*) after two or three years, the tropical clay soil has lost its fertility, and the group moves on to another part of the forest to start the cycle by slash and burn methods again;

(*e*) the old clearing reverts to secondary, less luxuriant, forest, known as *belukar* in Malaysia.

Shifting cultivation of the traditional type does not, however, lead to serious destruction of the forest. The density of population is so low that the forest has time to regenerate before it is used again.

The Senoi of the Malayan Peninsula

Many of the aboriginal groups of the remote Malayan highlands (Fig. 7.9) engage in both hunting and gathering, and shifting cultivation. The Senoi are an example. Their dwellings are long-houses built of

Plate 7.3   Senoi long-house, West Malaysia

bamboo with grass-thatch for roof material (Plate 7.3). Animals such as pigs and hens are kept to scavenge round the clearing. Inside the long-house (Plate 7.4) about thirty people live communally. The long-house is destroyed when the tribe moves to a new clearing.

During this century, the shifting cultivators have come increasingly into contact with more advanced groups, and have engaged in trade. Highland jungle produce, such as bamboo and fruit, is exchanged with lowland settled groups for axes, food vessels, matches and the like. The Malaysian aboriginals are increasingly merging with the settled agriculturalists of the lowlands. Their distinctive identity is being lost, together with their skills. At best they settle themselves on the fringe of the forest and make a living from small craft industries such as basket making and wood carving.

Plate 7.4   Inside a Senoi long-house

Exercises

PENANG	J	F	M	A	M	J	J	A	S	O	N	D		
Temperature (°C)	27	27	27	28	27	27	27	27	27	27	26	26	Range	2
Rainfall (mm)	100	75	125	180	280	180	225	330	480	410	280	125	Total	2 790

1. (a) On the basis of the figures given above, draw a temperature and rainfall graph for Penang.
   (b) Compare and contrast its characteristics with those for Iquitos (Fig. 7.2).
2. Explain why weather conditions in equatorial regions vary
   (a) little seasonally (b) greatly diurnally.
3. (a) Describe the characteristics of equatorial forest vegetation as shown on Fig. 7.4 and Plates 7.1 and 7.2.
   (b) Explain how this vegetation is adapted to physical conditions.

4. Make drawings or labelled diagrams to show the stages involved in shifting cultivation.
5. The type of environment which the Senoi people live in is sometimes described as 'hostile' in western texts.
   (a) In what ways would you find it hostile?
   (b) Try to imagine you were a member of the Senoi group coming to a British city. Write about ways in which you would be likely to find this environment hostile.
6. Outline the differences between the vegetation of equatorial and coniferous (Chapter 3) forests.

Commercial Plantation Agriculture: Rubber in West Malaysia

PLANTATION AGRICULTURE

Plantation agriculture is a form of commercial agriculture in that the produce is grown for sale, and generally, in tropical regions, for export. It is also a form of *monoculture* in that it involves the culture of one plant year after year. The main tropical plantation crops are rubber (especially Malaysia and Indonesia), cocoa (Ghana), palm oil (Nigeria), coffee (Brazil, Colombia, East African countries), tea (India, Sri Lanka, Japan, China, East African countries), sugar cane and bananas (Brazil, West Indies).

Plantation agriculture has a number of advantages.
(1) The fact that the same plants are all together makes collecting easy.
(2) There are considerable *economies of scale*, as commercial plantation agriculture is usually on a large scale, often controlled by multi-national corporations.
(3) Plantation agriculture is usually labour intensive, and provides work for local populations. In fact it has often been associated with exploitation of labour, especially migrant labour. The sugar plantations of Brazil and the West Indies, for example, were built up on slave labour.

(4) The influx of capital from outside makes possible the building of railways and roads to make the plantations accessible to ports for export. These lines of communication can open up the country for other purposes.

Large-scale plantations require much capital investment, as it may be some years before the trees or shrubs begin to produce.

RUBBER PLANTATIONS IN WEST MALAYSIA

Of the total world rubber production of 3.7 million tonnes in 1978, 1.5 million came from Malaysia and 0.9 from Indonesia. The rubber tree formerly grew wild in the Amazon forests. In the late nineteenth century, seeds were smuggled out of Brazil, via England, to form the basis of the rubber plantations in Southeast Asia. Plantation rubber was able to meet the huge twentieth-century demand for vehicle tyres and other products.

The west side of the Malayan peninsula has ideal conditions for rubber production:
(*a*) mean monthly temperatures between 25 °C and 28 °C;
(*b*) mean annual rainfalls of over 2000 mm with no month less than 75 mm;
(*c*) well-drained soils on the slopes of valleys which run west from the Malayan highlands (Fig. 7.5);
(*d*) access to ports such as Penang and Singapore (Fig. 7.5) via a well-developed road and rail system;
(*e*) a cheap and plentiful labour supply, mainly brought in from India.

Rubber is made from *latex*, the sap of the rubber tree, which is tapped by making a slanting cut in the trunk, allowing the latex to flow into a cup placed below the cut. The latex is a white liquid which is taken to a factory, diluted, sieved and coagulated by the addition of acid. It is then passed through rollers to form rubber sheets, which are then dried in the sun or in a smoking shed. Finally the sheets are packed into bales for export.

The rubber industry and the tin mining found in the same area (Fig. 7.5) make the standard of living in West Malaysia the highest in South-east Asia. The rubber industry, however, faces problems caused by fluctuating world prices, and the increasing competition of synthetic products. It is also at a stage when many of the trees planted in the early part of the century have reached the end of their productive life, of about thirty-five years. It is expensive to plant new trees, but these are higher yielders and eventually bring down costs of production.

Fig. 7.5 Major economic products of West Malaysia

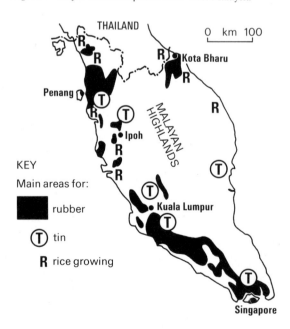

THAILAND

0 km 100

Kota Bharu

Penang

Ipoh

MALAYAN HIGHLANDS

KEY

Main areas for:

rubber

(T) tin

R rice growing

Kuala Lumpur

Singapore

Plate 7.5   Singapore, 1846

Singapore: a Seaport and City State

Singapore is a city state, independent from Malaysia since 1964, located off the south coast of the Malayan peninsula (Figs. 7.6 and 7.7). With an area of 580 km² and 2.3 million people, it has a density of population of over 4000 km², a figure surpassed only by Gibraltar, Macao, Monaco and Hong Kong, all very heavily urbanised territories.

SITE

The original site of Singapore city was at the mouth of the small Singapore River (Fig. 7.6). The site was selected by Raffles in 1819, and the early growth is shown on the print of 1846 (Plate 7.5). This was taken from Government Hill, and illustrates the importance of the port by this stage, with sailing ships lying in the safe anchorage of the 'inner roads'. Fig. 7.6 shows that today urban growth has spread over about half the island.

Fig. 7.6   Singapore: site and land-use

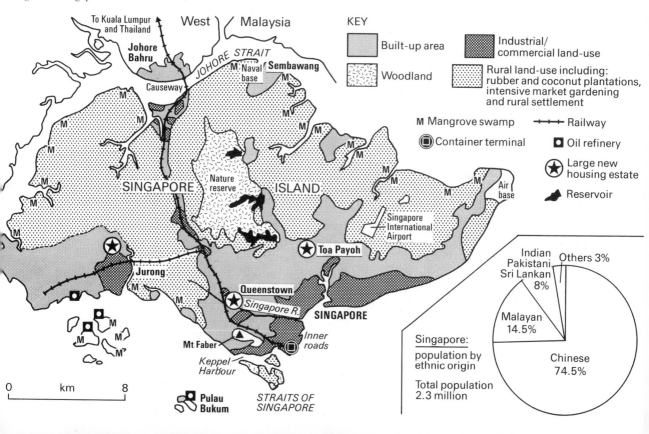

Singapore's general situation was the main reason for its growth into a great world seaport. Fig. 7.7 shows how it controls the Straits of Malacca, the traditional sea link between the Indian Ocean and the South China Sea. Singapore therefore became an international trading port on routes from the west to the east. Its importance was increased with the opening of the Suez Canal in 1869.

Singapore is also ideally placed for handling more local traffic from the islands of South-east Asia. Its growth was greatly increased by the development of rubber plantations and tin mines in Malaya, for which it became the main exporting port. In more recent times, it has achieved an important position in the world's oil trade, being well placed on routes from the Persian Gulf to the Far East.

FUNCTIONS

(1) As a *port*, Singapore was an excellent example of an *entrepot port*, that is a port where goods are trans-shipped from ocean-going vessels to smaller coastal vessels, which ply with the smaller ports of Indonesia and South-east Asia. One disadvantage of independence for Singapore, however, has been the fact that countries such as Malaysia and Indonesia have tended to develop their own ports for entrepot traffic, and by-pass Singapore. As its entrepot trade has declined, however, Singapore has extended its facilities for handling bulk products such as petroleum, and for container trade. Its exports today are fewer raw materials such as rubber and tin, and more products it manufactures itself, such as office and electrical machinery.

(2) Since independence, Singapore's *manufacturing* industries have grown rapidly. *Port industries*, such as oil refining, are located in the harbour areas and offshore islands. *Heavy industries*, such as steel, saw-milling, and cement, are found on the Jurong industrial estate (Fig. 7.6), which has harbour facilities and good road and rail access. The iron and steelworks depends on locally supplied scrap metal, and is powered by imported coal and oil. The steel supplies the city's expanding shipbuilding and construction industries. Most characteristic of all are the many *consumer goods* industries. Traditionally these were mainly textiles. Today there are increasingly food-processing plants (for frozen and packaged foods), and electronics and electrical products, often set up by West European and Japanese firms to take advantage of the cheap local labour supply.

(3) *Tertiary functions*: Plate 7.6 shows a series of tall office blocks towering over the Chinese quarter of Singapore. As a cosmopolitan international port, Singapore has long attracted migrants from other parts of Asia. The inset of Fig. 7.6 shows that three-quarters of the population is now Chinese.

Plate 7.6   Singapore river waterfront

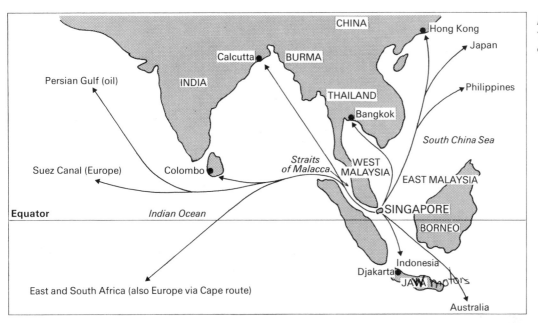

Fig. 7.7
The situation
of Singapore

Singapore's economic growth has been accompanied by many social problems, of which housing and traffic congestion are examples. The chief difficulty for an island state is finding land to build on. Congested central residential areas are being cleared. In place of these, vast new government sponsored high-rise flats are being built (Plate 7.7). The amount of washing on the lines gives some idea of the high population density in these flats.

Conserving the Equatorial Forest and its People: Amazonia

THE TRANSPORT REVOLUTION IN AMAZONIA

Before the 1970s, anyone crossing the Amazon forests (selvas) by air, would be able to see only rivers breaking through the dense forest. Follow this account of a flight north from Manaus (Fig. 7.8) in 1979:

> We flew at a height of about 1000 feet [c. 300 metres] over the limitless spread of trees... Across this the BR174 [highway] was a red line, ruled to the horizon [see Plate 7.8]. ...Fires appeared as smudges here and there, and there were never less than a half-dozen in sight [see Plate 7.9]... What the bird's-eye view made so startlingly clear was that the process the scientists called "desertification" was even more rapid than we had been led to expect. In many places...the arid ochre of the sub-soil already showed through. (from *Observer Colour Supplement* 22 April 1979)

Plate 7.7 Singapore tenements

Fig. 7.8 shows the new highway system that is opening up Brazil's north-west. The most famous is the Trans-Amazonian Highway, shown on Plate 7.8, over 5000 km long and running approximately 500 km south of the Amazon. Most of the roads are not paved, having a double strip of gravel topping or packed earth. Building such roads in this environment is very difficult. First the trees have to be cleared. Once these have gone, heavy tropical rains turn the clay soil into a quagmire.

89

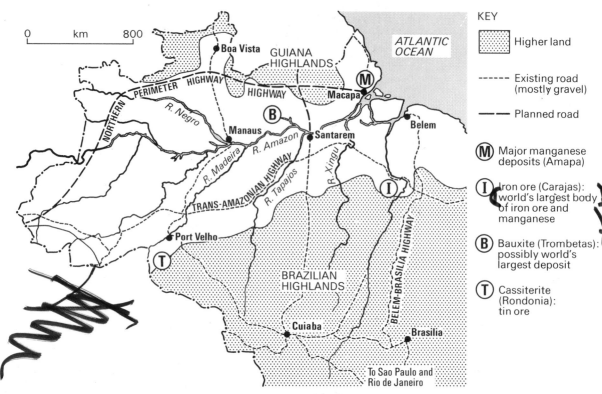

KEY

Higher land

------ Existing road (mostly gravel)

—·—·— Planned road

(M) Major manganese deposits (Amapa)

(I) Iron ore (Carajas): world's largest body of iron ore and manganese

(B) Bauxite (Trombetas): possibly world's largest deposit

(T) Cassiterite (Rondonia): tin ore

Fig. 7.8 The opening up of Brazil's north-west

Plate 7.8 The Trans-Amazonian highway

Plate 7.9 Forest firing in Amazonia

Tree stump legs (petrip)

ECONOMIC DEVELOPMENT

This great wilderness region of north-west Brazil is being opened up for economic development in a similar way to the opening up of the 'Wild West' of North America a century before. There are several reasons for this.

(1) The Brazilian government has planned that the opening up of this region will provide opportunities for migration for huge numbers of poverty-stricken people in its poor north-eastern region (Fig. 7.8). These have moved into Amazonia, and have burned down the forest (Plate 7.9) at an alarming rate, to make clearings for crops.

(2) Even more alarming, because of its large scale, is the burning down of forest to open up huge new cattle ranches and plantations, owned by rich business people from Sao Paulo or Rio de Janeiro.

(3) The most important reason has perhaps been to tap what has been found to be an enormous reserve of mineral wealth. Plate 7.10 shows the forest cleared for a settlement of 4000 people on the banks of the Trombetas, a tributary of the Amazon (Fig. 7.8). On the plateau behind this settlement is one of the world's largest bauxite deposits. The bauxite was first shipped from a newly built river port for export to North America and Europe, and will also be taken to an alumina plant on the Atlantic coast at Belem (Fig. 7.8). In addition vast reserves of manganese, iron and tin ores have been found (Fig. 7.8).

(4) Amazonia is also strategically important, in that there are a number of states along the isolated north-west frontier. Road access will help to control this frontier.

ECONOMIC DEVELOPMENT AND THE FOREST ENVIRONMENT

The world's conservationists have expressed alarm over the rapid destruction of the Amazon forest. There are various reason for this anxiety.

(1) Hardwood trees take a long time to grow, and over-rapid exploitation cannot be made good by re-planting, as in coniferous forests.

(2) The forest cover protects the ground, but it puts little organic matter into the soils, which are infertile clays (laterites). Removal of trees leads to swampy conditions on flat ground and soil erosion on slopes. The eroded soil is washed into rivers, silting up any reservoirs in their courses. The laterites, once exposed, can harden within five years to become a rock-like pavement in which nothing will grow except poor scrub.

(3) The forest cover allows slow run-off of water. Clearance causes rapid run-off, erratic river flow, and serious flooding, as happens regularly in Manaus, for example (pages 93–4).

(4) Forest clearance reduces rainfall totals, perhaps as much as 5% per annum, and increases temperature levels, creating a more arid environment over time.

Plate 7.10   Trombetas: a new town in Amazonia

Plate 7.11   Indian mother and child on a highway in
Amazonia

EFFECTS ON THE AMAZON INDIANS

Plate 7.11 shows a young Indian mother of the
Nhambiquara tribe on one of the new highways of
Amazonia, running across a drab landscape from
which almost all evidence of vegetation has been
cleared. The effect of the new developments on indigenous Indian groups has been devastating. Men have given
up their traditional skills and rely on women and children
bringing back western goods, often by begging at
the roadside. More and more are living in squalor
by the roads rather than in their forest villages.

The early stages of the development of Amazonia in
the 1960s were marked by the brutal expulsion and
murder of Indians by ranchers, mining gangs, and rubber collectors. Many have also been killed by 'western'
diseases such as smallpox and measles, to which the
people have little or no immunity. On top of this has
been the 'culture shock' of exposure to new forms of
language, religion, dress (see Plate 7.11) and enter-
tainment. Indian peoples in their natural state have
largely disappeared from the banks of the great rivers
of the Amazon basin and have been driven further
into the forest. Large numbers now live on 'Indian
reserves' set up by the Brazilian government.

Plate 7.12   Manaus: the Opera House and tall modern office blocks

Manaus: River Port and Regional Capital

The buildings on Plate 7.12 represent two boom periods in the history of Manaus. In the foreground is the huge piazza in front of the nineteenth-century Opera House. Manaus grew as a Portuguese slave-trading base on the Rio Negro, near its confluence with the Amazon (Fig. 7.8). A steamer service connected it with the Atlantic Ocean, 1500 km away, in the 1850s. Its great boom period came with the exploitation of rubber, brought from isolated rubber trees in the forest by individual collectors to central collecting points such as Manaus. Here the 'rubber barons' prospered and built a lavish opera house. Once the rubber seeds were smuggled out and rubber plantations were established in Malaysia, the Brazilian boom collapsed, and Manaus became a backwater.

For much of this century it functioned as a river port of minor importance, exporting products of the forest, such as Brazil nuts.

Its revival began in the 1960s with the opening of new roads in Amazonia. It now stands where the road from Porto Velho to Boa Vista crosses the Rio Negro. The stretch from Porto Velho to Manaus is one of the few paved stretches of Amazon highway. More important, however, was the decision of the regional government to make the city a 'free trade zone'. The town was exempted from federal taxes and import duties. Plate 7.13 shows one of the duty free stores in the city centre, and in the background of Plate 7.12 can be seen the tall office blocks that symbolise this second boom period for Manaus.

Plate 7.13   A duty free shop in Manaus

Modern cars choke the city streets blaring horns. Manaus remains the regional capital of a wilderness, but as one writer has commented: 'no savage Indians stalk across the zebra crossings'. Between 1967 and 1972 over eighty industrial projects were attracted, including a small charcoal-fired steelworks, an oil refinery, a shipyard, and a variety of consumer goods industries, making clocks, watches, jewellery, toys and domestic appliances, among many other products. In addition 1200 or more commercial firms came in,

setting up offices (Plate 7.12). A major international airport has been built, bringing in waves of tourists to buy at the duty free shops, and to take river trips and conducted tours of the surrounding jungle. Indians 'act out' their traditional life-style for the sake of the tourists. The city has now about 400 000 people, having attracted thousands of migrants to work in its new industries and offices. A serious housing problem has resulted, with shanties being built on unhealthy riverside marshes.

Exercises

7. Refer to Figs. 7.5, 7.9, 7.10 and 7.11.
   (a) Describe the distribution of population in West Malaysia (Fig.7.9).
   (b) Explain this distribution, with the help of Figs. 7.5, 7.10 and 7.11, and information in the text.
8. Refer to Fig. 7.6.
   (a) Describe the pattern of land-use found on Singapore Island.
   (b) Try to explain the location of (i) mangrove swamps; (ii) industrial and commercial land-use in general; (iii) oil refineries; (iv) 'new town' developments.

9. Compare the sites, situations and functions of Singapore and Manaus, referring especially to their rapid recent development.
10. (a) Explain why 'slash and burn' cultivation has over the centuries not destroyed the Malaysian forest, while the recent development of Amazonia is rapidly destroying the selvas.
   (b) Explain what is meant by 'culture shock', with reference to the aboriginal peoples of Malaysia, and the Indians of Amazonia.

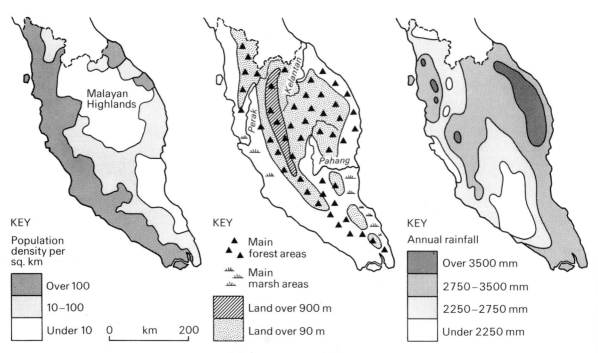

Fig. 7.9 West Malaysia: population distribution

Fig. 7.10 West Malaysia: relief and vegetation

Fig. 7.11 West Malaysia: annual rainfall distribution

94

SECTION C: Densely Populated Regions of the Tropics and Sub-tropics

8 The Monsoon Lands

LOCATION (Fig. 8.1)

The monsoon lands cover three separate climatic regions:

Tropical monsoon areas, including India, Pakistan, Bangladesh, Burma, Thailand, Kampuchea, Vietnam, southern China;

Temperate monsoon areas, including the rest of China and Japan;

Equatorial monsoon areas, including Malaysia, Indonesia and Sri Lanka, considered in the previous chapter.

These areas make up a large part of what is sometimes referred to as the *oriental world*.

PHYSICAL FEATURES

The Monsoon Climate (Fig. 8.2)

TEMPERATURE

The hottest month is usually May, averaging over 26 °C and sometimes as much as 30 °C. The coolest months, December and January, average from just under 20 °C to 24 °C in tropical monsoon, and −10 °C to +12 °C in temperate monsoon areas. The range of temperature is much greater in temperate than in tropical monsoon areas. In the tropical areas it is from 5 °C to 11 °C, and in temperate from 16 °C to 38 °C.

The high summer temperatures, especially just before the arrival of the wet monsoon, result from the high level of insolation, with the sun vertically overhead over the Tropic of Cancer in June. The temperature drops slightly with the arrival of the wet monsoon, when there is a greater amount of cloud. At this time, however, the humidity increases and weather conditions are oppressive. Winters are warm in tropical monsoon areas such as India and southern China, which are protected by the Himalayas and other mountain ranges from cold Siberian winds. In the temperate monsoon areas, however, winters can be very cold indeed, as in northern China, which is exposed to these cold Siberian winds, blowing out from a high-pressure area.

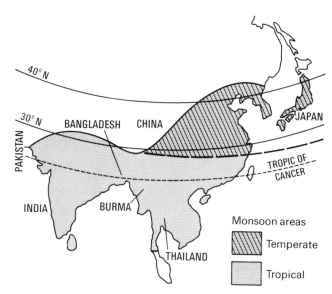

Fig. 8.1 The monsoon lands: location

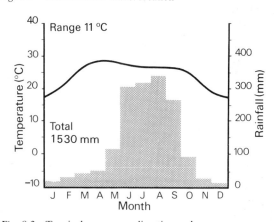

Fig. 8.2 Tropical monsoon: climatic graph

RAINFALL

The word monsoon means a 'seasonal reversal of winds', which accounts for the great variety in summer and winter rainfall conditions. There are considerable variations in the amounts of rain received, in the reliability of the rainfall, and in the date the wet monsoon arrives.

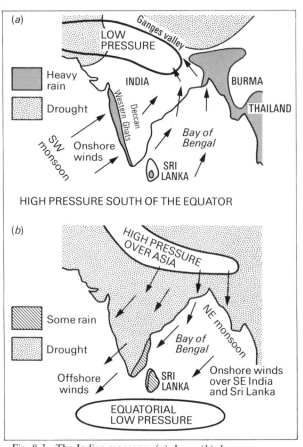

Fig. 8.3 The Indian monsoon: (a) June, (b) January

(1) In coastal areas, exposed to onshore winds, such as the west coasts of India, Burma and Thailand (Fig. 8.3a), rainfall is very heavy, reaching over 2500 mm per annum, the majority falling between June and October.

(2) Where mountains cause these onshore winds to rise, as in the Western Ghats of India, rainfall is heavier still (Fig. 8.4).

(3) Behind the mountains, rain shadow areas occur, as in the Deccan Plateau (Fig. 8.4), and here rainfall totals are lower.

(4) As the south-west monsoon sweeps up the Bay of Bengal (Fig. 8.3a), it is diverted by the Himalayan mountains up the Ganges valley, where rainfall totals decrease considerably further away from the sea, until in Pakistan the rainfall comes late, and is very unreliable, making irrigation necessary for farming.

(5) In winter, winds blow from the high pressure over the Asian interior towards the equatorial low (Fig. 8.3b), and are offshore winds, giving dry conditions to most areas.

(6) An exception is the south-eastern coast of India and Sri Lanka, where these winds are onshore, coming off the Bay of Bengal.

(7) In China and Japan, the wet monsoon comes from the south-east, giving heavy rainfall in the uplands of southern China, while the dry monsoon is from the north-west (Fig. 8.5).

Fig. 8.4 The Deccan Plateau: rain shadow

Fig. 8.5 China: rainfall conditions

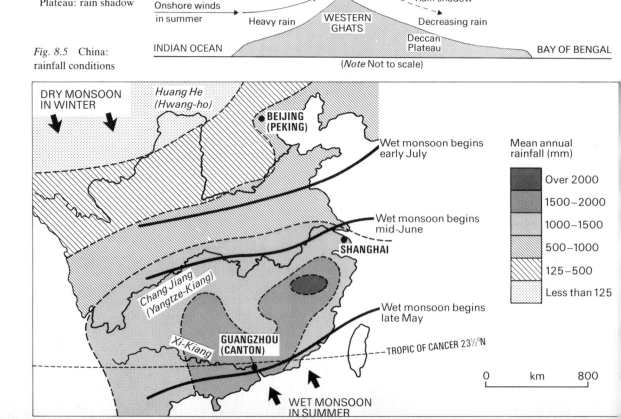

ECONOMIC DEVELOPMENT IN THE ORIENTAL WORLD:
AGRICULTURE AND FISHING

The 'Rice-Bowl' of Asia

LOCATION

Plate 8.1 is a vertical aerial view of a typical landscape in the lowlands of South-east Asia, in this case in Vietnam. It shows a close patchwork of flooded padi (rice) fields, and a dense rural population pattern, with villages built on dykes and hummocks above the flooded fields. The shaded area on Fig. 8.1, together with the equatorial areas of South-east Asia (Fig. 7.1) make up the 'rice-bowl' of Asia.

In this region, rice growing is usually a *subsistence* form of farming, the produce being grown for the family's own use. It is also an example of *labour-*

intensive agriculture, meaning that it relies on the presence of a large work force of peasant farmers. It is found in three types of area:

(*a*) on alluvial river lowlands, such as the Ganges valley in India, the Irrawaddy in Burma, the Menam in Thailand, and the Mekong in Kampuchea and Vietnam;

(*b*) in valleys in the hill country, where small padi fields are *terraced* on the hillsides, as in Assam in India, and in the islands of Indonesia;

(*c*) in drier areas such as the Deccan plateau in India, Pakistan, and in northern China, where the monsoon rain is sparse and unreliable and requires supplementing with *irrigation* water.

Plate 8.1   Vietnam: part of Asia's 'rice-bowl'

The process of rice growing is perhaps best explained by looking at the farmer's year, in a region where two crops (though not necessarily of rice) can be grown:

May: nursery beds are prepared and fertilised;

June: with the first monsoon rains, the rice seeds are sown in nursery beds, while the main padi fields are manured and the mud levelled;

July–August: the rice is transplanted from the nursery beds to the flooded padi fields where it grows rapidly to keep its head above water;

September–October: weeding and manuring of padi fields;

November–December: the fields are allowed to drain and harvesting takes place (Plate 8.2). The plants are cut by hand just above ground level, tied in bundles and taken to the village. Here they are beaten or threshed in special yards in the village to remove the grain, which is dried in the sun.

January: The fields are ploughed and harrowed, and a second crop of lentils, peas or beans may be planted;

March: the second crop is harvested.

Areas where double cropping is possible are at an advantage over those drier areas where it is not, because a larger and more varied food supply is available. The drier areas are particularly badly hit if the wet monsoon is late or gives little rain. Then it might not be possible to produce even one crop, and famine threatens. In drier monsoon areas, less rice and more millet or wheat is grown as the main grain crop.

Rice is a water-loving crop, and the heavy monsoon rain (or alternatively irrigation water) meets the requirement for flooded fields. The alluvial heavy soils of such rivers as the Ganges and Chang Jiang (Yangtze) provide the impervious muddy layer needed for rice growing. The flat flood plains also make flooding of the fields easy. Otherwise, flat terraces have to be built on slopes to hold in the water. The vast populations of the oriental world furnish the work-force for this labour-intensive form of farming. The hot summers and warm winters of the tropical monsoon areas provide the conditions for rapid plant growth, and usually allow the harvesting of two crops each year. Water buffaloes are used as beasts of burden, and these and other animals provide manure for the fields.

This is the traditional picture. In the last twenty years there have been attempts to modernise farming and increase yields by introducing new varieties of rice: the 'green revolution'. For these to be effective,

Plate 8.2   Rice harvesting in Indonesia

however, they need the use of artificial fertilisers. But the mass of poorer farmers cannot afford to buy fertilisers, and the new methods have been adopted only by larger and more well-to-do farmers. The traditional picture has been more dramatically changed in China, since 1949.

Farming in Communist China

In 1949, Mao Zedong (Mao-Tse Tung) and his communist forces won the civil war against the previous ruler, General Chiang Kai-shek. So far as farming was concerned, the following events were important:

1949–52 *Land Reform Act*: the government confiscated the holdings of the landlords, redistributing the land among the peasants.

1953–7 (i) *Mutual aid teams* were formed, made up of from six to fifteen households, who pooled their labour, animals and tools, but kept the crops produced on their own land.

(ii) *Elementary agricultural cooperatives* were formed, made up of from thirty to forty households, planning how land should be farmed, pooling the land and labour, and produce, in accordance with the size of holding and amount of time worked.

(iii) *Advanced agricultural cooperatives* were formed, made up of from 100 to 300 households, in which all land was pooled and individual ownership disappeared. The people were paid on the basis of days worked. There were about ¾ million advanced agricultural cooperatives by 1957.

1958 to date *People's Communes*

These were formed by combining cooperatives into huge rural units, with about 20 000 people in each. By the early 1970s there were 50 000 communes, with an average population of about 15 000, in which there were about 3500 households. Each commune is divided into fifteen *production brigades*, in turn subdivided into *production teams*. Each brigade controls an area of about 135 hectares. Each team, of 145 persons, controls 20 hectares of land, and makes up the equivalent of a village unit.

The brigade is responsible for overall planning, while the team controls the actual detail of the farming. Each team is an accounting unit, with its own balance sheet, responsible for contributing to state taxes, to a welfare fund for running clinics and schools, and for buying seeds. When this is done, the rest of the income, perhaps 55%, is distributed. The communes also usually run small-scale industries, controlled at the brigade level.

The commune system still takes advantage of the vast numbers of people in pursuing labour-intensive farming. But it has also made possible the introduction of machinery, even into rice production, in a way not possible in the less developed parts of the oriental world. Plate 8.3 shows a mechanical rice seeder at work on the flooded fields of Guangxi province in south-west China.

THE FARMING REGIONS OF CHINA

Fig. 8.5 showed how the climate of China is influenced by the wet and dry monsoons. The wet monsoon comes from the south-east, arriving in the Guangzhou (Canton) area late in May, the Chang Jiang (Yangtze) valley by mid-June, and the Huang He (Hwang-ho) valley by early July. Rainfall totals decrease considerably away from the south-east coast, Guangzhou receiving over 1600 mm, Shanghai 1100 mm and Beijing (Peking) just over 630 mm per annum. All areas have high summer temperatures, however, averaging over 26 °C (Table 8.1).

In winter, there is great variation in temperatures. Northern areas, such as around Beijing (Peking), are exposed to freezing Siberian winds, and average temperatures below freezing point. Areas further south are protected by mountains such as the Tsinling Shan (Fig. 8.6), and conditions are warm in the south, averaging over 13 °C in the coldest month. Winter is the dry season throughout China.

Plate 8.3 A mechanical rice seeder, China

These climatic contrasts are closely reflected in a distinct pattern of farming regions.

(1) The *dry west and north-west* concentrates on *pastoral farming*, with sheep and goats the main animals. Where water is available, oasis farming for cotton and fruits is practised.

(2) *Northern China* includes farming regions in which *wheat* or *millet* is the main grain crop. Other grain crops include kaoliang and maize. Conditions are not wet enough for the growth of rice. As in most of the rest of China, a wide variety of *vegetables* is produced.

(3) *The Chang Jiang (Yangtze) basin* is a transition region between the temperate monsoon of northern China and the tropical monsoon of the south. *Wheat* is the *winter grain* and *rice the summer*.

(4) In *southern China rice* is grown throughout the region, in valleys and on terraced slopes, and two crops can be produced every year. *Tea* growing is important in the south-east.

Table 8.1 Mean monthly average temperatures and rainfall at three Chinese stations

| | Guangzhou | | Shanghai | | Beijing | |
	°C	mm	°C	mm	°C	mm
J	13.3	23	3.3	51	−5.1	3
F	13.9	48	3.9	57	−1.7	5
M	17.2	107	7.8	86	5.0	5
A	21.7	173	13.3	94	13.9	15
M	26.7	269	18.3	91	20.0	36
J	27.2	269	22.8	188	24.4	76
J	28.3	205	26.7	150	26.1	239
A	28.3	219	26.7	145	24.4	160
S	26.7	165	22.8	119	20.0	66
O	23.9	86	17.2	79	12.2	15
N	19.4	31	11.1	51	3.3	8
D	15.6	23	5.6	33	−2.8	2
Annual:	range	total	range	total	range	total
	15	1618	23.4	1144	31.2	630

Fig. 8.6 Yellow River basin

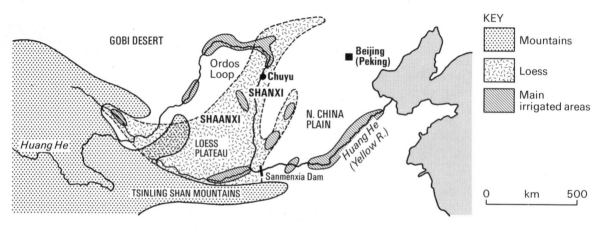

FARMING PROBLEMS IN THE YELLOW RIVER BASIN

The Yellow River (Huang He) has been called 'China's sorrow', having caused many disastrous floods as it has shifted its course across the North China Plain (Fig. 8.6). 'Taming' the Yellow River became a major objective of the communist government from 1949, both to stop flooding and the severe soil erosion which occurred in the loess plateau of Shaanxi (Shensi) and Shanxi (Shansi) provinces (Fig. 8.6).

Two of Mao Zedong's most famous decrees were: 'Work on the Yellow River must be done well'; and 'Attention must be paid to soil conservation'.

These decrees had the force of law.

The Huang He is called the Yellow River because of the vast amount of silt it carries, the highest of any river in the world. This is because it flows in a great loop through a loess plateau, made up of wind-blown and very fragile deposits. At one time the plateau was covered by trees and grasslands, but over the centuries the forests were felled and not replaced. As a result the loess was exposed, to cause some of the worst soil erosion in the world (Plate 8.4). The communist government has calculated that there are over 300 000 gullies in the region over 1 km in length. Farming is possible only in the valleys (Plate 8.4), unless the land can be rescued by laborious terracing.

Plate 8.4 Soil erosion in the loess region of China

Plate 8.5 Terraced fields on a Chinese commune

This has been a major objective of the communes in this region. Plate 8.5 shows part of a production team in a terraced landscape in north-west China, passing a sign containing sayings of Mao Zedong. The teams have also built earth dams in the gullies which build up sediment behind them for making new farming land. The people of the Chuyu district (Fig. 8.6) drew up the following plan in the form of slogans:

'High and remote hills, into forest,
Low hills, gentle slopes, into terraced fields,
Gullies, into orchards,
River banks, into farm gardens.'

In addition to the dammed-back gullies and terraced fields, irrigation water has been brought from the hills, or pumped from the river, and dykes have been built along the Yellow River to prevent flooding. Even greater dykes have been built on the North China Plain, and the Sanmenxia Dam was constructed (Fig. 8.6) to help to 'tame' the river. But the reservoir behind has become badly silted, for, despite the enormous efforts expended, the Yellow River refuses to be tamed, and continues to cause floods and bring down enormous quantities of silt.

Fishing in Japan

Japan is one of only seven countries in the world with national populations of over 100 million. Unlike countries such as China and India, however, Japan does not have the benefit of great lowland areas on which to house and feed its population. Lowland areas make up only one-eighth of the total area of Japan, and much of these are built over.

Japanese agriculture makes use of the land available to it as efficiently as possible, growing crops on every available lowland plot, and terracing hillsides, as is present high on the coastal hills of Plate 8.6., which also shows how in some places there is no coastal plain at all. Japanese farmers concentrate on rice and vegetable farming and much less on livestock farming. While there is an increasing amount of intensive livestock farming on western lines for dairy products, there is very little production of meat.

For animal protein in their diet, the Japanese are forced to depend on fish. Apart from rice and vegetables, fish is the key item. Japan has the world's largest fishing fleet, taking 15% of the world's catch. Only the USSR, with 13%, approaches this figure. Japan's fishing boats roam the world's oceans, catching whales in the northern Pacific and southern oceans, bonito and tuna in the Pacific, Indian and Atlantic oceans, and sardines and mackerel in home waters. Since World War 2, the fleet has become increasingly mechanised and efficient and is seen, with that of Russia, as the main threat to using up the world's fish stocks, and especially the stock of whales.

Plate 8.6 Fishing boats in a village near Numazu, Japan

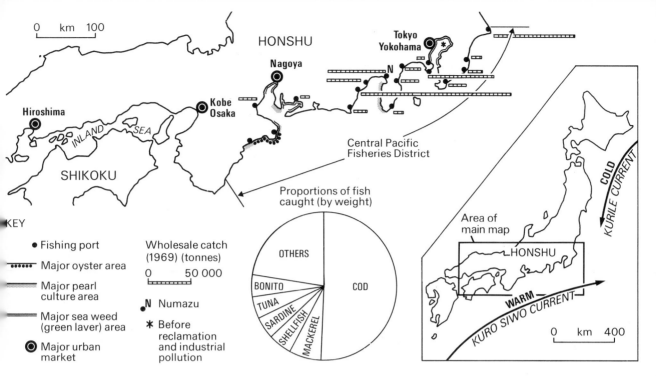

Fig. 8.7 Japan: the Central Pacific Fisheries District

The Japanese coasts are divided into fisheries districts; Fig. 8.7 shows one of these. Details are given in the pie chart of the catches made by the fishing ports in the Central Pacific District, which covers the great conurbations of Tokyo/Yokohama and Nagoya. One of the many small fishing ports, Numazu, marked by an N on the map, lies on the coast of Suruga Bay, shown on Plate 8.6. Like other fishing villages, it has tightly packed streets between the hills and the sea.

There are many advantages for fishing. The east coast of Japan is washed by the warm *Kuro Siwo* current, bringing north warm-water fish such as bonito, and the cold *Kurile* current, bringing south cold-water fish such as cod. While the fishing grounds are rich, they do not supply nearly enough for the vast population, and, as already noted, Japanese fishing boats roam the world's oceans. The boats shown on Plate 8.6, however, are smaller boats, which fish the waters round Japan.

The indented coast provides many small, sheltered fishing harbours, such as Numazu. The shallow waters of the bays and inlets, especially of the Inland Sea (Fig. 8.7) provide good conditions for 'sea farming', such as oyster farming, in which floating oyster 'rafts' support wire baskets in which edible and pearl oysters are reared. In addition, these coasts are famed for green laver, an edible seaweed considered a delicacy by the Japanese.

Above all, there is a huge demand for fish, greatest of all in this part of Japan, stretching from the Tokyo/Yokohama conurbation of 27 million people, through Nagoya, Osaka and Hiroshima, to the northern part of Kyushu.

Exercises

1. Refer to Table 8.1.
   (a) Draw climatic graphs to illustrate temperature and rainfall conditions at Guangzhou (Canton), Shanghai and Beijing (Peking).
   (b) How do the conditions at these three centres compare with those of the station illustrated on Fig. 8.2?
2. (a) Compare and contrast the monsoon climates of India and China.
   (b) Show how the monsoons in general affect farming activities in these two countries.
3. With the help of information, photographs and diagrams in the text, outline differences in rice farming in the communist and non-communist parts of the oriental world.
4. Refer back to Chapter 5. Outline the main similarities and differences between a commune in China and a kibbutz in Israel.
5. (a) Refer to the inset of Fig. 8.7 and with the help of information in the text suggest which fishing grounds the fleets of the Central Pacific Fisheries District are likely to use.
   (b) Why is fishing particularly important in this district and around the Inland Sea?

INDUSTRIALISATION AND URBANISATION IN THE ORIENTAL WORLD

The Damodar Valley Industrial Region of India

INDIAN MANUFACTURING INDUSTRY

India is a country in which manufacturing is carried on at a variety of different scales. Three main types can be identified:

(*a*) *Domestic industry*, in the villages and small towns, generally in the form of craft industries making products such as cloth and pottery for local consumption, and using family labour.

(*b*) *Small-scale factory industry*, such as the engineering works at Calcutta shown in Plate 8.7, which uses traditional methods to produce metal wheels and other products. Factories on this scale produce an immense variety of products. On the one hand, they may process raw materials, as in the case of the 'ginneries' of the cotton districts. On the other hand they may fabricate products derived from large-scale industry, including the products of the steel industry, for local markets.

(*c*) *Large-scale manufacturing* tends to be concentrated in the major towns and cities. Examples are the jute mills of Calcutta; the cotton mills of Bombay and Ahmadabad; and the iron and steel industry of the Damodar valley region.

Plate 8.7   Small-scale engineering in Calcutta

IRON AND STEEL IN THE DAMODAR VALLEY REGION

This region, centred on the town of Jamshedpur (Fig. 8.8), has been described as the 'Ruhr of India'. It is one of the greatest mining and heavy manufacturing regions in the oriental world. It has a whole series of advantages for iron and steel production.

Fig. 8.8   Damodar valley industrial region

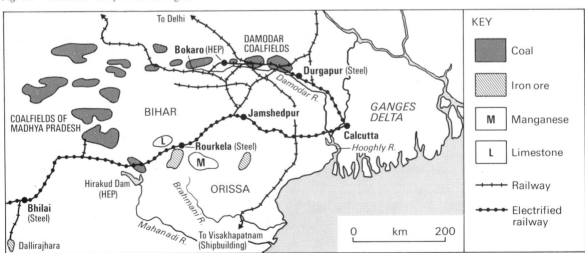

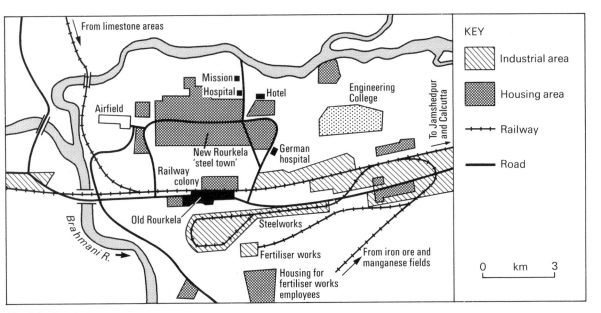

Fig. 8.9 Rourkela: steel town

Plate 8.8 Bhilai steelworks, India

(1) There are large reserves of coal, including coking coal, in the Damodar valley itself, and further west in the state of Madhya Pradesh (Fig. 8.8).

(2) In the hills of Bihar and Orissa to the south, are major deposits of iron ore, limestone (used as a flux in the steel industry) and manganese (used as an alloy), round the steel-making town of Rourkela (Figs. 8.8 and 8.9).

(3) Hydro-electric power (HEP) is available from the Bokaro power station on the Damodar and the Hirakud on the Mahanadi.

(4) A well-developed railway system, including four-track and electrified lines, is centred on Jamshedpur, and connects up with major Indian cities such as Calcutta, Madras and Bombay.

(5) A market for steel produce exists in the heavy engineering and vehicle industries of north-east India, such as car manufacturing (Hindustan motors) in Calcutta, and shipbuilding at Visakhapatnam (Fig. 8.8).

(6) The modern Indian steel industry resulted from the initiative of the Tata family, who built their works at Tatanagar near Jamshedpur, and a 'new town' to house the workers. In the last twenty years, new integrated steel plants have been built with the help of aid from abroad: from Britain, for Durgapur (Fig. 8.8); from West Germany for Rourkela (Fig. 8.9); and from the USSR for Bhilai (Fig. 8.8 and Plate 8.8), making use of the Dallirajhara iron ore deposits (67% pure) to the south. One of the great advantages of the Rourkela location is that the rail wagons that bring the coal from the Damodar valley can be loaded with iron ore for the journey back.

(7) These locational advantages, plus the low-cost Indian labour supply, make Indian steel the cheapest in the world.

Bombay: 'Gateway of India'

Plate 8.9 is a photograph of the waterfront of Bombay, showing the 'Gateway of India', the stone building on the right, erected in 1911 to commemorate a royal visit, and the Taj Mahal hotel behind. Both are representative of the period of British rule which began in the seventeenth century, when Bombay was the west coast head-quarters of the East India Company, and ended just after World War 2, when India was granted independence.

THE GROWTH OF BOMBAY

Bombay developed not so much because of the advantages of its site, 'a wilderness of malarious mudflats', as its situation, in a central position on the west coast of India, well placed for trade with Europe, especially after the opening of the Suez Canal in 1869. It grew enormously in the nineteenth century, from 150 000 in 1800 to 820 000 in 1900 as a result of:

(a) land reclamation of the malarious mudflats, making it less unhealthy as a place to live;

(b) the development of the Indian railway system by the British from the 1850s;

(c) the growth of the cotton manufacturing industry, using raw cotton from the Deccan plateau;

(d) the construction of docks on the east side of Bombay Island (Fig. 8.10).

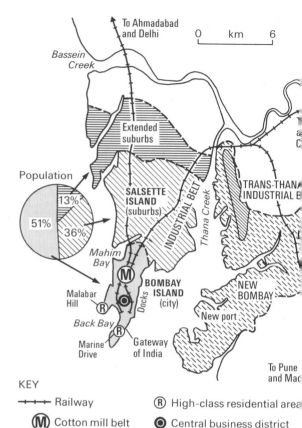

KEY

+—+—+ Railway

Ⓜ Cotton mill belt

Ⓡ High-class residential area

◉ Central business district

Fig. 8.10   The site of Bombay

Plate 8.9   'Gateway of India', Bombay

Plate 8.10 A Bombay street, with chawls, in the 1890s

Vast numbers of workers flooded in from the countryside for employment in the cotton mills, for whom the characteristic five-storeyed *chawls*, or tenements, were built. Plate 8.10 is a photograph of one of Bombay's streets in the 1890s.

BOMBAY TODAY

Manufacturing industry
Bombay remains one of India's great industrial cities. Its sixty cotton mills employ 30% of Bombay's factory workers, although this is a decline from 40% in 1960. The decline in textiles has been compensated by the growth of consumer goods industries, including vehicle construction, pharmaceuticals and electrical goods, and also by a great expansion of oil refining and petro-chemicals, with Bombay the nearest Indian port to the Persian Gulf. The main belt of cotton mills is on the north side of Bombay Island while the heavier industries and petro-chemicals are on either side of Thana Creek (Fig. 8.10).

Commerce
Bombay is also India's greatest seaport and commercial centre. The docks are, however, very congested, and a new port is planned across the water from Bombay Island in 'New Bombay'. 25% of Bombay's population belong to clerical and managerial groups, while 16% are shopkeepers and traders, and 6% are in the professions. Although Bombay has enormous social problems, its wage rates are on average double those of Calcutta.

Urban problems
While less desperate than those of Calcutta, the social problems of Bombay are, by West European standards, appalling. In the area between Back Bay and the cotton mill district, residential densities reach 250 000/km^2, as against less than 30 000 in well-to-do residential areas such as Malabar Hill and Marine Drive (Fig. 8.10). Most of Bombay's population lives in one of the following three types of 'housing'.

Plate 8.11 Part of a shanty town in Bombay next to modern office blocks

Sleeping on the streets is the way of life for 100 000 people, or 2% of the population.

> They were stretched out on the sidewalk, lying side by side; some were on pieces of cardboard but most slept flat on the cement, with no bedding and few clothes, their arms crooked under their heads. The children slept on their sides, the others on their backs. There was no sign anywhere of their possessions. I reached seventy-three and turned the corner, where down the road that ran next to the sea wall there were hundreds more – just bodies, no bundles or carts, nothing to distinguish one from another, no evidence of life.   (from Paul Theroux *The Great Railway Bazaar*, Ballantye, New York 1975)

Sometimes people choose to sleep on the streets rather than live in the shanty towns or the chawls. They are near their place of work, and sleeping out in the hot season is less unpleasant than the stifling atmosphere of the shanties and chawls. In the wet monsoon, many return temporarily to their villages to help with farming (see Chapter 14).

Shanty towns, of which there are about 150, house about 15% or one million of Bombay's population. The main one, just south of Mahim Bay houses about 300 000 squatters; a small portion of it can be seen on Plate 8.11. These shanty towns lack sewage and other facilities, and are liable to be blown down or flooded out during the wet monsoon season, when they are usually knee-deep in mud. Notice how well placed for employment opportunities the shanty town shown on Plate 8.11 is, with the central business district (CBD) of Bombay behind, and the docks in the distance.

Chawl districts (Plate 8.10) house no less than 75% of Bombay's population. Although of good standard for their time, most are now classified as slums. The ground floor is usually a shop, and above this are characteristically one-room tenements, each room sleeping up to ten people. While there is indoor sanitation, one toilet may serve up to 100 people. Some have water on tap, but many others have to rely on stand-pipes in the streets. So great is the pressure on accommodation, that even relatively well-paid office workers have to live in chawls, and even in the shanty towns. It is not rare to find smartly dressed clerks with brief cases leaving suburban shanty towns to catch the electrified suburban railway into the CBD. The more *affluent* portion of Bombay's population, about 10%, lives in tall blocks of flats in the Malabar Hill and Marine Drive areas, or out in the suburbs. By western standards, even these live in crowded conditions.

Plate 8.12 Central Tokyo

Japan's Post-war Industrial Miracle

Plate 8.12 is an aerial view of part of central Tokyo. While Tokyo is, in location, an oriental city, the urban landscape of Tokyo's CBD is very much that of a western city. In 1945, Tokyo was in ruins. Its great office blocks, urban highways, and dense traffic are all reflections of Japan's post-war industrial miracle.

Japan is today the world's third largest industrial power, after the USA and USSR, with a production roughly equal to West Germany and the United Kingdom combined. It is the world's leading exporter of manufactured goods, sending abroad 70% of the cameras it produces, nearly 60% of the ships and synthetic fibres, and nearly 50% of the watches and clocks, and textile machinery (Fig. 8.11). The achievement is all the more remarkable in that Japan completely lacks many of the basic raw materials and energy supplies required for manufacturing industry (Fig. 8.12).

The miracle has been achieved in three stages.

(1) During 1945–55 progress was at first slow, with expansion only in essential industries producing food and clothing. In 1950 the Korean war provided a boost to industry. The American occupation force was withdrawn, and Japan was looked to for economic support. Heavy industry was now expanded. The government

(*a*) protected home industry by import restrictions;

(*b*) provided favourable financial conditions, such as tax concessions, for expansion, especially in heavy industries; and

(*c*) imported new technology from abroad, which was quickly and skilfully improved in Japanese factories and laboratories.

(2) 1955–70 was a period of almost continuous rapid growth, with an immense investment in up-to-date manufacturing industry. By 1965, steel production had quadrupled from its 1955 level. In addition to growth in heavy industry, there was a phenomenal expansion in consumer goods industries, such as cars, watches and clocks, cameras, domestic appliances, radios and television sets, and office machinery.

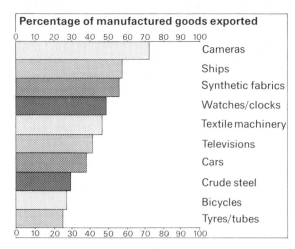

Percentage of manufactured goods exported

- Cameras
- Ships
- Synthetic fabrics
- Watches/clocks
- Textile machinery
- Televisions
- Cars
- Crude steel
- Bicycles
- Tyres/tubes

Fig. 8.11 Japan's industries

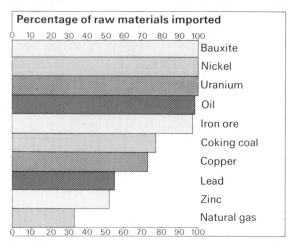

Percentage of raw materials imported

- Bauxite
- Nickel
- Uranium
- Oil
- Iron ore
- Coking coal
- Copper
- Lead
- Zinc
- Natural gas

Fig. 8.12 Japan's dependence on imported raw materials

This was accompanied by an enormous increase in trade, based on exported manufactured articles to Western Europe and the USA, in return for imported energy resources and raw materials, such as oil from the Persian Gulf and minerals from Australia (see Chapter 6). This period experienced a large amount of amalgamation of companies, creating huge combined enterprises with the advantage of 'economies of scale'. By 1965, industry was suffering from a shortage of labour. As the Japanese cities were already over-crowded, there was no prospect of bringing in imported labour. There was therefore a campaign to improve productivity and introduce labour-saving machinery.

(3) The 1970s have seen a slackening in the pace of economic growth, as world-wide recession has been experienced, in part as a result of the leap in world oil prices after 1973. The pace of growth had slackened from 12% of the gross national product per annum in the late 1960s, to 9% in the early 1970s, still very rapid indeed by British standards. Robot technology (Plate 8.13), quality control and harmonious labour relations have all helped to maintain Japan's economic miracle. Shortage of space has partly been answered by re-claiming land, as on Plate 8.14, in Tokyo Bay, (see Fig. 16.3), on which power stations, oil storage tanks, shipyards, steel and car plants can be constructed. Japan has had to pay a heavy social price for its economic miracle, however, as we shall see in Chapter 16.

Plate 8.13 The Datsun production line

110

Plate 8.14   Reclaimed land at Yokosuka, Tokyo Bay

Exercises

6. (*a*) Describe the land-use of Rourkela, as shown on Fig. 8.9.

(*b*) With the help of Fig. 8.8, outline the advantages of the location of the steelworks at Rourkela compared with those of Durgapur, under the headings of (i) energy supplies, (ii) raw materials, (iii) transport facilities, (iv) markets.

(*c*) Compare and contrast the factors favouring iron and steel industries in the Damodar valley region with those of Lulea (see Chapter 3).

7. With the help of Plates 8.11 and 8.12 compare the urban landscape of the central areas of Bombay and Tokyo.

8. Compare living conditions as shown in the foreground of Plate 8.11 with those in the street housing on Plate 8.10.

9. With the help of information in the text and an atlas, draw a labelled sketch map to show the advantages of the situation of Bombay. On it should be shown the whole of India; the Western Ghats; Delhi; Calcutta; Madras; Pune; Ahmadabad; main-line railways; the Persian Gulf; the Suez Canal; and Singapore.

10. With the help of Figs. 8.11 and 8.12 and information in the text, outline the nature of Japan's import and export trade.

11. With reference to Plates 8.7, 8.8, and 8.13, indicate how three different stages of industrial development are represented.

12. (*a*) Describe the industrial landscape development on Plate 8.14.

(*b*) Suggest three reasons why the power station in the right foreground is advantageously located.

9 Tropical Coasts and Islands

THE CARIBBEAN

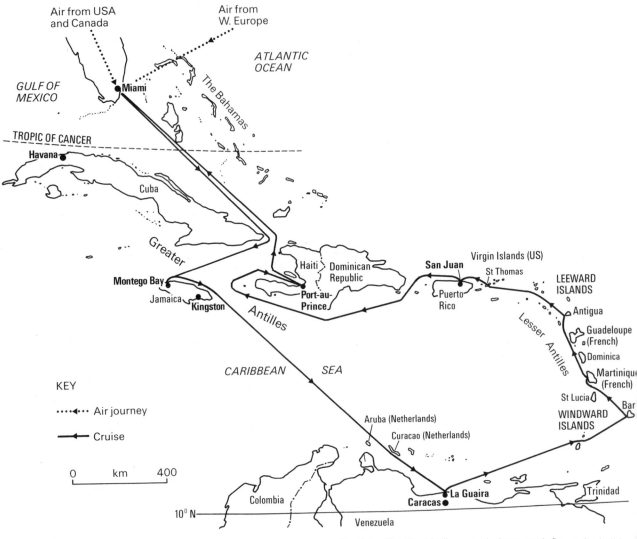

Fig. 9.1 The West Indies: a typical two-week fly–cruise holiday

Climate

TEMPERATURE

Although outside the equatorial region, some tropical areas have very uniform temperatures over the year, largely because of their maritime location. Thus the Caribbean islands (Fig. 9.1) lie in more or less the same latitudes as the Sahara, but do not have to endure the very high summer temperatures of the desert. All months are hot, with variations of between 24 °C in winter and 27 or 28 °C in summer. Another

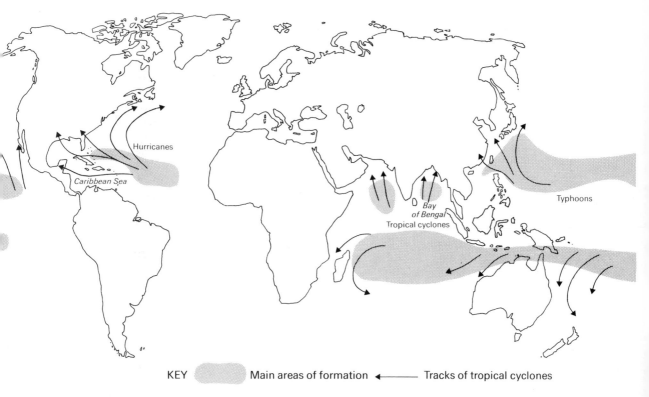

KEY ▨ Main areas of formation ◄——— Tracks of tropical cyclones

Fig. 9.2 Tropical cyclones

advantage of the maritime location is that sea breezes moderate the daytime temperatures.

RAINFALL

There is more variability in rainfall than in temperature conditions. Rainfall is caused mainly by the convergence of north-east and south-east trade winds at the *inter-tropical front*, which leads to rising air, condensation and rainfall. When the inter-tropical front is present, therefore, rainfall totals are high. But sometimes it does not reach as far north as the Caribbean islands, and when it does not, drought can occur.

Many of the Caribbean islands are mountainous, and rain shadow effects occur, with the north-east sides, which receive the north-east trades as onshore winds, wetter than the south-west, as in Barbados (Fig. 9.3).

HURRICANES

Tropical storms (Fig. 9.2) usually form in latitudes between 8° and 20° in both northern and southern hemispheres. They are called typhoons in the South China Sea, tropical cyclones in the Indian Ocean (see Chapter 16 on their effects on Bangladesh) and hurricanes in the Caribbean.

Hurricanes are similar in form to the depressions experienced in temperate latitudes, but they are much more violent. They are a means of transferring the sun's energy from tropical to temperate latitudes. They are circular in form and rotate anticlockwise in the northern and clockwise in the southern hemisphere. The spiral formation is closely related to the rotation of the earth's surface, causing the deflection of winds and air currents.

The circulation of a hurricane can be seen in Plate 9.1, a satellite photograph of Hurricane Allen hitting the coasts of Mexico and Texas in the summer of 1980, with the coastline superimposed in white. In the middle of the hurricane is an area of calm, with no cloud cover, known as the *eye*. This is the area of lowest pressure. Round the eye is a spiralling wall of cumulo-nimbus cloud, extending outwards for about 80 km. This is the zone of destruction, with winds sometimes exceeding 300 km per hour. Plate 9.2 shows conditions during a passage of a hurricane over the Florida coast.

113

Plate 9.1   A satellite photograph of Hurricane Allen 1980

(a) **Average hours of sunshine (April–October)**

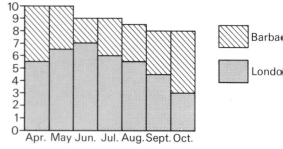

Barbados

London

(b) **Origin of visitors to Barbados, 1973**

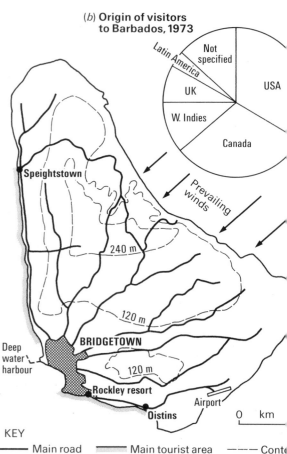

KEY

—— Main road   ▨ Main tourist area   ----- Cont

Fig. 9.3   Barbados

Plate 9.2   A hurricane on the Florida coast

The damage is caused not only by the high wind velocities, tearing away poorly constructed buildings, but also through coastal flooding caused by storm surges of the sea.

Tropical cyclones form in summer at the thermal equator (area of greatest heat, which lies north or south of the equator during the northern and southern summer respectively) and only form over sea areas. They occur where there are strong rising currents of air, removing air faster than it is flowing in. Although they cause great damage in coastal areas, they slow down rapidly on reaching land.

114

Tourism in the Caribbean

Rockley Resort

The new development situated in the south of the island, four miles from Bridgetown, consists of several groups of apartments, each group with its own swimming pool. Each apartment has a fully equipped kitchenette, air-conditioning, patio or balcony with garden view and private bath and shower. Rockley Resort has excellent facilities including a supermarket, tennis and squash courts, saunas, restaurant and open air bar/lounges. Close by is the Rockley Beach Club, just five minutes away by the hotel's free bus service. Situated on one of the south coast's finest beaches, the club comprises an open air restaurant serving snacks and barbecues, bars and changing rooms.
(from *P. and O. Air Holidays 'Caribbean and Mexico' Brochure*, 1981/2)

The above advertisement is quite typical of those in holiday brochures advertising the attractions of Caribbean islands, in this case Rockley Resort in Barbados (Fig. 9.3).

There has been an enormous increase in the international tourist industry since about 1960. In 1950 there were 25 million international tourists. By 1975, this figure had increased to over 200 million. Long-distance tourism has been encouraged by rising standards of living in westernised countries, with money to spare for expensive holidays; improvements in air transport; the development of relatively cheap package holidays; and conscious efforts made by countries, in this case tropical or sub-tropical countries, to encourage tourism by providing up-to-date tourist facilities.

One popular method is to combine fast air travel to reach a particular area, then to cover it by a more leisurely cruise. This is an important pattern in the Caribbean holiday industry, with tourists from North America or Europe flying to Miami, then taking a cruise ship. Fig. 9.1 shows a typical voyage that cruise ships follow. Plate 9.3 is a photograph of the harbour of St Thomas in the United States Virgin Islands (Fig. 9.1), one of the most popular stops, with cruise ships in port and a luxury hotel on the promontory in the background.

Plate 9.3   St Thomas harbour, United States Virgin Islands

Table 9.1 Number of tourists visiting Barbados, 1964 – 76

1964	57 600	1971	189 100
1965	68 400	1972	210 300
1966	79 100	1973	222 100
1967	91 600	1974	230 700
1968	115 700	1975	221 600
1969	134 300	1976	224 300
1970	156 400		

(from D.I. Marshall *Tourism and Employment in Barbados*, Occasional Papers Series No. 6, Institute of Social and Economic Research (Eastern Caribbean), University of the West Indies, Cave Hill Barbados)

The North American traffic is most important. Over one million visitors a year come to the Bahamas. Puerto Rico and the US Virgin Islands, all very popular with American tourists. Over half a million visit Jamaica, and between 100 000 and 500 000 the Dominican Republic, Haiti, Barbados, Curacao and Aruba (Fig. 9.1). Numbers alone, however, may conceal the importance of tourism to small islands: tiny Antigua's 70 000 annual tourists generate about 75% of its income. Table 9.1 illustrates the increasing importance of tourism in Barbados between 1964 and 1974, the first signs of check in the growth coming in 1975.

THE ATTRACTIONS OF CARIBBEAN ISLANDS

The most important attraction, emphasised by the tourist companies, is the tropical marine climate, with high but not excessive temperatures ranging from 25 °C to 28 °C. It is said that in some Caribbean hotels tourists are offered their money back if temperatures fall below 21 °C or rise above 31 °C. As inset (*a*) on Fig. 9.3 shows, there are long hours of sunshine, always eight or more per day between April and October which, as the diagram indicates, is many more than in London. The Caribbean comes out even better in the comparison for the winter, and December to April are particularly pleasant months, attracting winter tourists. Rain, when it comes, is of short duration, though it can be heavy. Tourists are not usually put off by the hurricane menace, for in any one place these are unlikely, and in any case their courses can generally be predicted.

Another major attraction is the quality of the scenery. Some islands have mountainous interiors, volcanoes, and interesting historical sites, such as English Harbour in Antigua, once the headquarters of the British navy in the Caribbean. Most important, however, is the coastal scenery, with unspoilt sandy beaches, cliffs, palm trees and clear waters, including ideal conditions for swimming, water skiing, surf riding and sailing on sheltered sides of islands. Plate 9.4 shows a typical scene on the coast of Antigua.

Air transport has made the Caribbean islands much more accessible. While many holiday makers fly direct to particular islands, one of the most popular methods, as we have seen, is to fly to a starting point, such as Miami, then take a cruise liner. The air fares are kept relatively cheap. Thus in 1977 an economy class flight from New York to Jamaica cost $334, as against $626 for one from New York to London.

Plate 9.4
A beach on Antigua

The tourist industry could not have got off the ground, however, had capital not been invested in building luxury hotels and apartments to attract North American and European visitors. Jamaica, for example, increased its accommodation from 3300 beds in 1955 to 22 000 in 1974. The tourist agencies also ensure that 'exotic' attractions are laid on for tourists, such as steel bands, and displays of local crafts and customs.

THE ADVANTAGES OF THE TOURIST INDUSTRY TO THE ISLANDS

Before the coming of the tourist industry the economies of many West Indian islands were precarious, being over-dependent on plantation products such as sugar and bananas, or on mineral wealth such as bauxite in Jamaica, all at the mercy of fluctuating world prices. Tourism helps to balance out the economy, earning 'invisible exports' through the money the tourists bring in. In 1974, Barbados earned almost as much from these as from 'visible' exports, mostly sugar cane.

Tourism is also a 'labour-intensive' industry, providing work in areas of high unemployment. In 1974, it provided 12 000 jobs in an overall work-force of 85 000 in Barbados. In Antigua, 900 hotel rooms generated about 1100 jobs.

Tourism also has what is called by economists a *multiplier effect*. That means it creates jobs not only directly in, for example, hotels, but also indirectly in servicing the hotels. For example, the hotels provide an enlarged local market for fish and agricultural produce, or for local crafts. The provision of hotels and other tourist facilities leads to an expansion of the construction industry, in building hotels, apartments, roads and airports.

PROBLEMS

The picture is not entirely a rosy one, however, and the 1970s have shown that tourism has far from solved the economic problems of Caribbean islands, as was thought possible in the rapid growth period of the 1960s. One reason has been the world recession from the mid-1970s, which has slackened off the growth in international tourism.

Tourism is in any case seasonal occupation, with slack periods when work is not available. This occurs in Barbados, for example, in May and June, and September and October. In Antigua, nearly one-third of the work-force lose their jobs in these periods. In some islands, the tourist industry is concentrated in lower grade hotels and apartments, which provide less employment than the luxury end of the market.

Some of the tourist traffic, such as that on cruise liners, brings less money to an island than guests who stay for a week or fortnight. The luxury hotels also tend to buy in a great deal of food from abroad in frozen form, at the expense of local produce. It has also been argued that tourism upsets the traditional culture of the islands, importing different sets of customs and values, displaying affluent western life-styles in the casinos and luxury hotels which are far beyond the reach of the local economy to offer to its own people. The control of new hotels over areas of beach sometimes leads to restriction of access to the local population, and resentment against tourists.

While luxury hotels are the most beneficial in respect of providing employment, and gain most foreign earnings, they are also expensive to build and require a high level of capital investment. If this comes from abroad, it means the earnings will be transferred outside the country also. If the capital is provided by the country itself, some would argue that it would be better invested in manufacturing industry.

Exercises

	J	F	M	A	M	J	J	A	S	O	N	D	
Temperature (°C)	25	25	25	25	26	26	27	28	28	27	26	25	Range 3
Rainfall (mm)	30	25	30	35	105	100	40	95	100	190	85	25	Total 860

1. (a) Draw a combined bar chart/graph to show the temperature and rainfall figures for Kingston, Jamaica (in a rain-shadow location), given in the above table.
2. (a) With the help of Plates 9.3 and 9.4 suggest reasons for the popularity of islands such as Antigua and the US Virgin Islands.
   (b) Find out why Cuba is not on the main tourist routes.

(b) How would you distinguish the tropical marine climate of Kingston from (i) an equatorial (ii) a tropical grassland (iii) a tropical monsoon climate.

3. (a) Draw a bar graph for the figures of the development of tourism in Barbados (Table 9.1). Why do most come from North America (Fig. 9.3b)?
   (b) Give reasons for the rapid growth of tourism and the signs of slackening of growth in the mid-1970s.

THE CANARY ISLANDS: TENERIFE

PROJECT: 'The Holiday Industry of Tenerife'

This project is based largely on the following resources, and also on earlier figures and plates in this chapter.

Fig. 9.4 Location and climatic features of the Canary Islands

Fig. 9.5 Map of Tenerife, with graph showing hours of sunshine

Fig. 9.6 Section across Tenerife

Plate 9.5 Mountains in the northern part of Tenerife

Plate 9.6 Puerto de la Cruz: main hotel district

Plate 9.7 Puerto de Santiago

Exercises

4. With the help of Figs. 9.1, 9.4, a world map and information in the text, compare and contrast the location and climatic features of the Caribbean and Canary Islands.

5. With the help of Figs. 9.3 and 9.5 compare and contrast the relief, climate and road patterns of Barbados and Tenerife.

6. Refer to Plates 9.5, 9.6, and 9.7, and write an account of the attractions of Tenerife to tourists.

7. In the light of the information in the text, state whether the following, taken from a travel brochure, is a fair summary:

The natural beauty of Tenerife is one reason for its many years of popularity. The timeless Mount Teide watches over the island. You can see it from almost anywhere you go, its conical peak rising to more than 12 000 feet. A cable-car trip to the summit is an awe-inspiring experience. Travel inland and Tenerife is a constant amazement as you leave the forests and banana plantations of the Orotava Valley for the contorted volcanic shapes of Las Canadas National Park. Drive along the island's central mountain ridge through Esperanza Forest and you can see far out across the Atlantic to Gran Canaria and La Palma. Or visit charming towns like La Orotava and Icod, where the famous 3 000-year-old Dragon Tree grows.

We offer hotels in three resorts, each with its own character and attraction. Puerto de la Cruz, Puerto de Santiago and Playa de las Americas

(from *Wings Holiday Brochure*, Summer 1981)

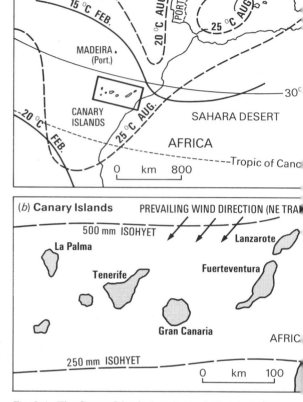

Fig. 9.4   The Canary Islands: location and climatic regions

Plate 9.5   Mountainous landscape, north-eastern Tenerife

Plate 9.6   Puerto de la Cruz, Tenerife

Plate 9.7   Puerto de Santiago on the south-west *coast* of Tenerife, with a black beach derived from volcanic deposits

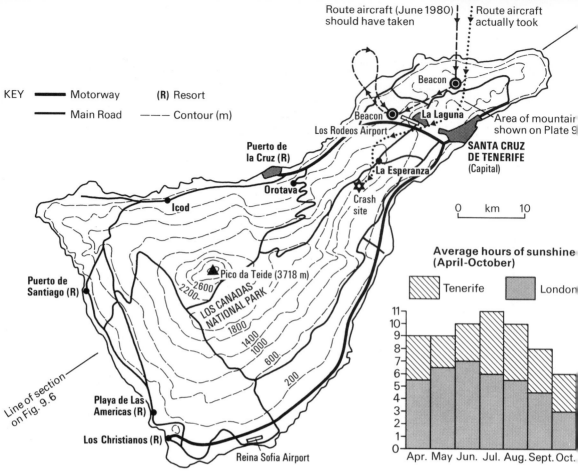

Fig. 9.5 Tenerife

Fig. 9.6 A section across Tenerife

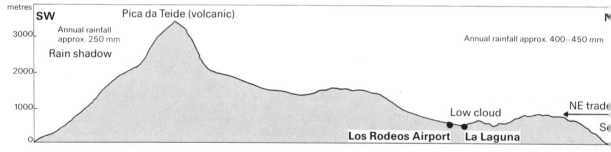

8. Fig. 9.5 shows the path of a British plane which crashed in a holiday flight to Los Rodeos airport, Tenerife, now rarely used.

(*a*) With the help of Fig. 9.5, Fig. 9.6 and Plate 9.5, whose general location is marked on Fig. 9.5, give reasons why Los Rodeos was a difficult airport to land at.

(*b*) Can you suggest a reason for the roundabout recommended flight path shown for landing at this airport?

(*c*) What advantages does the new airport at Reina Sofia appear to have over Los Rodeos?

(*d*) What impact is the increased use of Reina Sofia likely to have on the resorts of Puerto de la Cruz and Los Cristianos?

(*e*) With the help of Plates 9.6 and 9.7 and Fig. 9.5 suggest reasons why you would choose to visit Puerto de la Cruz rather than Puerto de Santiago, or vice versa.

9. Collect material from local travel agents on holidays in Barbados and Tenerife and work out the costs and time involved in travelling for a holiday in each, in summer and in winter. What factors would influence you in making a decision to choose to go to one rather than the other?

SECTION D: *Densely Populated Regions of Temperature Latitudes*
10 Agriculture in Capitalist and Communist Worlds

INTRODUCTION

In the regions we have studied so far, physical factors such as relief and climate are important in limiting farming activities. The Andean farmer, for example, cannot use combine harvesters on his small, steeply sloping and rocky fields. Without the summer rains both the Sahel nomad and the Indian rice farmer are in trouble. People of course adapt to, and seek to change, their physical circumstances, whether through applying irrigation water, as in the Israeli kibbutzim, or providing more land by clearing forest, as in Amazonia.

The regions we are about to study are also limited by physical factors, although to a lesser degree. While the Norwegian farmer cannot grow vines and the French farmer must produce sugar beet rather than sugar cane, in general, agriculture in temperate lati-tudes is favoured by wide expanses of level land; by climate (see below); and by thick loamy, peaty or clayey soils, well supplied with organic matter, built up through long periods of cultivation. In addition, they are areas of technologically advanced farming.

More interesting perhaps than the contrast between physical features, is the contrast between the modes of farming under different political systems: *capitalist farming*, which is farming for private profit, although often with a lot of government support and inter-ference, as practised, for example, in the European Community (formerly the European Economic Com-munity: EEC) countries and in North America; and *communist farming*, controlled by the state, as practised in the USSR and Eastern Europe.

Fig. 10.1   Temperate climatic regions

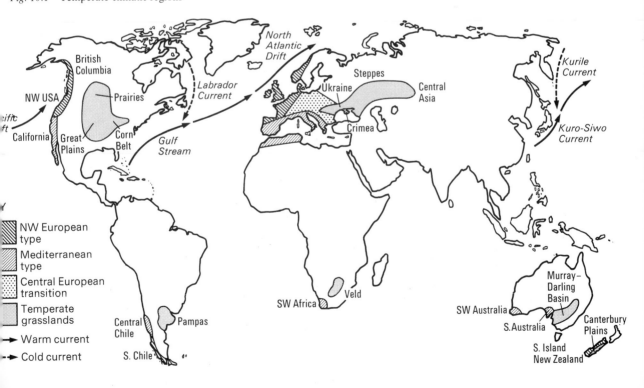

North-west European Type (CTWM: Cool Temperature West Marginal)

CLIMATE

Temperature
As Fig. 10.2a and b indicate, temperatures vary with latitude, in winter from 2 °C to 7 °C and summer from 13 °C to 19 °C. The temperature range is from about 11 °C to 13 °C. Another factor is distance from the sea. In winter, temperatures in the same latitude decrease away from the west coasts. Maritime influences in the shape of warm offshore currents and winds from the sea keep winter temperatures higher on these coasts. Thus as a result of the North Atlantic Drift (Fig. 10.1) Norwegian harbours, even north of the Arctic Circle, remain ice-free. In summer, the maritime influence leads to less warm temperatures at the coast than inland. Thus the annual range of temperature is less in coastal areas.

Rainfall
Rain falls at all seasons, but generally with more between August and January than between February and July, meaning there is a winter maximum (Fig. 10.2a and b). The main variations are caused by relief. There is about 750 mm on lowlands on the rain shadow side (the east side) of highlands; over 1000 m on west-coast lowlands; and over 2000 mm in mountainous areas facing westerly winds. Orographic (relief) effects therefore accentuate the tendency to regular rainfall resulting from the fact that these latitudes are in the main path of depressions from the west. These are more frequent in winter, giving heavier average rainfalls at that season. Although totals are heavy, there is a good deal of variability in the weather, and dry spells may on occasions occur even in the rainier winter season. There is some convectional rainfall in summer.

Fig. 10.2   North-west European type: climatic graphs

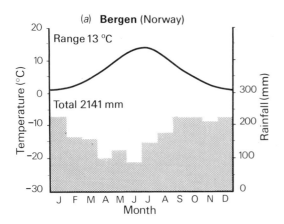

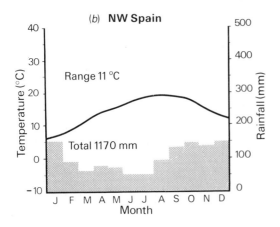

NATURAL VEGETATION (Fig. 10.3)

The natural vegetation is *deciduous forest*, with a bigger variety of trees than coniferous forest, although much less than equatorial. Trees include oak, beech, elm and ash. The fallen leaves in winter break down to form humus and the soils are naturally rich in organic matter. Most of the deciduous forest has, however, been cleared over the centuries to provide farming land.

Central European Transition

CLIMATE

In North America the Rocky Mountains provide a sharp break between the temperate maritime climates of the west coast and the temperate continental of the interior. In Europe, the presence of the North European Plain, from eastern France into the Low Countries, Germany and Eastern Europe, provides no such break. Thus a transition region exists between the wetter, less extreme and naturally forested areas of the west, and the drier, more extreme and grassland regions of the steppes. This means the North

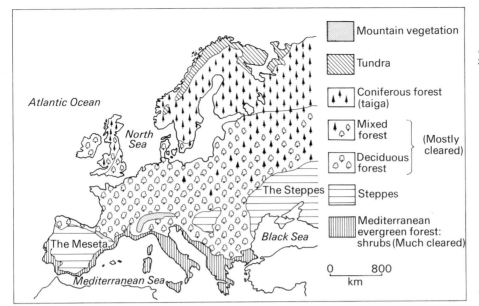

Fig. 10.3 Vegetation zones of Europe

Mountain vegetation
Tundra
Coniferous forest (taiga)
Mixed forest
Deciduous forest
} (Mostly cleared)
The Steppes — Steppes
Mediterranean evergreen forest: shrubs (Much cleared)

0   800
km

European Plain has colder winters than those of Western Europe, but less cold than those of the steppes. It has less rain than West European coasts, but does receive depressions from the west, and is wetter than the steppes region (Fig. 10.4).

NATURAL VEGETATION

This is more or less as for Western Europe, with most of the deciduous forest cleared for farmland. In the north-east the deciduous forest in the natural state shades into coniferous, and in the south-east into steppe grassland (Fig. 10.3), as in the Hungarian Plain and the Ukraine.

Mediterranean Type (WTWM: Warm Temperate West Marginal)

CLIMATE

Temperature
The hottest month generally averages from 21 °C to 27 °C, with less high temperatures on west coasts. The coolest month generally averages from 7 °C to 10 °C, with higher averages on the west coasts (Fig. 10.5). The annual range is from 14 °C to 17 °C, with a smaller range on west coasts. Clear skies in the drier summers allow intense insolation, giving high temperatures, especially inland. But on west coasts, as in California, cool currents can considerably reduce summer temperatures, bringing coastal fogs. In winter, however, the maritime influence results in milder weather conditions.

Fig. 10.4 Central European transition type: climatic graph

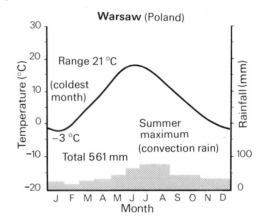

Warsaw (Poland)
Range 21 °C
(coldest month)
−3 °C
Total 561 mm
Summer maximum (convection rain)

Fig. 10.5 Mediterranean type: climatic graph

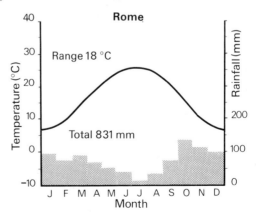

Rome
Range 18 °C
Total 831 mm

123

Rainfall

Annual totals vary considerably from as little as 175 mm to about 850 mm, with much more than this in some mountainous areas. There is a characteristically dry summer with high temperatures and drought conditions. Winter is the rainy season. In summer, Mediterranean areas are affected by the sub-tropical high pressure, giving offshore winds in most areas, and dry conditions. In winter, these areas are in the track of depressions from the west, with onshore winds bringing rainfall, especially heavy in mountainous areas.

MEDITERRANEAN VEGETATION

This is naturally *evergreen woodland* (Fig. 10.3), but much has been cleared by firing to provide agricultural land.

Characteristics

The natural evergreen forest includes evergreen oaks, cork oaks and pines. Some larger trees such as cedars are also found. In California, giant redwoods are still present, while in south-west Australia karri and jarrah are characteristic. When fired and not used for farmland, the forest is replaced by poor evergreen scrub. In Mediterranean Europe this includes *maquis*, a dense mass of low evergreen shrubs, with leathery or spiny leaves. In drier, often limestone, areas there are lower scrub-type plants, with much bare ground in between, known as *garigue*. Plate 10.1 is a photograph of Mediterranean evergreen shrub country in Sardinia.

Adaptation to climate

Winters are warm enough to allow evergreen plants to survive. In summer, conditions are desert-like, and plants must be able to withstand drought. This they do by having small, hairy or waxy leaves to reduce trans-

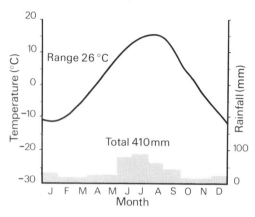

Fig. 10.6   Cool temperate grasslands: climatic graph

piration; long roots to reach underground supplies of water; bulbous roots to store food and moisture; and thick-skinned fruits. Garigue vegetation, on dry limestone soils, has to be particularly drought-resisting. Mediterranean tree crops, such as the vine and the olive, are drought resistant also. Larger trees are found in areas with most rainfall, as on the windward sides of uplands.

Temperate Grasslands

(Cool temperate (CT) or warm temperate (WT) continental interiors (CI))

CLIMATE

Temperature

In the cooler north of the Prairies and Steppes (CTCI), the hottest month averages from 16 °C to 21 °C. (Fig. 10.6). Further south, as in the Great Plains of the USA (WTCI), the comparable figures are

Plate 10.1   Mediterranean shrub vegetation, Sardinia

from 21 °C to 27 °C. The cool temperate areas have very cold winters, averaging from −4 °C to −10 °C (Fig. 10.6), while the warm temperate areas are still cold, averaging from 0 °C to −4 °C. The average range is from over 25 °C further north, to anything from 21 °C to 28 °C further south.

Temperatures are extreme because these continental interiors are isolated from the sea's influence, and are subject to very cold northerly winds in winter, from Arctic Canada (Prairies) and Siberia (Steppes).

Rainfall

Annual totals vary from under 500 mm in more northerly areas (Fig. 10.6) to approaching 750 mm further south. The rain falls mainly in summer. Precipitation is small in winter, and comes as light snowfall, though this can blow up into large drifts in blizzard conditions. In North America, rainfall totals increase eastwards from the Rockies.

Conditions are dry because the continental interiors are generally isolated from maritime influences. In North America, the western parts of the Prairies and

Great Plains are in the rain shadow of the Rockies. Further east, however, more rain is experienced as moist air comes through from the Gulf of Mexico, as in the Corn Belt of the USA (Fig. 10.1). The summer rainfall maximum results from depression activity and from convection. In winter the northern areas in particular are covered by high pressures giving descending air and dry conditions.

NATURAL VEGETATION

The grassland vegetation has been cleared over large areas for extensive grain farming. There is a transition from the richer grassland of wetter areas, such as the tall-grass prairie of North America, to the scrubbier grassland of drier areas, such as the short-grass prairie in the lee of the Rockies in North America, and over much of the steppes of the USSR. In wetter areas, the prairie grasses break down to provide a rich organic soil. Such soils are known as *chernozems*, and characteristically have dark surface layers, rich in humus.

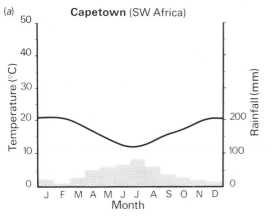

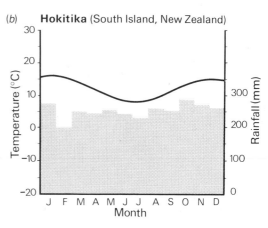

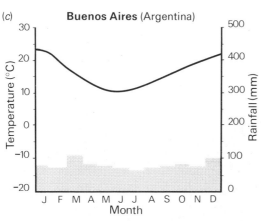

Fig. 10.7 Temperate climatic graphs, southern hemisphere

125

Exercises

1. Refer to Figs. 10.2*a*, and *b*, 10.4, 10.5 and 10.6. What features enable you to distinguish (*a*) a north-west European type of climate from a Mediterranean; (*b*) a north-west European type from a continental transition type; (*c*) a Mediterranean type from a continental interior (temperate grassland) type.

2. (*a*) Refer to Fig. 10.1. Describe the differing distribution of areas of temperate climatic type between the southern and northern hemispheres.
   (*b*) Describe the temperature and rainfall conditions of each station in Fig. 10.7*a*, *b* and *c*, trying to place each in its appropriate climatic type.
   (*c*) Why is there no continental transition type of climate in the southern hemisphere?
   (*d*) How is the climate of the Murray-Darling basin liable to differ from the steppes of central Asia?

3. Compare and contrast Mediterranean and desert vegetation (see Chapter 5) in terms of its characteristics and adaptation to climatic conditions.

INTENSIVE CAPITALIST FARMING IN THE EEC

Cooperative Mixed Farming in Denmark

The development of farming in Denmark since the beginning of the nineteenth century can be divided into three stages:

During much of the nineteenth century, Denmark was a granary for more densely populated countries in Europe. But the opening up of the Prairies in North America, and a reduction in trans-Atlantic freight rates, led to cheap grain flooding into European markets from the 1870s. As Danish grain could not compete, it was fed to livestock. Fortunately for Denmark, at about this time Britain adopted a freer trading policy to allow the import of foods for a rapidly growing population. The British acquired a taste for bacon, and an important and continuing trading link was established between Esbjerg, on the west coast of Jutland and British ports across the North Sea.

1880s TO ABOUT 1960

In the 1870s a Danish invention, a cream separator, allowed milk to be processed quickly on a factory basis. As a result, cooperative dairies, such as the Hjedding Dairy on Plate 10.2, were established. The skimmed milk was returned to the farm to feed pigs. The Danish Landrace pig was evolved as an ideal type for bacon production. From then on the quality of produce was strictly controlled in cooperative establishments, ensuring that only the highest grade butter, eggs and bacon reached the export market. The hygienic conditions under which the bacon is produced are seen on Plate 10.3. Over 90% of the output is con-

Plate 10.2   Hjedding Dairy, Denmark, in the late nineteenth century

Plate 10.3   Inside a Danish bacon factory

trolled under the cooperative system. Apart from quality control, the cooperatives, made up of independent farmers, ensure that their members obtain good prices for their produce, can buy materials and equipment at wholesale prices, and secure loans at low interest rates. Other cooperative organisations are concerned with advice and research.

EARLY 1960s TO THE PRESENT

In 1979 there were approximately 22 000 full-time male farmhands, only about one-fifth of the number employed in 1960. There has been a reduction in the prosperity of the small farmer, and a move towards larger, more mechanised and factory-type farming. The average size of holding increased from 16 hectares in 1960 to 25 in 1979. The scarcity of farm labour has particularly affected the dairying industry, and milk cattle have tended to be replaced by pigs and poultry, permanently housed indoors. The area under

cereals, and especially under barley, has been greatly increased. The undulating landscape of Denmark, built up of glacial deposits, remains intensively farmed, with a mixture of fields under grain, grass and green fodder crops (Plate 10.4). Agricultural land takes up over two-thirds of Denmark's total area, and of this about 70% is under cereals and approaching 30% under grass and green fodder crops. The grain is often harvested green for silage. 85% of the crops are used for stockfeed. The relatively low annual rainfall (630 mm) is ideally not wet enough for grass, and more suited to cereals. Denmark's cooperative system of *intensive mixed farming* is therefore well adapted to both physical and economic conditions.

Denmark joined the European Economic Community in 1973. This has widened Denmark's market for agricultural produce. While Britain remains the largest overseas market for bacon, butter and canned milk and meat, West Germany takes the largest share of

Plate 10.4   Mixed farming landscape in Jutland

Danish exports of cheese, poultry and eggs, and Italy of cattle and other meat products. Denmark must export to survive, as it has to import most of its industrial raw materials and energy resources. About two-thirds of Denmark's agricultural production is exported, and 60% of this export is to EEC countries. Another trend has been to more advanced means of transportation of produce, such as milk tankers and the containerised export of bacon and butter (Plate 10.5).

Entry to the EEC has meant that Danish agriculture is subject to an outside force, the common agricultural policy (CAP) of the Community. This has the effect of

(*a*) protecting farmers against the competition of imports from outside the EEC;

(*b*) guaranteeing prices for farm produce;

(*c*) storing agricultural surpluses, in some cases selling them off at cheap rates to countries outside the EEC;

(*d*) giving financial grants for modernisation.

Plate 10.5   Export of butter by container

Plate 10.6   Intensive glasshouse cultivation near the Hague

Plate 10.7   Bulb fields in the Netherlands

Market Gardening (Horticulture) in the Netherlands

Plates 10.6 and 10.7 illustrate an even more *capital-intensive* form of farming than that in Denmark, namely market gardening or horticulture. This takes place under glass (10.6) or in the open (10.7), in the former case producing lettuces, cucumbers, tomatoes, cut flowers and other crops, and in the other, bulb growing, one of the most characteristic farming activities of the polder lands of Holland. Bulb growing is found particularly in the sheltered areas behind the coastal dune belt, and in the river polders of the Betuwe district (Fig. 10.8). Plate 10.6 illustrates the high urban densities of population in the Netherlands, providing a local market for horticultural produce. Despite the high population density (340/km²), and despite the fact that only 4% of the land is devoted to horticulture, there is a considerable surplus of produce for export. In all, agriculture accounts for about one-quarter of the country's exports.

Fig. 10.8 indicates that a large percentage of the Netherlands is taken up by arable and pasture land, but here we shall be concentrating on the two activities of outdoor bulb growing and glasshouse cultivation. In the dune-sheltered polder belt of the Haarlem area, lime-rich sandy areas have been created by the digging away of old dunes. Sometimes the sand is mixed with peat to increase the organic content. The main bulbs grown are tulips, hyacinths and daffodils. The growers concentrate on producing healthy bulbs. The flowers are cut off at an early stage, but not before they have attracted tourists to the area.

As Plate 10.7 suggests, holdings are small, with tiny fields separated by drainage ditches. There has been a strong tendency to amalgamate holdings, but the average size is still only about 8 hectares. The production is therefore on a 'gardening' scale, and is labour intensive at certain seasons, such as the time in summer when the bulbs have to be cleaned, peeled, graded and packed. Temporary labour is employed for this purpose. Capital costs are great, both for machinery for beheading the flowers, raising the bulbs and sorting them, and for manure (from dairy farming areas), fertilisers and pesticides.

129

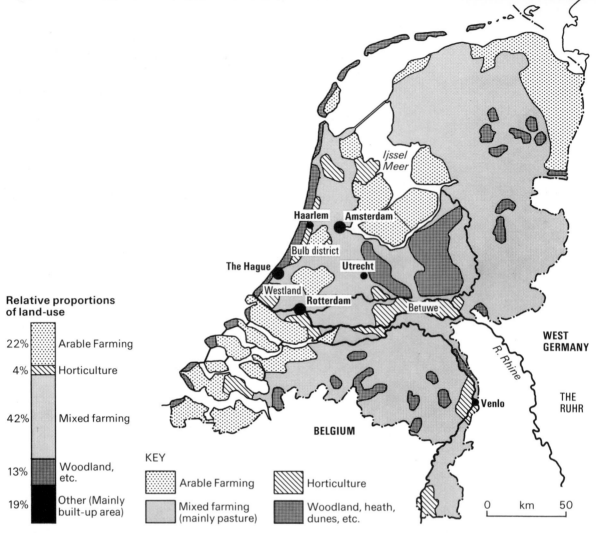

Relative proportions of land-use

- 22% Arable Farming
- 4% Horticulture
- 42% Mixed farming
- 13% Woodland, etc.
- 19% Other (Mainly built-up area)

KEY

- Arable Farming
- Horticulture
- Mixed farming (mainly pasture)
- Woodland, heath, dunes, etc.

0 km 50

Fig. 10.8 Agricultural land-use in the Netherlands

Plate 10.6 is in the Westland district between The Hague and Rotterdam. It is like a 'city of glass', more akin to an urban than a rural landscape. Here farming is even more intensive, with 'holdings' averaging about 1 hectare. Inside the glasshouses several crops are grown each year: perhaps spinach in spring, cucumbers in summer and lettuce in autumn and winter. Costs of production are considerable. In so densely populated a region, land values and therefore rents are high. Glasshouses require thermostatically controlled heating, generally based on home-produced natural gas. The plants also require carefully controlled watering. An automated 'micro-climate' is produced, sometimes by computer, ensuring the correct heating, moisture, ventilation and carbon dioxide content for each product. The 'soil' is sterilised each year and crop rotation practised to combat disease.

The average glasshouse holding employs two or three people, with casual help added at harvesting time. The produce is auctioned. There is a huge market for vegetable and floral produce in the Randstad Holland conurbation (see Chapter 13), but there are also large quantities produced for export. There are signs of the Westland area becoming gradually less important for glasshouse production. The glasshouses shown on the photograph have now been replaced by housing. The cost of land is excessively high in this area, which is also not so well placed for the German market as other horticultural areas such as the Betuwe and the rapidly growing Venlo region, right on the frontier (Fig. 10.8), near the densely populated Ruhr conurbation. In addition to export by road, expensive products such as cut flowers and table grapes may be exported by air from nearby Schipol airport (southwest of Amsterdam), mostly to south Germany and Scandinavian countries, but also to North America.

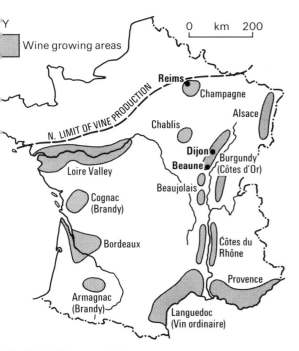

Wine growing areas

N. LIMIT OF VINE PRODUCTION

0   km   200

Reims

Champagne

Alsace

Chablis

Dijon

Beaune

Burgundy
(Côtes d'Or)

Beaujolais

Loire Valley

Cognac
(Brandy)

Bordeaux

Côtes du
Rhône

Provence

Armagnac
(Brandy)

Languedoc
(Vin ordinaire)

Fig. 10.9   Viticulture in France

Vine Growing (Viticulture) in Burgundy

While Italy is Europe's largest producer of wine, France is by far the most important producer in terms of the quality and variety of its wines. The most famous regions are round Bordeaux (producing clarets), the Reims area (producing Champagne), and in Burgundy (Fig. 10.9). In Burgundy, a string of high-quality wine-producing districts runs from north to south along the western slopes over-looking the Saone valley. Beaune is the main marketing centre while Dijon houses the head offices of many of the wine-trading firms.

The vine is a plant which can be grown on a great variety of soil types. These are reflected in the character of the wine produced. Vines are even more sensitive to small variations in weather. The difference between a good and a poor vintage often depends on minor variation in sunshine totals. In May, the frost danger is at its height and on clear nights stoves may be needed to heat up the air on the vineyards, sited on slopes so that the cold air will sink into the valley bottom below them. The vines flower in early June, and then the temperature is critical. If the weather is sunny and calm there is no problem. But if too cool and rainy, the crops can be seriously damaged. Different parts of France face different hazards. The northerly Champagne region is most liable to cool moist condi-

Plate 10.8   Nuits-Saint-Georges vineyards, Burgundy

tions in May and June. Bordeaux and Burgundy are not very different. On the other hand, Languedoc (Fig. 10.9) has little problem at this season. It produces vast quantities of wine, but of very ordinary quality ('vin ordinaire'). The problem here is that the summers are very hot, and while vines grow very well in hot conditions, they do not produce good-quality wines.

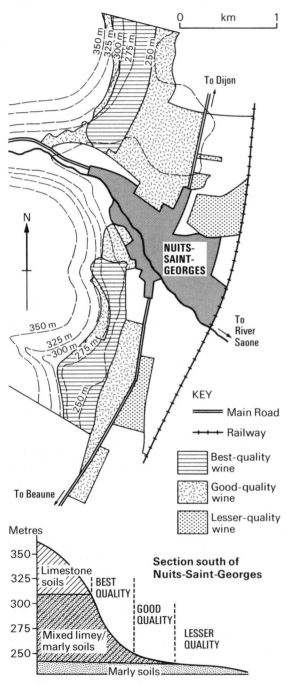

KEY

— Main Road

+—+ Railway

Best-quality wine

Good-quality wine

Lesser-quality wine

Section south of Nuits-Saint-Georges

Metres

350
Limestone soils
325
BEST QUALITY
300
GOOD QUALITY
275
Mixed limey/ marly soils
LESSER QUALITY
250
Marly soils

Note: Vertical scale exaggerated.
Soil boundaries approximate.

The famous vineyards of Nuits-Saint-Georges (Plate 10.8) are located on the road between Dijon and Beaune (Fig. 10.10), and illustrate the conditions needed for high-quality wines.

(1) The best vineyards in the area have the best *micro-climate*, found on slopes facing due east. This is because they catch the morning sun, which warms the ground gradually; lie on slopes above the valley floor, giving good air drainage and avoiding frost pockets; and are sheltered by the hills behind from moist westerly winds.

(2) While vines will grow in most types of soil, a high-quality wine demands a particular type of soil. As the inset to Fig. 10.10 shows, the higher slopes are made of thin and very light limestone soils, containing few vineyards. Lower down there is a marlstone band which gives too rich a soil for the best-quality wine. But between the two are soils of marl mixed with limestone material from above which are ideal. Here the highest-quality vineyards are located.

(3) Perhaps the most important factor of all, however, is the age-old tradition of skill which goes into the wine making, which in Burgundy dates back to Roman times.

(4) This is combined with a long-standing quality-control system that guarantees the quality of the wine. This ranges from the *Grand Cru* vineyards (and even the best Nuits-Saint-Georges does not meet this standard), producing very expensive wines; through *Premier Cru* (including the best Nuits-Saint-Georges), also expensive; then *Appellation Controlée, popular in the export market; followed by VDQS* wines, good quality 'local' wines, not much exported; and finally *vin ordinaire*, the everyday drink of millions of French people, increasingly being sold as 'plonk' in EEC countries where it competes with cheap Italian wines.

EXTENSIVE CAPITALIST FARMING IN NORTH AMERICA: THE PRAIRIE PROVINCES OF CANADA

The Prairie Provinces of Manitoba, Saskatchewan and Alberta (Fig. 10.11) form the northernmost part of the great grassland region of North America lying between the Appalachian and the Rocky Mountains, and running south from here to the Gulf of Mexico (Fig. 10.1). The cool temperate grasslands, which extend southwards into the USA, concentrate on the growing of wheat and barley. Further south, the warm temperate grasslands include the Corn Belt, concentrating on maize growing.

Fig. 10.10 Viticulture at Nuits-Saint-Georges, Burgundy

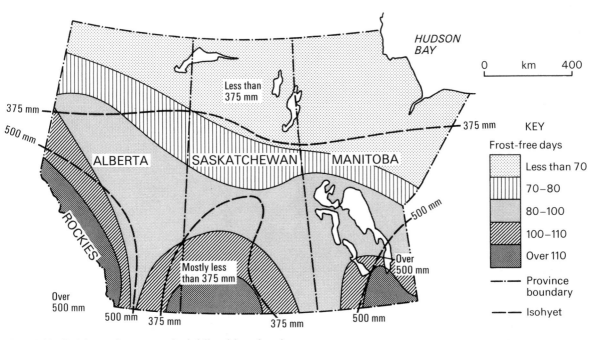

Fig. 10.11 Prairie provinces: annual rainfall and frost-free days

The Landscape and Settlement of the Prairies

The Prairies of Canada rise from east to west in a series of steps, the lowest near Lake Winnipeg and the highest lying against the Rockies in Alberta. The relatively flat or undulating surface is dissected by large rivers such as the North and South Saskatchewan. The climate becomes drier towards the west, with lower rainfall totals on average in the lee of the Rockies in southern Alberta and south-west Saskatchewan (Fig. 10.11). This is reflected in richer tall-grass Prairie in the east and short-grass Prairie further west. The moister areas also have the advantage of the richer *chernozem* soils, with less humus-rich *chestnut* soils in the drier areas.

A remarkable feature of the Prairie landscape is the regular grid-iron pattern of fields, roads and farm-tracks (Plate 10.9). Blocks of roads were laid out at intervals of just over 3 km and farms spread out evenly along them. When the railways reached the Prairies, settlers flooded in, and were granted blocks of land. These were smaller on the richer lands of the east than they were in the west. The roads connected the farms to the rail-heads, often marked by lines of grain elevators (Plate 10.9).

The most characteristic Prairie landscape is of fields of *grain*, traditionally wheat, but increasingly of barley. More and more farmers are diversifying into *mixed farming*, feeding barley to the livestock. Extensive grain farming still covers large areas of southern Saskatchewan and Manitoba, however (Fig. 10.12).

More scattered 'pioneer farming' is found on the margin between the grassland and the forest to the north (Fig. 10.12), and *cattle ranching*, centred on the Calgary area, and *dry farming* and *irrigation farming*, centred on the Lethbridge area, in the lee of the Rockies. *Dry farming* involves production of crops only every second year. The seeds are planted deep below the drier surface layers, and weeds, which take up moisture, are carefully kept down. The soils are not exhausted by continuous cropping and quite good yields of grain can be achieved in this way. Irrigation water is provided by Rocky Mountain streams such as the Bow River. The grazing areas are helped by the presence of the *Chinook*, a warm descending wind from the Rockies which melts the snow and opens up the pastures in spring.

Advantages of the Prairies for Grain Farming

(1) *Climatic* advantages include high summer temperatures (averaging over 15 °C) and summer rainfall

(Fig. 10.6) which promote rapid growth. The long daylight hours and dry autumns assist harvesting. The frost-free season of about 100–120 frost-free days in the main grain farming areas is sufficient for the growth of spring wheat.

(2) The level or rolling plains, and large field blocks, while making for a monotonous landscape (Plate 10.9), assist mechanisation, particularly the use of combine harvesters.

(3) In the wetter areas (Fig. 10.11), fertile black chernozem soils occur, deep and rich in humus.

(4) In general, the Prairie provinces have relatively low population densities, and most areas are losing population to the towns. The high degree of mechanisation, however, means that little farm labour is needed, and makes possible a vast production from the large amount of land available (*extensive farming*). While yields per hectare are relatively low by West European standards, the farming is very profitable.

(5) Roads and railways were easy to build over the level or gently undulating landscape. The low population density means that most of the production has always been intended for export, especially to West European markets and, since World War 2, increasingly to the Japanese and East European markets.

There are three main routes for export of grain (Fig. 10.12):

(*a*) 60% goes east to Thunder Bay (Plate 10.10) on Lake Superior, thence via the St Lawrence Seaway and Montreal to the north Atlantic trade route;

(*b*) in winter much is sent out via the ice-free port of Vancouver, particularly convenient for Japanese trade;

(*c*) a small amount is exported in summer via the port of Churchill on Hudson Bay, which freezes up in winter.

Plate 10.9 Extensive farming: the Prairie landscape

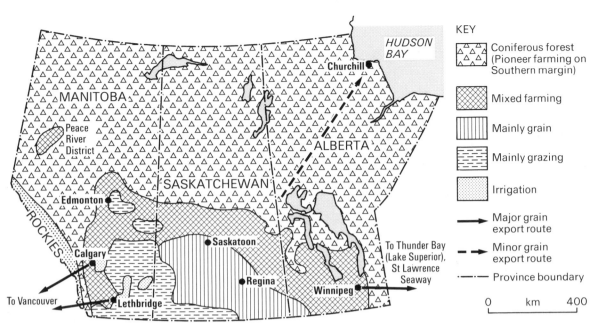

KEY

△△△ Coniferous forest
(Pioneer farming on
Southern margin)

▦ Mixed farming

▥ Mainly grain

▤ Mainly grazing

▦ Irrigation

→ Major grain
export route

–→ Minor grain
export route

–·– Province boundary

0   km   400

Fig. 10.12   Prairie provinces: agricultural zones

Plate 10.10   Grain elevators at Thunder Bay

135

Plate 10.11
Extensive farming:
a state farm (sovkhoz)
in Kazakhstan

Plate 10.12 Grain elevators in Kazakhstan

EXTENSIVE COMMUNIST FARMING IN THE USSR: THE STEPPES OF THE UKRAINE AND KAZAKHSTAN (Fig. 10.1)

Plate 10.11 could almost be a scene on the Canadian Prairies at harvest time, with combine harvesters at work on extensive fields of grain, broken up by shelter belts of trees. One differences is that the fields are even less divided, with no chequer-board of blocks as on Plate 10.9. The landscape is also marked by huge grain elevators at rail-heads (Plate 10.12).

Advantages for Grain Farming in the Steppes

The factors are similar to those of the Prairies. The long hot summers with rain at that season assist the growth and ripening of crops. In drier areas, irrigation water is available, from rivers such as the Dnieper, Don and Volga in European Russia, and the Ob and Yenisei in Siberia. Rainfall is particularly unreliable in the 'virgin lands' of Kazakhstan in the east. The level landscape and collective farming system have made possible an increase in mechanisation. As in the Prairies, the dark well-drained chernozem soils are rich in humus and lime. Drier areas have less rich chestnut soils, very liable to wind erosion when exposed. As in the Prairies, shelter belts are left to prevent serious losses of soil (Plate 10.11).

136

Plate 10.13
A sovkhoz settlement

Collective Farming

Between the two world wars, the communist government of the USSR, having taken power in 1917, brought to an end the old private farm system by making the peasant holdings collective, often by force. Since this agricultural revolution, two basic types of collective units have evolved.

THE KOLKHOZ

This is a type of large cooperative farm (perhaps 600 hectares), on land leased from the government and run by members of the cooperative, made up of about 400 families. The collective farm produce is sold to the state at fixed prices, and the income, after various expenses have been deducted, is divided among members. Members of the kolkhoz are allowed to work small private plots after they have fulfilled their obligation of a specified number of days at work on the main collective. On these plots, potatoes and other vegetables, milk and eggs are produced, both for family use and for sale.

The kolkhozes have not, however, been generally successful. The collective farming system was harshly imposed by the government, with many peasants of the Ukraine killed or deported in the process of change. The peasants found little incentive in the 'share-income' system of the kolkhoz. Most of the collectives had too many people in relation to the amount they produced. In addition, heavy industry was given priority over farming by Stalin's government, and investment was poor until after his death in the 1950s. After World War 2, attempts were made to increase the size and efficiency of the kolkhoz, but the trend was rather to a new type of collective, the *sovkhoz*, or state farm. The number of kolkhozes decreased from 127 000 in 1950 to 33 600 in 1970.

THE SOVKHOZ

This type of cooperative farm is entirely state owned. The workers are hired in the same way as factory workers. The farm is directed by agricultural managers, and is much larger than the kolkhoz up to 50 000 hectares, with a community of perhaps 1500 people, living in a large village or small town (Plate 10.13). The state farms are more typical of newly opened areas, such as the virgin lands of Kazakhstan. They are more highly mechanised and often more specialised than the kolkhozes. They may, for example, concentrate on producing a particular crop such as cotton.

There were only 4200 sovkhozes in 1940, but 15 000 in 1970. The number of farm workers in them increased from 2.3 million in 1940 to 8.9 million in 1970. Their increased importance reflects the higher priority now given to farming by the Soviet government. From the 1960s, attempts were made to increase efficiency by agricultural planning through regional economic councils, rather than by inefficient central direction. These regional councils set productivity targets, as was typical in manufacturing industry. Greater personal incentive was offered by breaking down the production brigades on the state farms into teams of five or six, and giving bonuses for good production levels. There has been increased investment in farm machinery, and in improvements in irrigation, farm buildings, processing plants and farm roads.

Many of the sovkhozes are, however, in areas with less than 500 mm of rainfall, which makes crop yields unreliable. Productivity remains low, with the Soviet farm worker producing perhaps one-fifth of his American counterpart. While yields have greatly improved, there is still a frequent need to import grain from North America.

137

Table 10.1 EEC agricultural statistics
(a) *Agricultural land and farms, 1978*[1]

	Total area (million hectares)	Agricultural area (million hectares)	No. of farms (1000s)	Hectares per farm
West Germany	24.9	13.2	843.6	14.6
France	54.9	32.2	1126.0	25.9
Italy	30.1	17.5	2053.4[3]	7.8[3]
Netherlands	3.7	2.1	134.4	15.2
Belgium	3.1	1.4	96.8	14.8
Luxembourg	0.3	0.1	5.0	25.9
Great Britain	24.4	18.5	260.2	66.0
Ireland	7.0	4.8[2]	260.1[3]	20.5[3]
Denmark	4.3	2.9	122.3	23.9
Total EEC	152.7	92.7	4901.8	17.2[3]
Denmark, % of EEC	2.8	3.2	2.5	–

[1] Including market gardening. [2] 1976. [3] 1975.

(c) *Population 1978*

	Total population (millions)	Working population (millions)	Population employed in agriculture[1] forestry, fishing Total (millions)	Percentage of working population
West Germany	61.3	24.7	1.6	6.5
France	53.4	20.9	1.9	9.1
Italy	56.8	19.9	3.1	15.5
Netherlands	14.0	4.6	0.3	6.2
Belgium	9.8	3.7	0.1	3.2
Luxembourg	0.4	0.2	–	5.6
Great Britain	55.9	24.6	0.7	2.7
Ireland	3.3	1.0	0.2	22.2
Denmark	5.1	2.5	0.2	8.8
Total EEC	260.0	102.1	8.1	8.0
Denmark, % of EEC	2.0	2.4	2.7	–

[1] Including market gardening.

(b) *Total livestock, December 1979* (in millions)

	Cattle	Cows	Pigs	Sows with young
West Germany	15.0	5.6	22.4	1.7
France	23.7	10.2	10.5	0.8
Italy	8.8	3.8	8.8	0.6
Netherlands	5.0	2.3	10.0	0.7
Belgium	2.9	1.1	5.0	0.4
Luxembourg	0.2	0.1	0.1	–
Great Britain	13.3	4.9	7.8	0.6
Ireland	6.2	2.0	1.1	0.1
Denmark	2.9	1.1	9.6	0.7
Total EEC	78.0	31.1	75.3	5.6
Denmark, % of EEC	3.8	3.7	12.7	11.8

(d) *1979 Production* (in 1000 tonnes)

	Cereals	Milk	Beef & veal	Pig meat
West Germany	22 707	22 028	1522	3100
France	44 062	23 500	1955	1729
Italy	16 602	7 925	861	974
Netherlands	1 287	11 219	415	1298
Belgium	1 980	3 060	269	670
Luxembourg	144	251	8	7
Great Britain	17 307	15 382	1052	944
Ireland	1 730	4 650	406	150
Denmark	7 673	5 026	256	905
Total EEC	113 492	93 041	6744	9777
Denmark, % of EEC	6.8	5.4	3.8	9.3

(from *Agriculture in Denmark. Annotated Statistics 1980 Danish Farmers Union*)

Exercises

4. What are the main differences between (a) intensive and extensive farming; (b) intensive farming in the 'rice-bowl' of Asia (Chapter 8) and in Western Europe?

5. Indicate the main differences between cooperative farming in Denmark, USSR, China and Israel.

6. Compare and contrast the human-made landscapes of Plates 10.4, 10.7 and 10.9.

7. Refer to Table 10.1. With its help, and information in the text, (a) outline the importance of agriculture to the Danish economy; (b) compare this with two other European countries which you may choose from the table.

8. Refer to Fig. 10.8.
   (a) Describe the distribution of (i) horticultural (ii) mixed farming areas.
   (b) What are the advantages and disadvantages for horticulture in (i) Westland (ii) the Venlo area.

9. (a What are the main differences in location and climatic conditions between the Champagne area and Languedoc?
   (b) Why is climate a more important factor in viticulture in Burgundy than in horticulture in Westland?

10. (a) What are the main differences between a communist and a capitalist agricultural economy?
   (b) With the help of photographs, diagrams and information in the text, show how these are reflected in the farming landscape and activities of the Prairies and the Steppes.

11. Outline the main changes which have taken place since World War 2 in farming in (a) Denmark (b) the USSR.

11 Manufacturing Industry in Capitalist and Communist Worlds

INTRODUCTION

It is useful to distinguish between two major *categories* of manufacturing industry.

(1) The first can be called *nineteenth-century type* manufacturing industry. This grew out of the invention of the steam engine and the *industrial revolution* which followed, leading to the development of factory industry then factory towns. The location of such industries was usually fixed by the presence of

(*a*) *water supply*, in the first place as a source of power, and then for processing;

(*b*) *energy supplies*, in the form of coal; and

(*c*) *bulky raw materials*, such as iron ore for the iron and steel industry (Fig. 11.1).

(*d*) *waterside location*, either at seaports, river ports or canal ports where necessary raw materials could be imported. Flour milling and sugar refining were nineteenth-century examples.

Many nineteenth-century industries which were involved with bulky raw materials are called *heavy industries* (for example, iron and steel).

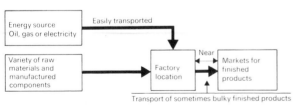

(*a*) **Nineteenth-century industries**
Raw material orientation

(*b*) **Twentieth-century industries**
Market orientation

Fig. 11.1 Factors influencing industrial location

(2) The second group have grown to prominence in the *twentieth century*. They include a vast range of consumer goods industries. Many of them are concerned with a lot of smaller components (Fig. 11.1), and are sometimes termed *light industries*. The nineteenth-century type industries have of course continued into the twentieth century. Twentieth-century industries are less tied to the location of raw materials, and can flourish in a variety of locations, which has led to them being called 'footloose'.

Various *factors* have promoted the growth of light or consumer goods industries.

(*a*) Increasing affluence in western society has enlarged the demand for consumer goods. These include a variety of products, such as processed foods, electrical goods, plastics and, above all, cars.

(*b*) Such industries usually have 'multiplier' effects, generating other industries which manufacture necessary components. The car industry is a classic example, each car being made up of thousands of components.

(*c*) As such industries rely much less than nineteenth-century industries on bulky raw materials, they are less tied to particular locations. Components factories do, however, tend to congregate in areas with good access to the industries they supply.

(*d*) As the name suggests, consumer goods industries supply consumers and therefore are concerned with getting their products quickly to market (Fig. 11.1). They are therefore often found either in large centres of population, or in areas with rapid access to such centres, such as along motorways.

(*e*) Most industries of this type use electricity, oil or gas as sources of power, and are therefore not tied to coalfield locations.

(*f*) As they are more flexible in their location, they can easily be encouraged, by government policy and grants, to transfer to new areas, such as those of high unemployment.

Industry in Communist States

While similar economic factors operate in *communist* states, the degree of government intervention is much greater. One of the first priorities of the Soviet government following the communist Revolution of 1917 was the wholesale reorganisation of industry, and in the first place heavy industry. Instead of being arranged on a capitalist basis, in which individual or group enterprise provided capital for setting up factories, and took the profits which resulted, manufacturing was nationalised and wholly controlled by the state. In general, consumer goods industries are not as well developed in communist states as in Western Europe, North America and Japan, because society in such states is less affluent, and the government gives less priority to the production of consumer goods.

Stages of Industrial Development

Manufacturing industry in western countries has tended to develop, over a period of over two hundred years, in the following sequence:

(*a*) *Infancy*: manufacturing undertaken on a domestic basis, as in hand-loom weaving.

(*b*) *Youth*: early factory development, often in rural locations where water supply and/or raw materials were available.

(*c*) *Maturity*: development of factory towns containing many industrial plants, often with connections between them; commercial support systems, for example in wholesaling, insurance, etc.

(*d*) *Old age*: factories in decline as new and better locations for old industries open up, or new industries develop elsewhere; unemployment characteristic.

(*e*) *Rejuvenation*: government help and/or local initiatives bring in new employment.

Plate 11.2   Aging textile mill at Biddeford, Maine

NINETEENTH-CENTURY TYPE INDUSTRIES: TEXTILE MANUFACTURING IN NEW ENGLAND

New England is an old-established manufacturing region which has been through all the stages of industrial development.

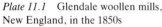

Plate 11.1   Glendale woollen mills, New England, in the 1850s

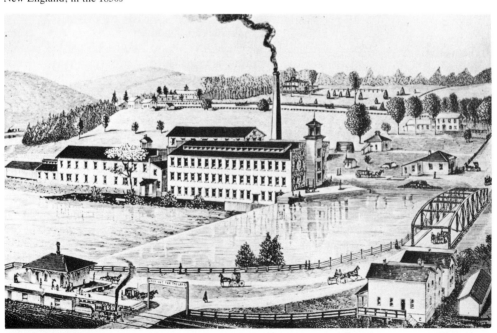

Fig. 11.2 New England industrial location

Infancy

New England was the first part of the eastern seaboard of America to be permanently settled by Europeans. They brought their ways of life and crafts with them. A subsistence economy existed in dispersed farmsteads and nucleated villages, in which *domestic industry*, producing, for example, cloth, pottery and leather goods, developed.

Youth

New England continued to attract settlers from Europe and was the first part of the USA where widespread factory development took place. Early factories had a rural riverside location (Plate 11.1). New England had no important industrial raw materials, nor any energy sources apart from water power. But domestic craft industries such as wool and timber provided a basis for the establishment of textile and paper mills. These were concentrated at water-power sites, such as Biddeford on the Saco River in Maine (Plate

11.2) and more particularly along the Merrimack valley at Lawrence, Lowell, Nashua and Manchester (Fig. 11.2).

Maturity

Investment in industry led to the developmemt of towns at sites such as that in Plate 11.1. One of the factory towns was Manchester, New Hampshire, shown in Plate 11.3 as it is today, in the valley of the Merrimack River. Notice the concentration of textile mills at the riverside.

One of the factors stimulating urban development was the influx of labour from Europe throughout the nineteenth century, a high percentage of which settled on the north-eastern seaboard. In 1921, for example, 83% of workers in Lawrence had either been born abroad, or had parents who had been born abroad. By 1870, New England had over 21% of manufacturing employment in the USA. It had some of the largest textile plants in the world, such as the woollen mill at

141

Plate 11.3 (*opposite*) Manchester, New Hampshire

Old Age

From the 1920s, however, decline set in. Between 1919 and 1939, the numbers employed in manufacturing in New England declined by about 20%. By 1940, it had only just over 11% of the USA's manufacturing employment. One of the causes of the decline was the great economic depression of the 1930s. Another was the progress of the textile industry in the southern states of the country. These had the advantages of being near cotton producing areas, cheaper sources of energy, cheaper land, and a cheaper labour supply. By this time, trade unionism was strong in the north-east, and wage rates were higher and working conditions better, but more expensive for the owners to support. The factories in the south were newer and had more up-to-date machinery. In addition, the most rapidly expanding market for textile goods was in the south.

Notice the difference between the fresh-looking woollen mill on Plate 11.1 and the faded appearance of the Biddeford mills on Plate 11.2, symbol of an industrial region in old age, with problems such as blighted areas with decrepit property, sources of energy (here water power) no longer required, and an industrial plant not necessarily suited to modern use. Towns such as Biddeford, Lawrence, Lowell and Manchester became areas of high unemployment.

Rejuvenation

This began first in the towns of southern Connecticut, Rhode Island and southern Massachusetts (Fig. 11.2), as America's entry into World War 2 led to a huge demand for military goods. There was a switch from *non-durable* goods such as textiles and paper, to *durable goods* such as metal-using industries. Among the most important of these were armaments, the aerospace industry and, later, electronics. The industrial structure became much better balanced through relying less on a few old-established industries. An important reason for the success of the southern parts of New England in leading this new industrial revolution was the existence in the area of some of the most famous scientific and research institutions in the world, such as Harvard and Yale universities, and Massachusetts Institute of Technology.

As the extract from the *Hartford Courant* which follows indicates, this rejuvenation has spread to the northern textile centres, the new electronics firms making use of the old textile mills and taking advantage of state tax concessions.

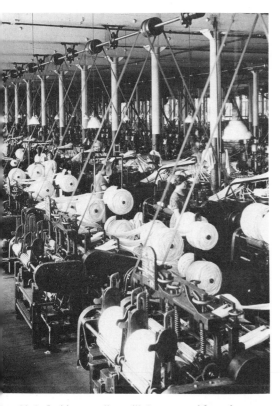

Plate 11.4   Inside a woollen mill, Lawrence, Massachusetts

Lawrence shown on Plate 11.4, typical of the advanced technology of the late nineteenth century. Its products could be sold in the urban areas of the densely populated north-eastern seaboard, stretching from the Boston area to Washington DC, and further afield in the rapidly developing USA.

New England's early lead was, for a time, of great benefit. The region illustrated the importance of *industrial inertia*, meaning that once a high capital investment in manufacturing has been made, it tends to persist even after the initial advantages have disappeared. When coal replaced water power, for example, industrial development continued to flourish, even though New England had to bring in coal from outside.

Manchester Rides Crest of New Hampshire Economic Boom

By Mary Walton
Knight-Ridder Newspapers

MANCHESTER, N.H. — Backs turned to the peaceful Merrimack River, the glorious Victorian mills of blood-red brick solemnly confront this city of wide streets and small buildings.

Once this was the largest textile manufacturing complex in the world, a turn-of-the century melting pot for 17 000 immigrants. Manchester then had no other identity than the mills of the mighty Amoskeag Manufacturing Co.

When Amoskeag went bankrupt in 1936 – the giant looms stilled and the shuttles silenced – Manchester, too, withered. The city was not alone. Virtually all of New England's mill towns sank into depression as one by one the textile and shoe factories closed, many to move south where there was cheap labor.
...

But now there is new life in the old mills. Manchester is showing unmistakable signs of prosperity. And, thanks to a happy confluence of geography and economics, New Hampshire is enjoying growth unmatched in the Northeast. With increases of 24.8 percent in population – to 920 610 – and 25.5 percent in manufacturing jobs between 1970 and 1980, New Hampshire is, in fact, something of a hot spot right in the middle of the Frost Belt.

Manchester's three industrial parks are filling up, Prentiss says, and Digital Equipment Corp., one of the country's largest computer companies, plans a $10 million assembly plant in one of them.... Meanwhile, Hendrix Electronics Inc. moved out of an industrial park and into larger quarters in the 95-year-old Jefferson mill. City officials hope it's the start of a trend.

The comeback of the old mill towns results from several natural and man-made conditions that account for New Hampshire's new-found popularity. One is that electronics companies like Hendrix, with roots in Massachusetts, have spilled into New Hampshire, attracted by the availability of large industrial sites and the willingness of local officials to accommodate them in such matters as zoning and road improvements.

'Local officials have been very encouraging', said Richard Berube, public relations director for Digital Equipment....

Digital now has eight facilities in southern New Hampshire, where it employs 6000 workers and plans further expansion.

New Hampshire has no sales tax and no income tax, so that a company moving into the state from Massachusetts, in effect, is giving employees immediate relief from a 5.37 percent income tax and a 5 percent sales tax....

But the tax situation was not a major incentive for Digital.... More important...was the nose-to-the grindstone attitude of the work force, what he calls 'the old work ethic and craftsmanship of New England'.

Nor does Digital, which also has plants in Arizona, New Mexico, Colorado and South Carolina, experience problems in recruiting people to work in one of the nation's snowiest states, Berube added.

Boosters are fond of pointing out that parts of New Hampshire are just 45 minutes from ski areas, beaches and Boston, which is brimming with history, education and culture. 'That turns out to be important stuff', Berube said.

(from the *Hartford Courant* 27 May 1981)

NINETEENTH-CENTURY TYPE INDUSTRIES: IRON AND STEEL MANUFACTURING IN THE DNEIPER–DONBAS REGION

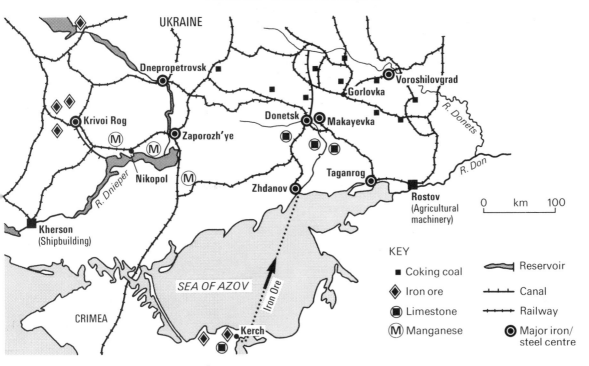

Fig. 11.3   Dneiper–Donbas heavy industrial region

Apart from the USA, the USSR is the world's leading manufacturing country, and it surpasses the USA in its production of coal, coke, pig-iron and steel. Its heavy industries are concentrated in three main areas: the newer Kuzbas region of Siberia (see Fig. 3.11); the Urals; and the Dneiper–Donbas region of the Ukraine (Fig. 11.3).

Locations

In the Dneiper–Donbas region, iron and steel manufacturing is found in four main types of location

(*a*) *coal-based*, as at Donetsk and Makeyevka on the Donbas coalfield;

(*b*) *ore-based*, as at Krivoi Rog on the iron-ore fields and near manganese deposits;

(*c*) *intermediate locations* between Donbas coal and Krivoi Rog ore, such as Dnepropetrovsk and Zaporozh'ye on the Dneiper River;

(*d*) *coastal locations*, such as Zhdanov (Plate 11.5) and Taganrog on the Sea of Azov, using Donbas coal and iron ore brought by sea, to another type of intermediate location.

Plate 11.5   Azovstal steelworks at Zhdanov, Ukraine

Advantages for Iron and Steel Manufacturing

The basic location factors for steel making in a communist country are similar to those in a capitalist country. The Dneiper–Donbas region is unusually rich in energy supplies and raw materials required for steel.

(1) There is high-grade coking coal in the Donbas field, where Donetsk (Plate 11.6) is the mining capital of the region, with a population of over one million.

(2) There are also coal-measure iron ores which allowed the early development of iron making through the initiative of an imported Welsh iron-master, Hughes, and the founding of Yuzovka (meaning Hughesville, later called Stalino and now Donetsk).

(3) When the coal-measure ores were exhausted, high-grade ores in the Krivoi Rog area (Fig. 11.3) were exploited, followed by low-grade ores from Kerch in the Crimea, sent by sea to the Ukraine.

(4) There were also supplies of limestone flux, required in blast furnaces for the smelting of pig-iron, in the Donbas.

(5) Manganese is necessary as an alloy in the manufacture of high-grade steels, and there are plentiful supplies in the Nikopol area, which can be extracted by open-cast methods. Zaporozh'ye is a major centre for high-quality steels (Fig. 11.3).

(6) The railway from Krivoi Rog to the Donbas in the 1880s was a major stimulus to industrial development, with the level terrain of the Ukraine making rail construction easy.

(7) Transport by waterway is also important, including the Kerch ores by sea to Zhdanov, and by canals from Donetsk to the Donets River (Fig. 11.3) and from the Don to the Volga (see Chapter 12).

(8) There is a large market in the region for iron and steel products in the engineering industries of Rostov and Kharkov (agricultural machinery for the Steppes); Gorlovka (mining machinery), Voroshilovgrad (diesel engines and locomotives) and Kherson (shipbuilding) (Fig. 11.3).

Plate 11.6   Donetsk, Ukraine

Communist System

Under the communist system, the whole of economic activity is under state control, with development geared to 'five-year plans'. Donetsk is not only a coal mining and iron and steel centre today, but has a variety of engineering industries, and has diversified into lighter industries such as clothing and toy-making. It is the major cultural centre of the Donbas, with an opera house, a theatre, libraries and over 200 educational establishments. The local miners' football team is seen on Plate 11.7 playing in the Russian League against Moscow's Spartak in the state-built stadium, with coal pit heaps in the background. Plate 11.6 shows state-financed apartments for the workers, with mining tips in the background which the state is now reclaiming to improve the urban landscape.

Plate 11.7 Donetsk miners' team playing against Moscow's Spartak

Exercises

1. Refer to Plate 11.1. Under the headings (a) general setting; (b) nature of the factory; (c) water supplies; (d) transport facilities, write an account of the industrial development shown.
2. Refer to Plate 11.3. With the help of tracing paper, draw a labelled sketch of Manchester, to show (a) the Merrimack River; (b) the forested setting; (c) industrial land-use; (d) the central business district; (e) residential land-use; (f) main lines of transport.
3. Refer to Plate 11.3, the newspaper extract (page 00) and information in the text, and write an account of the five stages of development of manufacturing industry in Manchester, New Hampshire.
4. With the help of Figs. 11.2 and 11.3 and Plates 11.2 and 11.5, compare the factory locations shown in Biddeford and Zhdanov.
5. Compare the land-use shown on the photographs of Manchester (Plate 11.3) and Donetsk (Plate 11.6).
6. With the help of Fig. 11.3 and information in the text, explain why steelworks are found in four types of location in the Dnieper–Donbas region. Why is the Dnieper–Donbas an industrial region (see Fig. 11.1)?
7. Why is the Donbas a much larger steel-making area than northern Sweden (see Chapter 3)?
8. Refer to Fig. 11.4. The government of this country has decided to close the old steelworks at X and build a new integrated steelworks elsewhere. Consider the pros and cons of each of the possible sites marked A to G, and justify one as the best choice, using ideas from the discussions of steel making at Lulea (Chapter 3); Rourkela (Chapter 8); and in the Donbas.

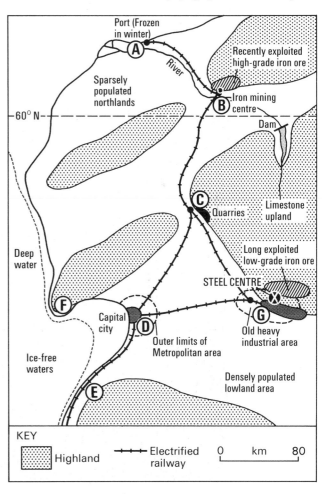

Fig. 11.4 Find the location of the integrated steelworks

147

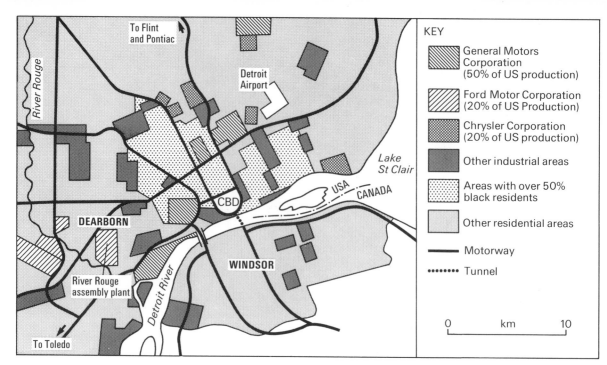

Fig. 11.5 The site of Detroit

TWENTIETH–CENTURY TYPE INDUSTRIES: CAR MANUFACTURING AT DETROIT

Early Growth

The motor car industry symbolised the growth in the importance of consumer demand with rising affluence in the twentieth century, particularly in the USA. Its world capital is Detroit, whose CBD is shown on Plate 11.8 overlooking the Detroit River (Fig. 11.5). Henry Ford was born in Dearborn, a suburb of Detroit (Fig. 11.5) and began making cars there. The first trial run of one of his cars was in 1896 and the Ford Motor Company was formed in 1903. The development of this and other motor companies in the area was helped by Detroit bankers, who supported the initiatives being taken to establish expensive car plants.

Plate 11.8 The central business district of Detroit

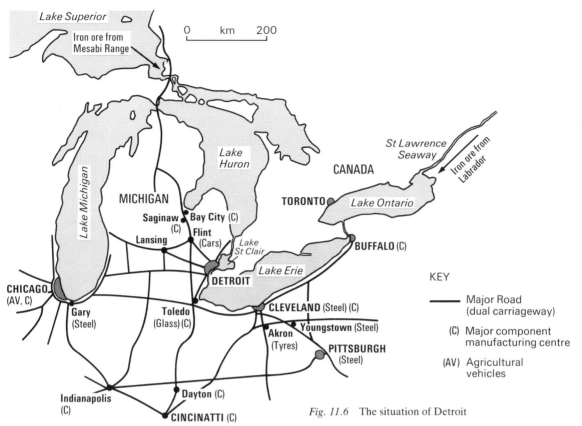

Fig. 11.6 The situation of Detroit

Ford took factory industry a stage further by developing mass production of cars on assembly lines. This was made possible by the standardisation of parts, with each employee responsible for doing the same job over and over again. 'Economies of scale' resulted, which meant that cars could be made cheaply for a mass market. Over 15 million 'Model T' Fords were sold between 1908 and 1927. The assembly line process became the pattern for all mass car manufacturing.

Advantages of the Detroit Area for Car Manufacturing

The first reason why Detroit grew as a car centre was the chance fact that Henry Ford was born there, and was supported by local bankers. Detroit's location proved very advantageous for the growth of car manufacturing, which spread to other Michigan towns such as Lansing and Flint (Fig. 11.6). The three giants of American car manufacturing, today responsible for 90% of US vehicle production, Ford, General Motors, and Chrysler, all established themselves at Detroit (Fig. 11.5).

Assembly line plants need to store cars after manufacture, and so require large areas of level land, which are readily available in the gently rolling landscape of Michigan (Plate 11.9). The Detroit area has also a central location in the United States' north-east manufacturing belt (Fig. 11.6), with railways and motorways centring on it. Apart from California, this is the richest part of North America. In the USA as a whole there are over 100 million private cars and 26 million other vehicles; 10% of US wealth goes into buying, maintaining and insuring cars. The Great Lakes system is very useful for the transport of raw materials such as steel products, and for sending out finished cars. Detroit is on the river which connects Lake Huron and Lake Erie (Fig. 11.6 and Plate 11.8).

Cars are made up of thousands of components, and there are complex linkages all over this region between raw material, component and car firms. Thus iron ore from the Mesabi Range and Labrador comes via the Great Lakes and St Lawrence Seaway (Fig. 11.6) to steel manufacturing centres which supply sheet steel for the car industry. Tyre manufacturing is centred on Akron and glass on Toledo; 16% of US steel, 33% of US rubber and 31% of US glass goes into vehicle production.

Once the car industry is established in an area it usually remains, as a result of industrial inertia. One reason for this is that car plants tend to gather together with components suppliers. Another is that

Plate 11.9 The Ford car plant, Detroit, in the 1930s

car plants such as Ford's at Dearborn, shown in Plate 11.9 taken in the 1930s, represent an enormous investment. It is, however, also advantageous to develop car assembly plants in other areas, near large consumer markets. There are major car assembly plants outside Michigan in states such as Georgia and California, serving other markets. The components still tend to be manufactured in the original region, however.

Recent Problems in the Detroit area

During the 1970s the car industry started to face serious economic problems, and the cities in which factories were found faced serious social problems.

(1) *Economic problems* began when world oil prices rose dramatically after 1973. American oil supplies had become increasingly inadequate to meet the home demand, and huge import bills for oil resulted. Large American cars were noted 'gas guzzlers' and American assembly lines were geared to producing such cars. Ford refused to alter this policy. The American market demanded smaller more economical cars, however, and imports from Europe and Japan flooded in. Sales of large cars plunged. Chrysler went bankrupt and had to be rescued by the American government. Ford and General Motors suffered huge losses. The problem of supplying small cars was temporarily met by multi-national firms such as Ford (in Europe) making use of European designs for smaller cars, and producing them in the USA. In addition, government legislation demanded improved safety standards and better control of exhaust fumes causing atmospheric pollution. These measures have increased the cost of building cars. The economic decline in the car industry has also seriously affected components suppliers. Not only Detroit, but also towns such as Akron, Toledo and Cleveland have been hit by the recession in the car industry.

(2) *Social problems* have arisen from the fact that originally much of the work-force for the Detroit car industry flooded in from the southern states in the early decades of this century. The poorer-paid workers were mainly blacks who settled in decaying residential areas near the city centre which were convenient for travelling to work at the car plants (Fig. 11.5).

At the same time, the car revolutionised urban living, making it possible for people who could afford it (mainly whites) to live further and further away from the city centre, in pleasant semi-rural areas. Plate 11.10 shows the General Motors technical and research centre on the outskirts of Detroit, which employs highly paid engineers and designers. The centre is attractively landscaped and conveniently placed for salaried employees coming to work by car.

Detroit is thus a highly segregated city residentially, with large percentages of coloured people in areas around the centre. In 1967 Detroit experienced some of the worst racial riots in the history of the USA, and it remains a violent city, with unemployment in the car industry now adding to the social problems.

Plate 11.10   General Motors technical and research centre, Detroit

TWENTIETH–CENTURY TYPE INDUSTRIES: MICRO–ELECTRONICS IN 'SILICON VALLEY', CALIFORNIA

The landing of men on the moon was the most spectacular human achievement of the 1960s. It required computer networks that could perform more than 50 million calculations per minute, a product of a highly sophisticated new technology provided by the electronics industry. This also made possible a communications system which allowed television coverage of the event throughout the world.

At the end of World War 2, the Santa Clara valley at the southern end of San Francisco Bay (Fig. 11.7) was still a rural backwater. It was a valley of vineyards and apricot, plum and apple orchards. San Jose was the assembly point for Mexican fruit pickers, and the main marketing centre for the valley. Today the orchards have gone, and the landscape is covered with sprawling suburbs, freeways and attractively landscaped industrial parks. The northern part of the valley is now termed 'Silicon Valley', the heart of a new technological world of micro-electronics.

The Growth of the Electronics Industry

A critical event was the founding of Stanford University at Palo Alto in the 1890s. This became a world leader in electronics technology research in the late 1930s and 1940s. After World War 2, Berkeley University, on the other side of the bay (Fig. 11.7), became one of the world's leading research centres in computer science. These institutions provided the 'brains' behind the electronics revolution. In addition, an 'industrial park' was established in connection with Stanford University, on which sites were leased to firms which could apply the research in practical industrial products. The 'industrial park' landscape spread south to Mountain View (Plate 11.11) and Sunnyvale in Santa Clara County, reaching its regional centre, San Jose. The area became known as 'Silicon Valley', its prosperity based on a new industrial revolution caused by the invention of the silicon chip.

151

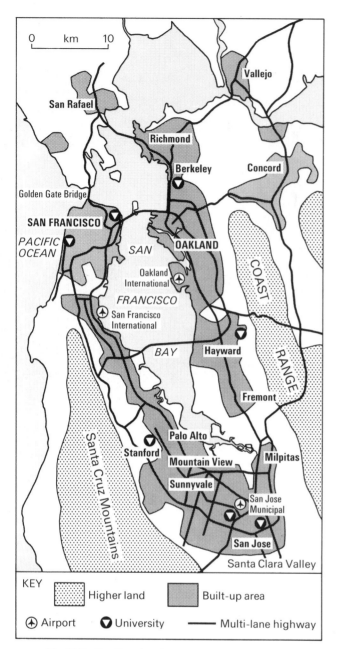

Fig. 11.7 San Francisco Bay area

Plate 11.11 Mountain View industrial estate, Silicon Valley

facture transistors. Young inventors employed by Shockley and the Fairchild groups wished to gain the economic benefits of their research, however, and moved out to found their own firms in a second generation of electronics companies.

Two of these were Signetics and Intel, pioneers of silicon chip technology, the basis of the microprocessor revolution. A silicon chip costing £5 could do the work of a machine which twenty years earlier would have cost £100 000. Computers, formerly affordable only by large industrial concerns or for military or other state purposes, could now be bought for use in offices, schools and even homes. Microelectronics is the technology behind not only the launching of the space shuttle (Plate 2.3) and car manufacturing by robot (Plate 8.13), but also behind electronic games, quartz-controlled electronic wrist-watches and pacemakers to regulate heart-beats.

Advantages of Silicon Valley

As with the car industry in Detroit, the microelectronics industry of Silicon Valley has resulted from local initiative, in this case the research excellence of two universities and a system which allows this pure research to be applied rapidly to industry. The most important need is to attract and keep high-quality research workers. These are in short supply and can readily move to other firms, or set up new firms themselves, taking with them their skills and industrial information.

Another vital event which took place after World War 2 was the invention by William Shockley in 1948 of the transistor, a much smaller device than the conventional valve, enabling the production of, for example, much smaller radios. Shockley set up his own firm in Palo Alto, appointing young scientists to translate his ideas into practice. The Fairchild Camera and Instrument Company, already well established in the aerial camera and electronics businesses, moved into a plant at Mountain View in the late 1950s, to manu-

The electronics firms therefore aim to provide pleasant environments to work in. Plate 11.11 shows part of the landscaped industrial park at Mountain View (Fig. 11.7). Conditions inside the plants are also of high standards. Plate 11.12, taken inside the Fairchild plant at Mountain View, shows computer-controlled systems which transfer the integrated circuit patterns to the silicon wafer. The greatest care has to be taken to ensure that the wafer is absolutely uncontaminated. The workers are required to wear sterilised hats, smocks, boots and glasses.

Apart from the working environment, the area provides more general attractions. San Francisco is one of the great cultural centres of the USA. The Santa Cruz mountain and the Pacific beaches and cliffs provide scenic attractions. Further east there is the wilderness country of the Sierra Nevada and the desert scenery.

Like the car industry, micro-electronics brings with it a wide variety of components manufacturers, and it is convenient that these should congregate in close proximity, as they do in the San Francisco Bay area. It must be stressed, however, that electronics is a major growth industry, found all over the USA. As we have seen, there is a concentration of aerospace and electronics industries in southern New England (page 141).

In the micro-electronics industry, components and finished products are small and of high value. Hence air freight is often used. San Jose municipal airport has grown rapidly as a result, and nearby are also San Francisco and Oakland international airports (Fig. 11.7).

The growth of Silicon Valley has also brought economic and social problems. Suburbs and orchards do not mix. The fruit and vine growers have had to move

Plate 11.12   Inside the Fairchild micro-processor plant, Mountain View

south. A sprawling mass of suburbs and expressways has disturbed the Santa Clara valley, which is now part of the San Francisco conurbation. House prices in the San Jose area have rocketed as affluent personnel of the electronics and aerospace industries demand low-density housing, which takes up a lot of space. Lack of land for further industrial parks may well now restrict development.

Exercises

9. (a) Outline the similarities and differences between the technologies of textile and car manufacturing.
(b) What is meant by 'economies of scale'? Why are these vital in car manufacturing?
10. Compare and contrast the factors influencing the location of car manufacturing and micro-electronic plants.

11. Contrast the landscapes shown on Plates 11.9 and 11.11. Why are they different?
12. Outline similarities and differences in the industrial landscapes of Manchester, New Hampshire (Plate 11.3) and Detroit (Plate 11.9).

12 Transportation in Capitalist and Communist Worlds

INLAND WATERWAYS: THE VOLGA

In the early days of the industrial revolution, inland waterway traffic was the most efficient means of shifting bulky goods such as coal, cloth and chemical products. Canals were built to connect raw material and coal supplies with industrial towns, and industrial towns with ports. Today, rail and road systems provide more rapid ways of transporting goods. But inland waterways remain the cheapest method. While the small canals of the early industrial revolution period are now little used, great waterways such as the rivers Rhine and Volga remain very important.

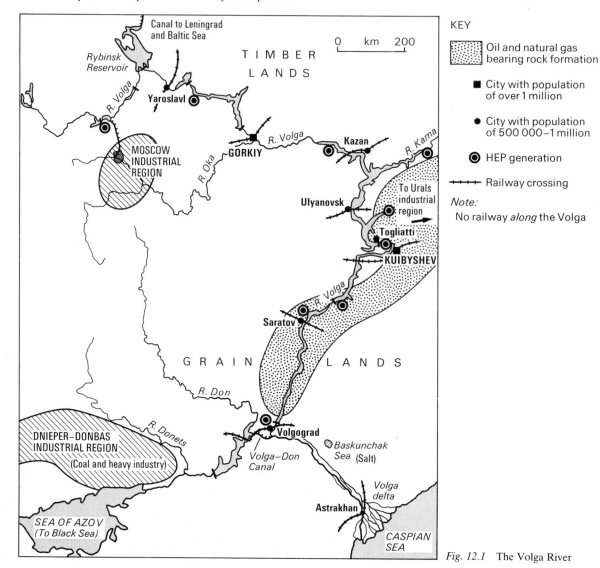

KEY

- Oil and natural gas bearing rock formation
- ■ City with population of over 1 million
- ● City with population of 500 000–1 million
- ◎ HEP generation
- ┿ Railway crossing

Note:
No railway *along* the Volga

Fig. 12.1 The Volga River

154

Plate 12.1 A hydro-electric power station at Kuibyshev, Volga River

Navigation on the Volga

The Volga is navigable by barges from the Moscow area to the Caspian Sea (Fig. 12.1). Its importance has increased with the construction of the Volga–Don canal, connecting it to the Black Sea, and with the enlargement of the Mariinsky canal to Leningrad and the Baltic Sea. Navigation has been improved by the construction of large dams, which even out flow and impound vast navigable reservoirs, such as the one at Kuibyshev shown on Plate 12.1. These contain locks to allow barges to pass through.

The Volga has certain disadvantages for navigation, however, as it freezes for five months in the north and four months in the south. In addition, variations in flow are caused by meltwater in spring, and drought, giving low water, in summer. Shifting channels are found in the braided section and delta in the south. The Volga also flows into an inland sea, the shores of which are generally sparsely populated.

Hydro-electric Power

At first sight, the Volga waterway would not seem the most likely of rivers for large-scale hydro-electric power generation. It does not rise in a high mountainous region, where tall dams might be built to hold back long narrow reservoirs. It does not rise in, or flow through, regions of high rainfall. It makes up for these deficiencies, however, by sheer size and volume of water. Low wide dams have been built at, for example, Kuibyshev (Plate 12.1), Saratov and Volgograd (Fig. 12.1) to supply power not only to industrial towns along the river, but also to the Urals and Donbas industrial regions. The reservoirs also supply *irrigation water* to the surrounding steppe lands.

Inland Trade

The Volga is of great importance to the industrial system of the USSR because, with its tributaries and connecting canals, it joins the main industrial regions of the country: the Moscow region, the Urals, the Ukraine (Donbas) and the Leningrad region (Fig. 12.1). The main traffic on the river includes:

(*a*) grain from Volgograd, moving upstream to Kuibyshev, for transfer to railways connecting with the Moscow and Urals regions;

(*b*) timber barges, coming downstream from the upper Volga and Kama River, to provide for the treeless steppe region to the south;

(*c*) petroleum, and petroleum products, transported either downstream from the Volga-Urals fields (Fig. 12.1) or upstream from Baku via Astrakhan;

(*d*) coal from the Donbas, by way of the Volga–Don canal;

(*e*) cement and other building materials, chiefly moving upstream to the Moscow region;

(*f*) industrial products, such as cars from Togliatti (Plate 12.2 and Fig. 12.1).

River Ports

Some of the largest cities of the USSR, apart from Moscow and Leningrad, are located on the Volga waterway. They are mostly river ports, such as Volgograd (formerly Stalingrad). All are at *break of bulk* sites, where goods are transported from rail or road to river, or vice versa (Plate 12.2), and many are at major *bridging points* where railways cross the river.

At these points, *processing industries* have developed, such as: fish at Astrakhan (sturgeon for caviare); flour milling at Gorkiy, Kuibyshev, Saratov and Volgograd; oil refining and petro-chemicals and heavy chemicals at Volgograd, Saratov, Kazan and Kuibyshev; and timber processing at Volgograd. Car manufacturing at Togliatti is a comparatively recent development, using West European designs.

Plate 12.2 River transport of cars from Togliatti

Plate 12.3 The Storstrøm Bridge, Denmark

Fig. 12.2 Danish main-line railways

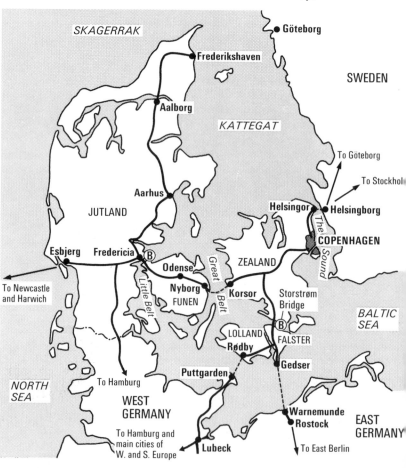

DENMARK

Population	**5.1 million**
Rail network	**2300 km**
Area	**43 000 km²**
Density of population	**119 per km²**

KEY

————— Main-line railway

------- Main rail ferry (Many not shown)

Ⓑ Bridge

0   km   100

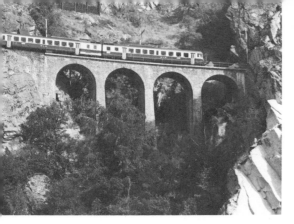

Plate 12.4   Swiss railway near the Lötschberg Tunnel south of Berne

BARRIERS TO TRANSPORT: RAILWAYS IN DENMARK AND SWITZERLAND

Barriers

Plate 12.3 is a photograph of one of the longest bridges in Europe, the Storstrøm Bridge, connecting the Danish islands of Zealand and Falster (Fig. 12.2). This carries the main-line railway from Copenhagen south towards the mainland of Europe.

Plate 12.4 shows a section of the Swiss railway system south of Berne as it crosses an Alpine mountain tract near the Lötschberg Tunnel (Fig. 12.3). The two photographs illustrate two of the major physical barriers to transport systems: bodies of water, and mountains.

Notice on Fig. 12.2 how Danish territory is broken up into a main peninsula, Jutland, and a whole series of islands, divided by straits, such as the Great Belt and Little Belt. The capital city, Copenhagen, is on the edge of the present territory, but once had a more central position, when Denmark controlled Norway and Sweden. As transport systems usually radiate out from the major city of a country, Copenhagen's position on the edge of one of its islands makes access to the rest of the country a problem.

As Fig. 12.3 indicates, the major part of Switzerland's main-line railway system is concentrated on the relatively level land of the Swiss Plateau. Elsewhere, it is forced into valleys and gaps in the mountains and, in the case of the Alps, can only break through by major tunnels. In addition, many bridges are required to negotiate steep-sided valleys, and complicated loops are needed to climb valley sides at a reasonable gradient (Fig. 12.4). Such engineering makes rail building expensive, and in general these physical barriers, whether of water or of relief, make journeys slower.

Fig. 12.3   Swiss main-line railways

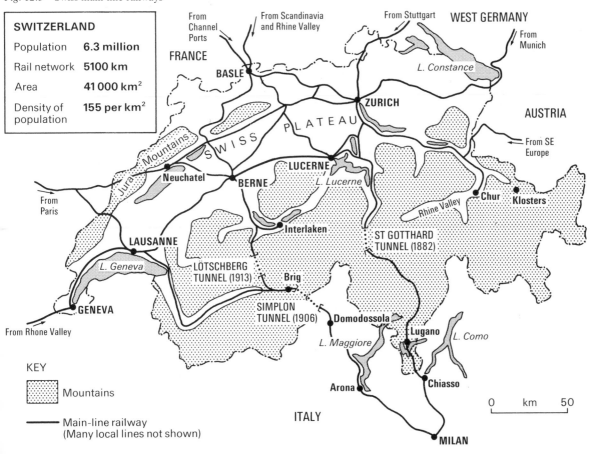

SWITZERLAND	
Population	**6.3 million**
Rail network	**5100 km**
Area	**41 000 km²**
Density of population	**155 per km²**

KEY

▨ Mountains

── Main-line railway
(Many local lines not shown)

Danish Railways

Denmark's physical structure has always meant that ferries or bridges have been necessary to provide connecting links between land transport. Danish State Railways own a large number of ferries and ships. The main rail ferries are (Fig. 12.2):

(*a*) Korsor–Nyborg, across the Great Belt;

(*b*) Helsingor–Helsingborg, across the Sound to Sweden;

(*c*) Rødby–Puttgarden, across the Baltic Sea to West Germany;

(*d*) Gedser–Warnemunde, across the Baltic Sea to East Germany, a service much less used since World War 2.

The problems caused by the distribution of land and sea can be illustrated by the times taken for trains to connect Copenhagen with distant parts of the country. Take the inter-city service to Frederikshaven in the northern part of Jutland. The *straight-line distance* between the two places is approximately 225 km. *By train*, the journey is 591 km. A fast train leaving Copenhagen at 7.15 in the morning arrives at Korsor about one hour later, then takes a further hour or more to cross the Great Belt to Nyborg. It eventually arrives in Frederikshaven at 14.02, a journey of nearly seven hours. If a straight route were available, the journey between the two cities would take about two hours. Compare the inter-city service from London to Cardiff, a journey of 233 km, which takes less than two hours.

Similar breaks are experienced by inter-continental expresses. It takes less than an hour for an express, crossing the Storstrøm Bridge and the level landscape

Plate 12.5 Rødby station, Denmark

of Denmark, to travel from Copenhagen to Rødby station (Plate 12.5 and Fig. 12.2). But from here, the short Baltic Sea crossing by train ferry has to be made, and it is two more hours before Puttgarden (Plate 12.6) is reached.

Swiss Railways

In Switzerland there are nearly 5500 railways bridges and 670 tunnels, of which three, the Simplon (over 20 km); the St Gotthard (over 15 km) and the Lötschberg (15 km) are among the longest in the world (Fig. 12.3). Plates 12.7 and 12.8, and Fig. 12.4 illustrate the type of landscape which requires small as well as large tunnels, bridges, and loops, to establish con-

Plate 12.6 Rail ferry at Puttgarden

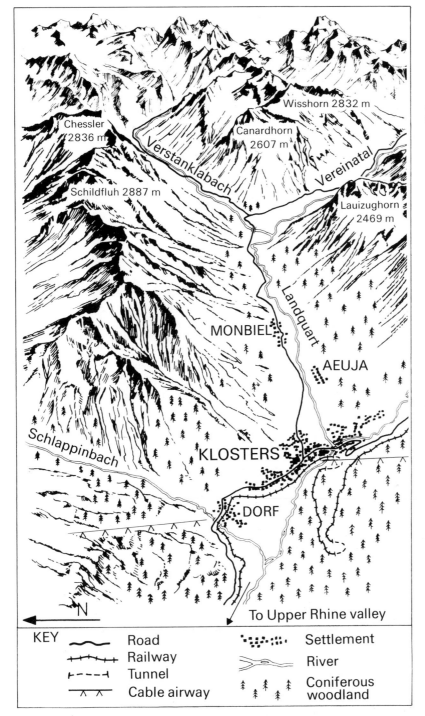

Fig. 12.4 Klosters and Landquart valley

Chessler 2836 m

Wisshorn 2832 m

Canardhorn 2607 m

Verstanklabach

Vereinatal

Schildfluh 2887 m

Lauizughorn 2469 m

Landquart

MONBIEL

AEUJA

Schlappinbach

KLOSTERS

DORF

N

To Upper Rhine valley

KEY   Road   Settlement
Railway   River
Tunnel   Coniferous
Cable airway   woodland

nections between places on opposite sides of valleys and mountain ranges. Notice on Plate 12.7 that, after crossing the railway bridge at Klosters, the line is about to enter a tunnel under the slope in the left foreground. Another problem in mountain areas is the likelihood of snowfall in winter, making it necessary to use snow-ploughs to keep tracks clear (Plate 12.8).

In such conditions, travel is generally slower. Plate

Plate 12.7 Klosters, Switzerland

12.8 shows the train which connects Klosters with Davos, a resort only 15 km away. Yet the journey, without a stop, takes 25 minutes. To travel between London and Cardiff at this average speed would require a journey of 6½ hours.

These figures suggest that for travellers a more important measure of access than distance on the ground is *time distance*: that is, the time it takes to get between two places. It is important to realise that Switzerland and Denmark have advanced railway systems, and the relative slowness of some of their services is the result of *physical barriers*. There are of course other less advanced countries, and also more advanced ones, where slowness of rail travel even over level landscapes is the result of old-fashioned trains, or poorly maintained track.

Plate 12.8
Above Klosters

Plate 12.9 Mannheim and Ludwigshafen, river ports on the Rhine

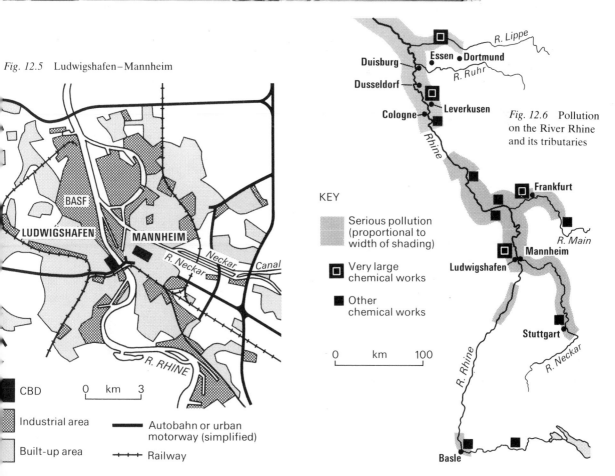

Fig. 12.5 Ludwigshafen–Mannheim

BASF

LUDWIGSHAFEN

MANNHEIM

R. Neckar

Neckar Canal

R. RHINE

CBD

0   km   3

Industrial area

Built-up area

Autobahn or urban motorway (simplified)

Railway

Fig. 12.6 Pollution on the River Rhine and its tributaries

R. Lippe

Duisburg   Essen Dortmund

R. Ruhr

Dusseldorf

Cologne   Leverkusen

Rhine

Frankfurt

R. Main

Mannheim

Ludwigshafen

Stuttgart

R. Neckar

R. Rhine

Basle

KEY

Serious pollution (proportional to width of shading)

Very large chemical works

Other chemical works

0   km   100

Exercises

1. (a) Divide the following list of products into two columns, representing those (i) most, (ii) least, likely to be transported by the Volga waterway: diamonds; grain; grapes; petroleum; timber. Give reasons in each case for your choice.

(b) Explain the importance of the Volga waterway in the transport system of European Russia.

2. Refer to:

Plate 12.9, of the Rhine–Neckar junction, with the river port of Mannheim in the background and part of the BASF heavy chemical works at Ludwigshafen in the right foreground.

Fig. 12.5, a land-use map of Ludwigshafen–Mannheim;

Fig. 12.6, a map of the Rhine and important tributaries in West Germany;

an *atlas map* of the Rhine valley as a whole.

(a) Describe the land-use shown on Plate 12.9.

(b) What indications are there on this photograph and on Fig.12.5 of the importance of Ludwigshafen and Mannheim? What site factors have contributed to this importance?

(c) What advantages are there in a riverside location for heavy chemical industries, bearing in mind that they developed on the basis of such raw materials as coal tar, salt and sulphur? What problems are created by the presence of such industries?

(d) With the help of the photograph and maps, suggest reasons why the Rhine is a more important inland waterway than the Volga.

3. (a) Explain the importance of the concept of *time distance*, with illustrations.

(b) The *detour index* (DI) between two places can be calculated by dividing the travelling distance (x) by the straight-line distance ('as the crow flies') (y), and multiplying the result by 100, that is

$$DI = \frac{x}{y} \times 100$$

A high detour index is an indication that places are not well connected, with a long travelling distance between them. With the help of Figs.12.2 and 12.3, work out the detour indices of

(i) Copenhagen and Frederikshaven;

(ii) Geneva and Milan;

(iii) Basle and Zurich.

Which of the three pairs are best and worst connected, according to the detour index?

4. Refer to Figs. 12.2 and 12.3, the information in their insets, and relevant photographs in the text.

(a) Compare the sizes, shapes, populations and rail networks of Denmark and Switzerland.

(b) Indicate how the rail networks have been affected by physical factors.

5. Refer to Fig.12.4 and Plates 12.7 and 12.8.

(a) Describe the landscape of the Klosters area in summer and winter.

(b) Name the peak in the background of Plate 12.8.

(c) Describe the problems facing rail transport in the Klosters area, referring specifically to Fig. 12.4 and Plates 12.7 and 12.8.

(d) What suggests that Klosters is an important tourist centre?

Fig. 12.7 Variation in wealth of regions in the European Community

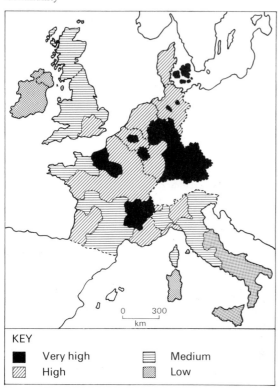

KEY

■ Very high	▤ Medium
▨ High	▦ Low

Fig. 12.8 The EEC: proportion of work-force in farming, fishing and forestry

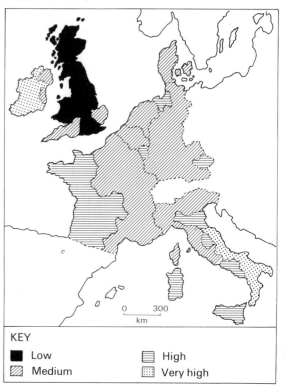

KEY

■ Low	▤ High
▨ Medium	▦ Very high

THE ITALIAN AUTOSTRADA NETWORK AND REGIONAL DEVELOPMENT
IN THE MEZZOGIORNO

A Problem Region of the EEC: the Mezzogiorno

As Fig.12.7 indicates, the two poorest countries of the European Community, before Greece joined, were Ireland and Italy. Both remain 'poor neighbours' in the rich West European community. Fig. 12.8 suggests that one reason for this situation may be the nature of the economic activities practised in these areas. It is clear that the poorest regions are those in which the largest proportions of the work-force are engaged in primary production: farming, fishing and forestry.

The southern part of the Italian peninsula, together with Sicily and Sardinia, make up the Mezzogiorno. As Fig. 12.9 shows, large areas of the Mezzogiorno are densely populated, and the poverty of the region is increased by the high birth rate. As a result, for the last hundred years there has been migration out of the area, to the industrial north of Italy, other parts of Europe, and North America.

Fig. 12.9 Italy: distribution of population

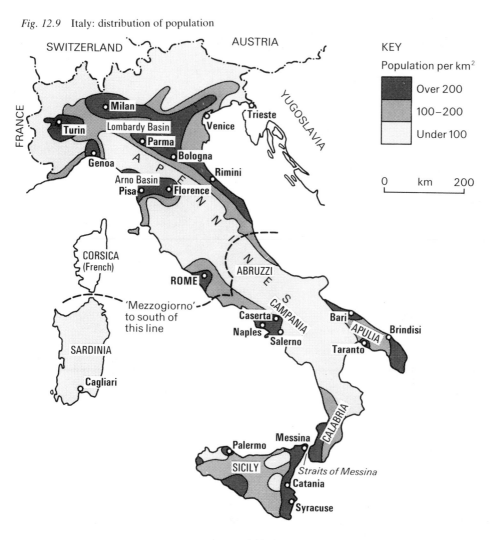

Much of the interior of the region is of *rugged relief* (Fig. 12.10), the Apennine mountains making up the backbone of peninsular Italy. The dry limestone soils and summer *drought* limit farming possibilities, and *soil erosion* is a problem on the the slopes of clay areas where trees have been removed, and rainfall tends to come in short sharp bursts.

Farming methods in the region have developed very little, with tenant farmers living in defensive hill-top villages, and having to travel long distances to scattered fields. The farmers have traditionally had short tenures, which discourages them from making long-term improvements. There has been no tradition of commerce and industry over much of the south, with a few exceptions such as Naples. Few mineral or power resources exist in the region.

Fig. 12.10   The Italian autostrada network

Redeveloping the Mezzogiorno

MOTORWAYS: THE 'AUTOSTRADA'

Until recent years, the Mezzogiorno was isolated from north Italian and European contacts, with poor communications between north and south Italy. A major change has come with the completion of the *autostrada del sol*, which links Milan with Naples and Reggio di Calabria (Fig. 12.10). Another motorway now runs down the east side of the peninsula to Bari and Taranto. A bridge is also planned to cross the Straits of Messina to link up with the Sicilian road system. As Plate 12.10 shows, the motorways in the south have often to negotiate difficult relief, which adds to the expense of building them.

Plate 12.10 An autostrada in the Mezzogiorno

INDUSTRIAL DEVELOPMENT

The proportion of work-force engaged in farming in the Mezzogiorno was over 30% in 1971, a high figure by European standards, although much lower than in the region twenty years previously, when 55% of the active population were farmers. Although wages were still low by European standards, the average income per head improved by 250% between 1960 and 1970 in Apulia (Fig. 12.9). In the Mezzogiorno as a whole, between 1951 and 1968, 600 000 new jobs had been created in manufacturing, and 500 000 in service industries. One of the main reasons for the expansion of industry was the development of better communications.

The government has also intervened in other ways. It has given grants to encourage northern firms to ex-

pand in the south, together with tax concessions and preference when government contracts are granted. In addition, labour is abundant and relatively cheap in the south. Thus great car firms (Fiat and Alfa Sud) and office machinery firms (Olivetti) have built factories in the Naples–Caserta area. One of the most important growth areas is centred on the Bari–Brindisi–Taranto triangle in Apulia. The Italsider steelworks at Taranto (Plate 12.11) imports coking coal and iron ore by sea, and exports finished products, such as oil pipelines, to Libya and the Middle East. Brindisi has petro-chemical, metallurgical, and food processing plants, while the many small factories on the Bari industrial estate employ 15 000 workers making small precision engineering products, and consumer goods.

The autostrada network has also encouraged the development of tourism, south of the Naples–Sorrento area. The south has beautiful mountain scenery, Mediterranean beaches and cliffs at the coast, and historic buildings. But the region remains distant from the most populated and wealthy parts of Europe, and the towns of the south cannot compete with the attractions of, for example, Rome, Florence and Venice.

The region remains poor, although less poor than it was. Industrial development has not been wholly successful. For example, car assembly plants in the south still bring in components from the north. The lack of an industrial tradition means the region is short on

skilled workers and management, which are also brought in from the north. While industrial development has made growth points such as Bari, Brindisi and Taranto less poor, it has not greatly helped rural areas.

Although the autostrada system has made a difference, it cannot alter the fact that the Mezzogiorno remains remote from the core areas of the European Community. People still have to leave the south to seek jobs in the industrial north of Italy, and further afield as guestworkers in Switzerland and West Germany (Chapter 13).

AIR TRANSPORT IN THE USA

Growth

Fig. 12.11 shows that in the USA air transport took over in the later 1950s from rail and buses as the most important form of domestic passenger transport between cities, and increased remarkably in the 1960s, from round about 30 000 million to over 100 000 million passenger miles. One of the main reasons for the expansion of air transport is the improvement it makes in time distance. Fig. 12.12 shows how the USA 'shrank' between 1860 and 1960. In 1860 it took over ten days; in 1960 less than ten hours, to cross the country. The great airports, rather than bus or railway

Plate 12.11
Italsider steelworks,
Taranto

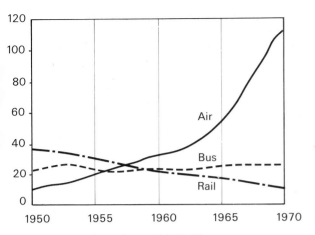

Fig. 12.11   US inter-city travel 1950–70

stations, are now the busiest communications hubs in the country. Another reason for the success of air transport is the actual size of the country, which extends for thousands of kilometres from east to west. In Britain for example, there is little gain in time distance in travelling from, say, Manchester to London by air as against train, after the time lost in getting from city centre to airport is taken into consideration. But in the USA, the gain in travel time which comes from travelling by air from, say, New York to Los Angeles, is very considerable. The two cities are about 4000 km and four time zones (Fig. 12.13) apart.

Fig. 12.13 shows the major airports of the USA. The largest of these, the combined New York airports, Chicago, Atlanta, San Francisco/Oakland, and Los Angeles, all service over 20 million passengers a year. Of British airports only Heathrow is in this category. There are nine other airports which carry between 10 and 20 million passengers.

The Growth, Decline and Fall of Braniff International

One of the major American airlines was Braniff International, one of whose Jumbo jets is shown on Plate 12.12. This company illustrates a series of stages of growth and, in the economic recession of the late 1970s and 1980s, of decline typical of the development of other American airlines (Fig. 12.14).

(1) *Initial routes*: The first route, in 1928, was between Tulsa and Oklahoma City, and was extended to Wichita Falls in 1930. Its planes carried six passengers, who were usually oil workers, for this area was in the heart of the Texas–Oklahoma–Kansas oilfields.

(2) *Regional sphere of influence*: By the mid-1930s, Braniff was an important regional airline, with routes to Kansas City, St Louis and Chicago to the northeast, and Fort Worth, Dallas and other Texas cities to the south and west. By 1952, it was the most important central United States airline, having bought out Mid-Continent airlines, which gave it routes north to Omaha, Minneapolis–St Paul and Winnipeg. It also shared routes west to Denver and east to Memphis and Atlanta with another airline (Fig. 12.13).

(3) *National sphere of influence*: In 1955, Braniff achieved a link with Washington and New York which gave it national status. Its first jet service, between

Fig. 12.12   US trans-continental routes: reduction in journey time from 1850 to 1960

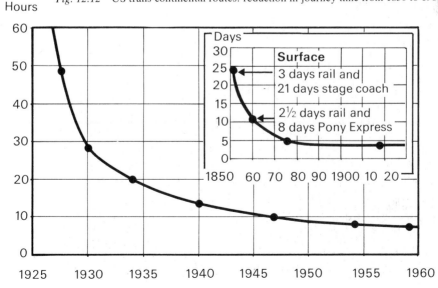

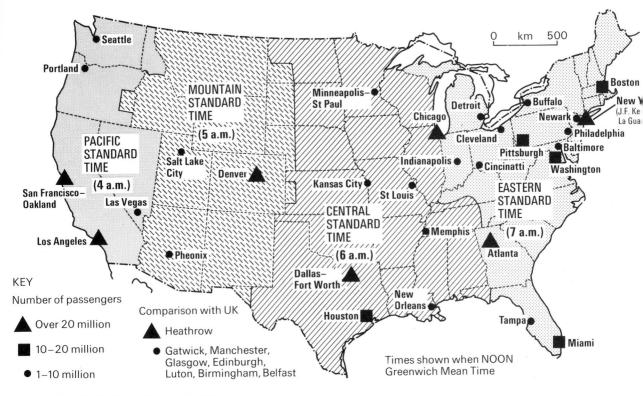

Fig. 12.13　Major US airports, 1980

Dallas and New York, began in 1959.

(4) *Braniff International* by this time was already operating services to Mexico, and to South American cities, in competition with Panam, the major American international airline. During the 1960s these routes were expanded, and during the 1970s, trans-Atlantic services to London were established, with Jumbo jets.

(5) The tremendous rise in the price of aviation fuel in the 1970s hit all major airlines. Price cutting between the airlines, especially on trans-Atlantic routes, has increased losses and has put, for example, Laker Airways out of business. In the USA, economic recession has led to a slump in internal passenger traffic. Despite the fact that Braniff carried 300 000 passengers a day, and was the USA's tenth largest airline, by late 1981 it had lost over one-quarter of its internal passengers and nearly 10% of its international. In May 1982 Braniff International declared itself bankrupt, as the newspaper extract indicates.

Plate 12.12　Braniff Jumbo jet

Braniff airline collapses owing 733m dollars

From Alex Brummer in Washington

Braniff International, the Dallas-based airline which carried more than 12 million passengers last year, yesterday gave up its fight for survival and began bankruptcy proceedings.

(from *The Guardian*, 14 May 1982)

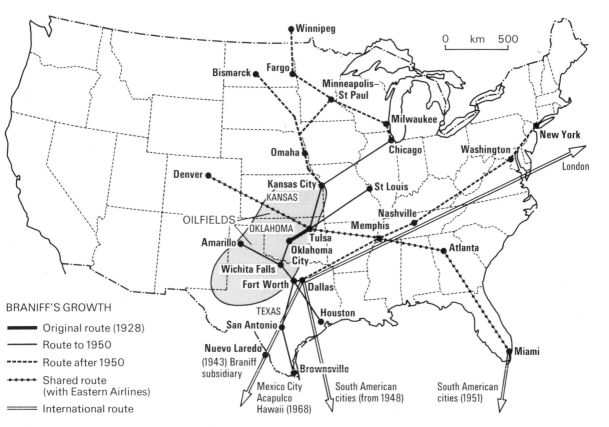

Fig. 12.14   The expansion of Braniff International Airlines

BRANIFF'S GROWTH

━━━━━ Original route (1928)

─────── Route to 1950

- - - - - Route after 1950

••••••• Shared route
          (with Eastern Airlines)

═══════ International route

Plate 12.13   Dallas – Fort Worth international airport

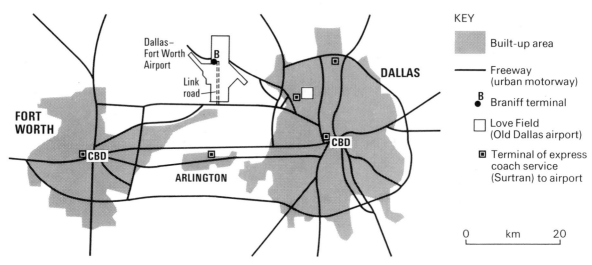

Fig. 12.15 Dallas–Fort Worth international airport

Dallas–Fort Worth airport

Plate 12.13 is a photograph of one of the USA's major airports, Dallas–Fort Worth, opened in 1974 at a cost of $700 million, a symbol of the wealth of this part of Texas. The airport is approximately 30 km from the centres of both Dallas and Fort Worth, and covers approximately 70 km². The airport is well served by freeways (Fig. 12.15), and the semi-circular shape of the terminals (Plate 12.13) is designed to bring the car parking bays as close as possible to the air parking bays. A fully automated passenger transit system connects the different air terminals.

Plate 12.14 shows something of the interior of Dallas–Fort Worth airport, including the former Braniff ticket and reservation counter, shops, and restaurant and waiting areas. These are all essential where pas-

sengers may have to wait to change planes, or for delayed flights.

Dallas–Fort Worth airport illustrates how important such a facility is to the local community, expensive though it is to build. It employs over 14 000 people, who own between them about 30 000 cars; 70% are home owners. The average salary of the employees is over $16 000 per annum, and the employee payroll is over $230 million. It is calculated that the airport with all its expenditures had a total economic impact on the local communities in 1978 of $1.5 billion. This excludes the five million tourists and nearly two million convention (conference) delegates coming to the airport each year.

Plate 12.14 Inside Dallas – Fort Worth airport terminal

Factors Influencing Airport Location

(1) As Plate 12.13 suggests, an international airport needs a *large expanse of flat land*, sufficient for at least two runways of over 3600 m in length, required by large jets for landing and take-off. In addition, space is needed for access roads, customs services, terminals, hangars for aircraft, sheds for airport vehicles and warehouses for goods storage.

(2) The airport should also preferably be in an area clear of mountains, which provide a hazard if they affect the approach to the runways, as in Tenerife (Chapter 9).

(3) Airports should also be located in areas of good visibility, not subject to frequent fogs or excessively heavy rainfall.

(4) They should also be located away from the centres of cities, although at the same time good road links with the city centre are required, as at Dallas–Fort Worth (Fig. 12.15). Other alternatives are fast rail (as at London Gatwick) or underground (London Heathrow) links.

(5) Large airports cause problems of noise pollution, and should preferably be located in such a direction that the landing and take-off paths of aircraft do not provide noise corridors which affect too many people. This is often not possible, and millions of urban dwellers over the world are disturbed by aircraft noise (see Chapter 16).

(6) Another problem is congestion on land and in the air. For some very large cities one airport is not enough. Care has to be taken that flight corridors do not cross each other. New York has three international airports: John F. Kennedy, La Guardia, and Newark, which lead to congestion of air space and can make changes of flights very inconvenient. One means of connecting these airports with each other and with the Manhattan business district is by helicopter. The Panam building provides a central landing ground (Plate 12.15).

Exercises

6. (a) Describe carefully the distributions of GDP per head of population in the EEC (Fig. 12.7) and of proportions employed in primary production (Fig. 12.8)
   (b) Outline the connections you notice between these two distributions.

7. Describe the distribution of population in Italy (Fig. 12.9). Indicate the extent to which (a) relief (b) motorway development (Fig.12.10) is related to the population pattern.

8. (a) With reference to Plate 12.10, describe the physical and human landscape of this part of Calabria in the Mezzogiorno, and the problems which it suggests.
   (b) Outline the factors which make the Italian Mezzogiorno in general one of the problem regions of Europe.

9. The table below shows the flight times from New York to other selected US airports. With the help of Fig. 12.13 work out the local time of arrival for a flight leaving New York at mid-day; copy the table and write your answers in the empty column.

Destination	Flight time	Local time of arrival
Miami	2hr 40 min	
Los Angeles	5hr 05 min	
Phoenix	3hr 50 min	
Chicago	1hr 20 min	

10. (a) Make clear the difference between domestic and international air passenger traffic. Why is New York more important than Dallas–Fort Worth for international passenger traffic?
    (b) With the help of Plate 12.13 and Fig. 12.15 describe the location of Dallas–Fort Worth airport and explain why it is an advantageous one.
    (c) What advantages for a community arise from it being the location of a major airport? What are the disadvantages?
    (d) Write a brief account of the factors which in the late 1970s and early 1980s caused a decline in both domestic and international air passenger traffic.

Plate 12.15 Airport connection by helicopter, New York

13 Urbanisation in Capitalist and Communist Worlds

ANTWERP: A COMMERCIAL PORT OF THE EEC

Growth

Antwerp was originally built on a defensive site on two low ridges on the east bank of the River Scheldt in Belgium. It became a prosperous trading centre for cloth and spices during the fifteenth century. It then declined, under Spanish occupation, from the sixteenth to eighteenth centuries, when the Scheldt was closed to traffic. Antwerp grew rapidly in the nineteenth century with the re-opening of the Scheldt. It bought out the tolls which the Dutch levied on ships moving through the Scheldt estuary, which passes through Dutch territory (Fig. 13.1).

Another reason for growth was the industrial development of Belgium, based on coal from the Sambre – Meuse coalfields. Canals such as the Albert canal connected Antwerp to this growing hinterland, while railways extended Antwerp's influence beyond Belgian frontiers, to the Ruhr and Lorraine industrial regions of Germany and France respectively (Fig. 13.2).

Until the rapid suburban development of this century, Antwerp's site remained compact, and can be seen in the middle ground of Plate 13.1. Plenty of space remained for building docks, which grew on the east bank of the river, to the north of the town, on flat, easily excavated land. Plate 13.2 shows one of the series of docks connected to the Albert Canal, the Leopold Dock. This is a dock where goods are transshipped from ocean-going vessels to canal barges, as well as being unloaded to dockside warehouses for transfer to land transport.

Antwerp's growth has also been helped by its overseas connections, such as the trading links with its former African colony, the Belgian Congo (now Zaire), an important source of minerals, such as copper and diamonds, and equatorial produce. More important, Antwerp is adjacent to the busiest part of the world's busiest sea, the southern part of the North Sea, at the end of great ocean trade routes across the Atlantic, from the Mediterranean and, in more recent times, the Persian Gulf (Fig. 13.3).

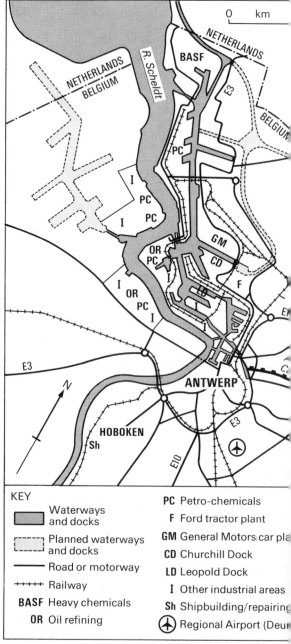

KEY

▨ Waterways and docks	**PC** Petro-chemicals
▢ Planned waterways and docks	**F** Ford tractor plant
— Road or motorway	**GM** General Motors car pla
+++++ Railway	**CD** Churchill Dock
BASF Heavy chemicals	**LD** Leopold Dock
OR Oil refining	**I** Other industrial areas
	Sh Shipbuilding/repairing
	⊕ Regional Airport (Deur

Fig. 13.1   The port of Antwerp

172

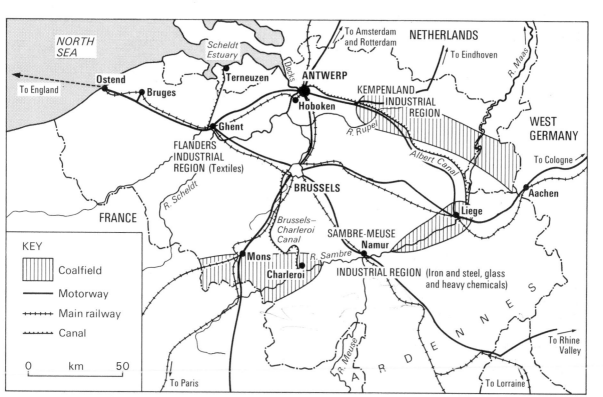

Fig. 13.2   The hinterland of Antwerp

Plate 13.1   Central Antwerp and the River Scheldt

Plate 13.2 Leopold Dock, Port of Antwerp

Fig. 13.3 World trade and Antwerp

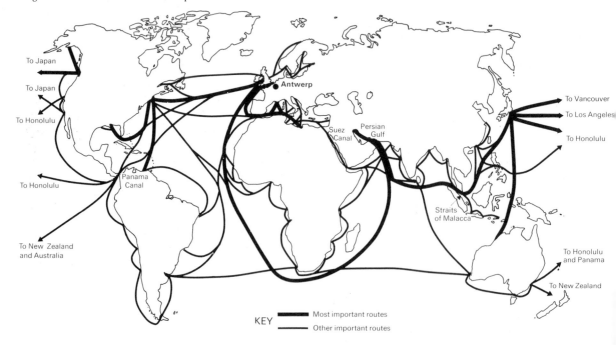

Table 13.1   Antwerp's locational advantage

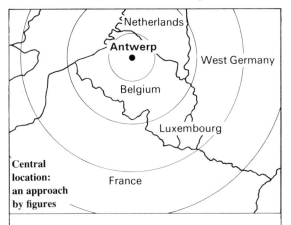

Central location: an approach by figures

All main European seaports stress their favourable location with regard to a part of the consumer market. This, however, does not mean that all these ports are entitled to the same extent to claim this advantage, which is especially important in connection with the choice of location places for distribution warehouses. A simple illustration of the differences between the seaports as far as their geographical location with regard to the important centres of population in a certain area is concerned is given by the following examples.

In Benelux, France and West Germany there are 24 large cities or conurbations, with over 400 000 inhabitants.

On the basis of the distance by road from the ports of Antwerp, Rotterdam, Amsterdam, Bremen, Hamburg, Dunkirk, Le Havre and Marseille to each of these 24 conurbations, the average distance in kilometres from the various ports to reach each of the inhabitants of the centres of population can be calculated. Technically spoken this is called a 'weighed average distance', because apart from the distance in kilometres also the importance of each of the conurbations (based on the number of inhabitants) as a consumption centre is considered.

The figures for the 8 ports are:

	weighed average distance	Antwerp = 100
Antwerp	368	100
Rotterdam	408	111
Amsterdam	432	117
Dunkirk	433	118
Le Havre	540	147
Bremen	560	152
Hamburg	646	176
Marseille	935	254

These figures show that serving these large conurbations in Benelux, France and West Germany from Antwerp brings an advantage in distance ranging from 11% with regard to Rotterdam, to 154% with regard to Marseille.

Recent Developments

ANTWERP AND THE EEC

Table 13.1, produced by the Port of Antwerp Promotion Association, shows how the great port of Western Europe compete for the expanded trade brought by belonging to the European Community. Antwerp is shown as having the best location of all, in terms of its access to the great conurbations of Western Europe. Antwerp is a huge port, handling over 70 million tonnes of cargo each year, far more than any British port. It is the fourth most important port of the EEC in tonnage handled, after Rotterdam, Marseilles and Le Havre.

Antwerp's links with other EEC countries have been strengthened by the opening of a new canal to the Rhine (1975), running to Dordrecht, which has reduced the time taken to reach the Rhine from Antwerp from 20–36 hours to 8–12 hours. Other recent links are the motorways running near Antwerp (Fig. 13.1), including European through-routes such as the E3 to the Netherlands and Scandinavia to the north, and France and Spain to the south; the E10, south to Paris; and the E39 to Aachen and the Rhine valley (Fig. 13.2). Of Antwerp's total trade, 64% is with Belgium itself and Luxembourg, 14% with West Germany, and 8.5% with France. About half the traffic is trans-shipped to and from the inland waterway system, by barge (Plate 13.2), and about 30% to and from rail. Road traffic is the fastest growing, however.

NEW DEVELOPMENTS IN ANTWERP'S DOCKLAND

Fig. 13.1 indicates how the docks have spread northwards on the east bank of the Scheldt; those north of the General Motors works having been built during the 1960s. Further developments are planned on the west bank. Dockside land is now occupied by a whole series of major multi-national concerns, particularly in heavy chemicals (BASF), petro-chemicals and oil refining. Older industries along the Scheldt are the shipyards of Hoboken and the vehicle manufacturing plants of General Motors and Ford. The docks altogether employ 75 000 people. Each quay in the docks has access to roads and railway tracks. There is much specialised equipment, for the bulk handling of coal, ores and grain, for example.

Plate 13.3   Container terminal, Churchill Dock, Port of Antwerp

CONTAINERISATION

The most important development in Antwerp and other major ports has been the move to containerisation. Plate 13.3 shows Antwerp's main container terminal at Churchill Dock, with its eight giant gantry cranes for transferring the containers to and from the quayside loading areas, linked with road and rail connections. There has been rapid growth from the mid-1960s, with the number of containers handled increasing from 50 000 in 1966 to 450 000 in 1980.

Containers are standardised steel-framed boxes, which are stacked in the holds of ships, and up to eight high on the decks as well (Plate 13.3). Containerisation has many advantages. A container quay with two cranes can handle five times as much tonnage as a conventional quay. The loading and offloading capacity per docker is increased ten times. One large container ship can do the work of between six and twelve conventional cargo liners. Container ships spend on average about 25% of their time in dock, compared with 60% for conventional cargo boats. This quick turnround makes them much more economic. Containerisation substitutes capital for labour, which has reduced costs in a period when wages have increased rapidly. There is also much less cargo lost through damage and pilferage than under the old system.

On the other hand, there are certain disadvantages. The greater efficiency means there is a smaller demand for ships, which has worsened the recession in the world's shipbuilding industry. Fewer dock-workers are needed, which has increased unemployment in many ports. In addition, fewer docks are needed. Many of Liverpool's, and most of London's docks, for example, are now closed, with trade concentrated on the container terminals of these ports, at Seaforth and Tilbury respectively.

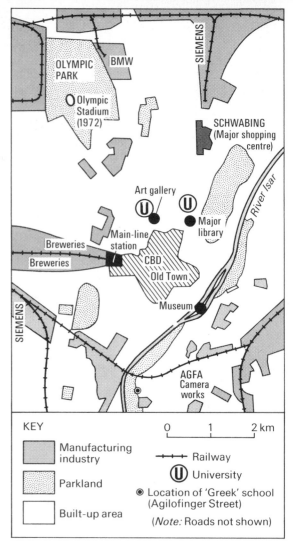

Fig. 13.4   Central Munich

MUNICH: INDUSTRIAL REGENERATION AND GUESTWORKERS

Growth

Munich is the third largest city of West Germany (after West Berlin and Hamburg), with a population of 1.3 million. Its early growth was on a dry-point site on the west bank of the River Isar (the 'old town' area on Fig. 13.4). It grew to importance as the capital city of the independent state of Bavaria, and in the nineteenth century became one of the great cultural centres of Europe, with universities, art galleries, museums, theatres and major libraries (Fig. 13.4). It was also a major industrial centre, with engineering works, paper and printing, and famous breweries, one

Plate 13.4   Munich station, and a brewery

of which is shown alongside the approaches to Munich station on Plate 13.4. Munich's growth was also helped by its strategic situation on European routes. Fig. 13.5 shows it as a rail-hub on trans-continental routes from Hamburg to Innsbruck; Berlin to Innsbruck; Cologne and Frankfurt to Vienna; and Mannheim and Stuttgart to Vienna. After the unification of Germany in the late nineteenth century, Munich became one of the new state's great regional capitals. Since World War 2 it has continued as the capital of the largest of the 'länder' (countries) of the Federal Republic (West Germany).

Fig. 13.5   Munich as a railway focus

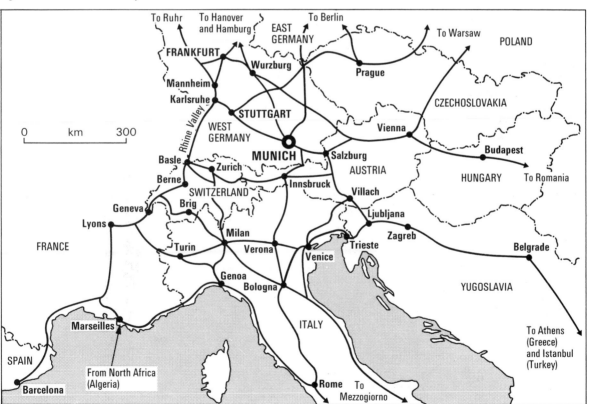

West Germany's Economic Miracle

Like other West German cities, Munich lay in ruins at the end of World War 2. Between 1945 and 1950 the occupied country was in a state of economic collapse. It had lost over four million military, killed in the war, while over half a million civilians had lost their lives through the bombing of cities. In addition, the country's Jewish population had either emigrated or been largely wiped out under the Nazi regime. West Germany's demographic problem is illustrated in Fig. 13.6. Note the gaps resulting from two world wars. In 1975, among fifty-year olds, there were only about 70 men for every 100 women; while among seventy-five-year olds, there were only just over 50 men for every 100 women.

Yet by the 1970s West Germany had become one of the most prosperous countries in the world, with economic growth well ahead of that of the United Kingdom, for example. Munich had grown into one of the country's most prosperous cities, and hosted the 1974 Olympic Games, for which it built an underground railway and a huge Olympic Village (see Fig. 13.4 and Plate 13.5). It is a major industrial centre, with prestige companies such as the BMW car manufacturing firm, whose plant is beside the Olympic Park on Plate 13.5, and Siemen's, a multinational electrical engineering corporation (Fig. 13.4). Post-war development in the region has been mainly in high-technology industries such as electronics, electrical, precision and optical engineering, and aerospace industries. This

Plate 13.5 The Olympic Park and BMW works, Munich

late start has been an advantage in that, unlike old industrial regions such as the Ruhr, for example, Munich has avoided problems of pollution and dereliction, and concentrated on the cleaner capital goods sections of industry.

Guestworkers

The great shortage of male workers illustrated on Fig. 13.6 would have been a grave handicap to industrial recovery had guestworkers not been imported. Plate 13.6 shows foreign labour on one of the BMW assembly lines at Munich. At first the imported labour was mainly made up of German-speaking deportees from Eastern Europe, expelled when the communists took over after 1945. Then, until the building of the Berlin Wall and the closure of the East German frontier in 1961, the West German economy was helped by the flight of workers from East Germany. The gap left was then filled by an influx of guestworkers from poorer countries of southern Europe, in particular Italians and Spaniards in the 1960s and Yugoslavs, Greeks and Turks in the early 1970s. Plate 13.7 shows coaches near Munich station waiting to carry Yugoslav guestworkers back to Zagreb, perhaps for a holiday or a weekend visit. Many more come in by rail to Munich station (Plate 13.4). Of the guestworker force in West Germany in 1975, 27% was from Turkey, 17% from Yugoslavia, 15% from Italy and 10% from Greece.

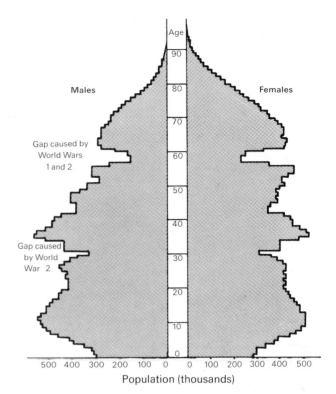

Fig. 13.6 West Germany: age and sex structure of population, 1975

Plate 13.6 Guestworkers on a BMW assembly line in Munich

Plate 13.7 Yugoslav guestworkers' buses, Munich

Plate 13.8 Agilofinger Street Primary School for Greek children, Munich

The guestworkers are generally employed in jobs unpopular with native German workers. These include less skilled jobs, as in the construction industry; more dangerous jobs, as in asbestos works and in coal mining; more menial jobs, such as street cleaning; poorly paid jobs, such as in catering; and labour-shortage activities, such as agriculture. Nevertheless the guestworkers are much better off than at home, and send enormous amounts of money back home to support their families, a total of 8.45 million deutschmarks in 1973.

In Munich, the guestworkers are most heavily concentrated in older areas adjoining the central business district (traditionally the 'blighted zone' of the city) (Fig. 13.7). About 17% of the city's population is made up of guestworkers, and there are three districts with over 30%. Fig. 13.7 shows the proportion of guestworkers' children to total primary school children in Munich, showing the concentration in the older quarters of the city. Plate 13.8 shows a typical Bavarian style school building in Agilofinger Street (see Fig. 13.4) which now concentrates on the education of

Fig. 13.7 Proportion of guestworkers' children to total primary school children in different parts of Munich

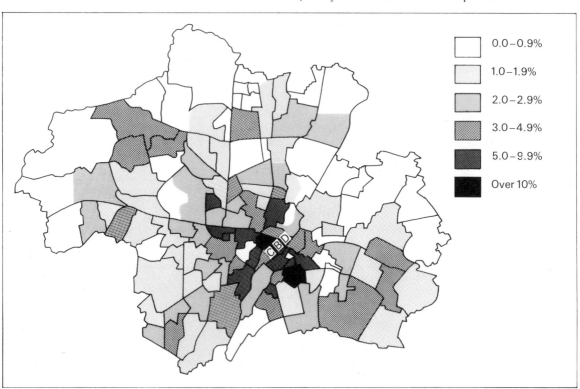

	0.0−0.9%
	1.0−1.9%
	2.0−2.9%
	3.0−4.9%
	5.0−9.9%
	Over 10%

Greek guestworker children. On the walls in its classrooms are maps of Greece, and posters and workcards in the Greek language. Here the children learn also to speak German.

The guestworkers who have helped to create West Germany's economic miracle are also a cause of social concern. Look at the accompanying extract from a Munich newspaper. It says: 'Foreigner? But I've settled here. A million guestworkers' children are growing up in the Federal Republic. They're asking themselves, and mostly in German: Where do we belong?'. Many of the guestworkers have been successful, and wish to settle down in West Germany. These are often more skilled people, however, who are needed in their own countries. Although the guestworkers send back large amounts of money, their home villages lose their labour and agriculture declines. Family life is shattered, and when they return, their new skills, of car assembly, for example, are of no practical benefit. The dilemma is shown in the following statements, one from a factory manager, and the other from an immigration officer:

'It is inconceivable that we could continue running the factory without large amounts of new foreign labour.'

'It is morally wrong to build the development of our wealth on the backs of foreign manpower.'

»Ausländer? Aber ich bin hier doch gewöhnt...«

Eine Million Gastarbeiterkinder wachsen in der Bundesrepublik auf. Sie fragen sich, und das zumeist in Deutsch: » Wohin gehören wir? «

(from Raumwissenschaftliches Curriculum – Forschungsprojekt des Zentralverbandes der Deutschen Geographen)

Exercises

1. Contrast the dockland activities on Plates 13.2 and 13.3. What are the advantages and disadvantages of containerisation?
2. (a) How have Antwerp's linkages in Europe and beyond changed between the nineteenth century and today?
   (b) Refer to Table 13.1 and describe in your own words what the figures in the Antwerp = 100 column indicate.
   (c) Why, if Antwerp's location index is so good, does it remain a less important port than Rotterdam? (Refer also to Fig. 13.2 and atlas maps of Western Europe.)
3. (a) Draw a pie chart to illustrate the following percentages of guestworkers in West Germany (1975): Turkey 27%; Yugoslavia 17%; Italy 15%; Greece 10%; Spain 6%; Portugal 3%; others 22%.
   (b) With the help of the text and Fig. 13.5, suggest why a large proportion of guestworkers come to cities such as Munich, Stuttgart and Frankfurt.
4. (a) Describe and explain the main features of the population pyramid for West Germany in 1975 (Fig. 13.6).
   (b) Describe and try to account for the distribution of guestworkers' children shown on Fig. 13.7.
5. Outline the pros and cons of the use of guestworkers, with special reference to the two quotations which end the section on guestworkers.

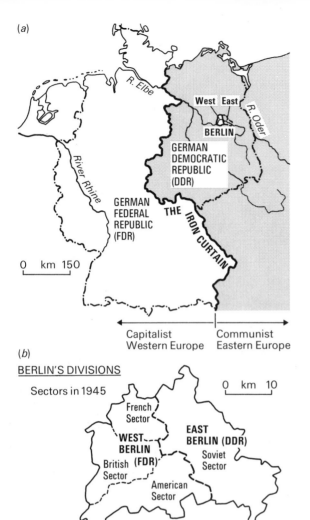

(a)

West | East
BERLIN
GERMAN DEMOCRATIC REPUBLIC (DDR)
GERMAN FEDERAL REPUBLIC (FDR)
THE IRON CURTAIN
R. Elbe
R. Oder
River Rhine

0 km 150

Capitalist Western Europe | Communist Eastern Europe

(b)

BERLIN'S DIVISIONS

Sectors in 1945

0 km 10

French Sector
WEST BERLIN (FDR)
British Sector
American Sector
EAST BERLIN (DDR)
Soviet Sector

BERLIN: WHERE CAPITALISM MEETS COMMUNISM

The Berlin Wall

After the end of World War 2, Germany's capital city, Berlin, was split up into zones by the occupying forces: the Americans, British and French in West Berlin, and the Russians in East Berlin (Fig. 13.8 and Plate 2.7a). In Germany as a whole, Berlin lay in the heart of territory occupied by Soviet forces. This became the German Democratic Republic (DDR) or East Germany. Those parts of Germany occupied by western forces became the German Federal Republic (FDR), or West Germany. West Berlin was left as a capitalist island behind the 'iron curtain', in communist Eastern Europe (Fig. 13.8).

The division of Berlin left many sources of conflict. One was that West Berlin was used by many East Germans to escape to the west. This seriously affected the East German economy, and for this and political reasons the East Germans suddenly erected the Berlin Wall in 1961 (Plate 13.9). This is seen in quite different ways by the two sides. The graffiti on the wall on the west side says: 'Stop: here ends freedom'. The East Germans regard the wall as 'a bastion against Fascism'. To the west, the wall is a symbol of oppression, and many East Germans have lost their lives trying to escape over it.

Fig. 13.8   Germany after World War 2

Plate 13.9
The Berlin Wall, with East Berlin beyond

The Aftermath of World War 2

In 1939, Berlin was one of the great capitals of Europe, with a population of 4.3 million people. It grew remarkably from the late nineteenth century, when the separate German states, such as Prussia and Bavaria, were united as Germany, with Berlin as the capital. It was the most important railway focus and the greatest manufacturing city of central Europe. It became the pride of Hitler's Germany between the wars.

Plate 13.10 Berlin in May 1949

Like other German cities, Berlin was devastated by war, both by bombing and by Russian shelling in the final battle for the city. Plate 13.10 shows the ruins of Berlin in 1949, four years after the end of the war. Apart from some new official buildings in the centre of the photograph, reclamation of this central area, near the junction of the British, American and Russian sectors (Fig. 13.8) had not begun. Recovery was at first very slow, and the people lived in great hardship. Redevelopment speeded up in the 1950s and 1960s, but even in the 1970s evidence of war damage remained, especially in East Berlin.

Since the division of Berlin, West Berlin has been rebuilt as a capitalist city. Plate 13.11 shows the centre dominated by the Kaiser Wilhelm Memorial Church. Running away to the left is the tree-lined boulevard of Kurfurstendamm, the main shopping and entertainments street of West Berlin. The bridge over the urban motorway on the right is the approach to the main station, on the line which connects passengers to West Germany (Fig. 13.9). East Berlin has been redeveloped as a communist capital, with modern offices and apartments near the city centre (Plate 13.12), making it the showpiece of East Germany.

Plate 13.11   West Berlin

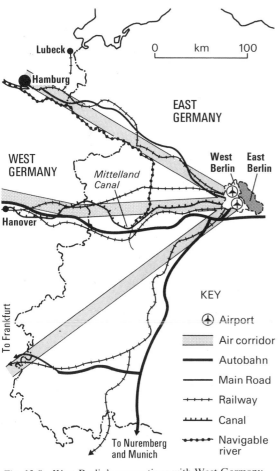

Fig. 13.9   West Berlin's connections with West Germany

Plate 13.12   The centre of East Berlin

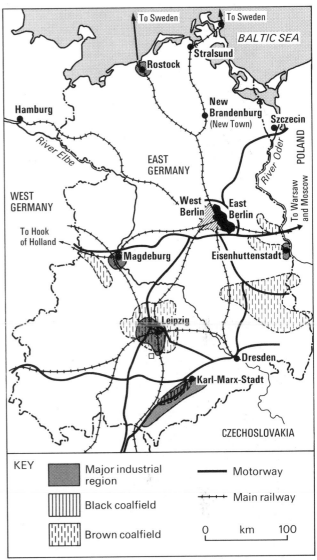

Fig. 13.10   East Berlin's connections

Contrasts between West and East Berlin

Redevelopment of Berlin under capitalist and communist regimes has been very different. Major reasons for the differences include the separate political beliefs of what a city should be, and also the geographical fact that West Berlin is isolated from the rest of West Germany, while East Berlin is physically connected to East Germany. The differences can be summarised as follows:

185

	West Berlin	**East Berlin**
Access	West Berlin is an 'island' 200 km from the 'mainland' (Fig. 13.8). This isolation produces a claustrophobic atmosphere. It is difficult to attract people from West Germany to work and live in West Berlin.	East Berlin is, like other capital cities, fully integrated with its territory, although the presence of West Berlin makes some connections difficult (Fig. 13.10).
Population	West Berlin has a population of 1.9 million, but this is likely to fall because a high percentage of the population is over 60. Many young married couples migrate to West Germany.	East Berlin has a smaller population than West Berlin, 1.1 million, and a very different population structure, with a much higher percentage of the population in working groups. Loss of population was stopped by the Berlin Wall.
Labour	Before 1961, 76 000 East Berliners worked in West Berlin. The 'Wall' resulted in a drastic labour shortage, made up by recruiting guestworkers (see page 179).	Since the building of the 'Wall' the labour shortage has been reduced. About 10% of the work-force commutes into the city.
Urban renewal	Rebuilding has been fast because of huge subsidies from West Germany, but extremely difficult owing to shortage of land. A continuing housing shortage has caused social unrest. Planning has been on 'western' lines with, for example, Kurfurstendamm (Plate 13.11) rebuilt as a shopping and leisure complex.	Rebuilding has been slower than in West Berlin. It speeded up as the economy improved after the building of the Berlin Wall. Planning has been on Soviet lines, with tall blocks of flats near the city centre (Plate 13.12). Land shortage is less of a problem, and the population density is less than in West Berlin.
Water supply and waste disposal	This is difficult for West Berlin owing to its isolation. It relies on ground water deposits from sands and gravels of the Spree valley. Waste disposal is by incineration. Sewage is dealt with by East Berlin. Fear of epidemics ensures that it is done properly.	East Berlin has fewer problems than West Berlin, as it is connected with the national systems.
Transport	There is only one through-railway (shown on Plate 13.11), which carries the trans-continental services from Western Europe to the Soviet Union. Links with West Germany are limited to the railways, canals, autobahns, and air corridors shown on Fig. 13.9.	The disruption caused by the division of Berlin has resulted in the closure of a number of stations. A ring railway was built in the 1950s to avoid West Berlin, which is much used for commuting. There are also motorways round the city (Fig. 13.10)
Manufacturing	West Berlin remains a major manufacturing centre, with industries similar to those of pre-war: electrical engineering; general engineering; food processing; textiles and clothing. Coal and oil have to be imported from West Germany.	Here manufacturing is less important, as East Germany's major industrial regions lie elsewhere, to the east along the Oder valley and further south in the coalfield areas (Fig. 13.10). There are, however, electrical engineering, textile, tool-making and vehicle industries. Consumers goods industries are given less priority than in the west.
Tertiary sector	*Commercial* activities are much less important than before the war, as these have shifted to West Germany. Berlin remains West Germany's main *cultural* centre, however, with major film-making and television studios, and concert halls and theatres. It is seen as a 'showplace' for the west.	Tertiary activities are very important, as East Berlin is the capital of a very centralised communist state. Large numbers are employed in government services, administrating the activities of the DDR. East Berlin is also an important cultural centre, with a similar range of facilities to West Berlin. It is used as a 'showplace' for the east.

186

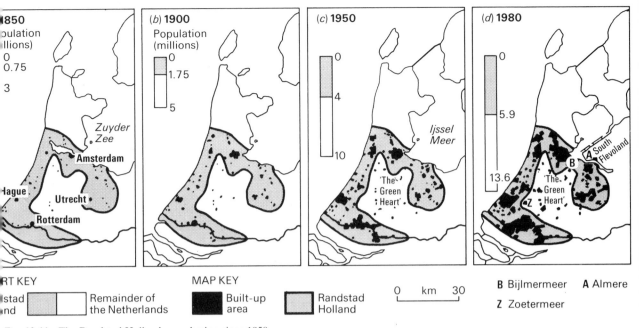

Zuyder Zee
Amsterdam
Hague
Utrecht
Rotterdam

(b) **1900**
Population (millions)
0

1.75

5

(c) **1950**
0

4

10

Ijssel Meer

'The Green Heart'

(d) **1980**
0

5.9

13.6

South Flevoland
B
A

'The Green Heart'
Z

RT KEY

stad | Remainder of
nd | the Netherlands

MAP KEY

Built-up area | Randstad Holland

0   km   30

B Bijlmermeer   **A** Almere

Z Zoetermeer

Fig. 13.11   The Randstad Holland conurbation since 1850

RANDSTAD HOLLAND: THE WEST NETHERLANDS CONURBATION

Conurbations

Conurbations are large and often sprawling urban areas made up by the growing together of formerly separate towns and cities. Randstad Holland (Fig. 13.11) is in the shape of a horseshoe, open at the south-eastern end. The maps show how it has grown by the merging of towns and cities, today forming an urban ring round a rural area known as the 'green heart'. Notice from the bar charts on Fig. 13.11 how the population of the Randstad has grown from ¾ million in 1850 to 4 million in 1950 and nearly 6 million in 1980, almost half the population of the Netherlands. The four largest cities are Rotterdam, the largest port in the world; Amsterdam, the main commercial and cultural centre of the Netherlands; The Hague, the seat of government; and Utrecht, the main railway focus. Notice on Fig. 13.11 how even the 'green heart' is now under attack from urban growth.

Physical Factors

The reasons for the 'horseshoe' growth round a 'green heart' are the result of physical features. Towns have grown in three main areas:

(a) along the sand dune coast, as in the case of The Hague;

(b) on glacial sand and gravel deposits in the east, as in the Utrecht area;

(c) along dykes beside rivers or at outlets to the sea, as in the case of Amsterdam and Rotterdam.

Urbanisation and its Problems

The population density of the West Netherlands is 905/km^2 compared with 412/km^2 in the Netherlands as a whole. Randstad covers 16.7% of the total area, but has 42.6% of the national population. The rapid growth in population had, by the second half of this century, caused considerable urban sprawl (Fig. 13.11). Many problems have resulted.

(1) As central areas of the cities have become older, the *quality of housing* has declined, made worse by housing shortage and over-crowding in tenement blocks, such as those shown near the centre of Amsterdam in Plate 13.13. The foundations of such tenements, built on low-lying polder land, are now often in poor condition.

(2) The desire to move out of city centres has led to *suburbanisation*, the process causing urban sprawl and conurbation development. While there was a 10% increase in population during 1974–7 in the Randstad area, there was a 1% decrease in the nine main towns as a result of the suburbanisation process.

(3) Like other western countries, the Netherlands has become a *multi-ethnic society*, with considerable numbers of people from former colonies in South-east Asia and the West Indies. Like the coloured populations in Britain, these have tended to concentrate in overcrowded tenement areas near the centre of large cities.

(4) In so crowded an environment, *congestion* is a major problem. Although the Netherlands has an efficient railway and motorway system, the Randstad suffers from typical western city problems of rush hour delays.

(5) The concentration of industry in such areas also leads to problems of atmospheric and river *pollution*, particularly great in the Rotterdam area, where oil refineries and chemical works are concentrated.

(6) Unlike most conurbations, Randstad Holland has no one central city, and therefore no organisation based on a single centre. The major cities have their own histories and different functions. There is no feeling of 'belonging' to Randstad. This variation makes planning more difficult.

Urban Planning

Solutions to problems of declining central areas and urban spread have been sought in different ways.

OVERSPILL DEVELOPMENTS WITHIN PRESENT CITY LIMITS

One example of such overspill development is at Bijlmermeer, on the south-east side of Amsterdam (Fig. 13.11). This huge scheme, designed to cater for 100 000 people, is shown on Plate 13.14. It is made up of elongated tenement blocks, eleven storeys high, with green areas between. Road traffic is separated from pedestrian. The development is linked with Amsterdam (in the background of the photograph) by a new 'metro' link, shown under construction on the photograph, and now complete. Like many other West European developments on this inhuman scale, Bijlmermeer has been unsuccessful, and is avoided as much as possible by people needing housing. The most deprived groups, particularly coloured people from former Dutch colonies abroad, have, through lack of the prospect of finding other accommodation, moved into Bijlmermeer, which is becoming something of a ghetto as a result.

Plate 13.13 Central Amsterdam: nineteenth-century tenements

Pressure of population within Randstad, has led to an attack on the 'green heart', especially in the area east of The Hague (Fig. 13.11). A *new town*, Zoetermeer, has been built to take overspill population from The Hague area. It was still a large rural village, with 8500 inhabitants in 1960. In 1980 it had nearly 64 000. One very interesting feature of Zoetermeer's growth, seen spreading onto the polder land on Plate 13.15, is the evidence of the decline in popularity of high-rise housing. Notice the great mixture in the residential areas.

In the first neighbourhood, built between 1966 and 1975, 70% of the residences were high-rise. In the fourth, built between 1974 and 1982, there were only 10% high-rise, and in the fifth neighbourhood there are to be none.

Although an industrial estate has been established, most of the work-force, about 13 500 out of 23 500, commute into The Hague. Zoetermeer is well connected by a rapid-transit railway, shown on the right of Plate 13.15.

Plate 13.14 Bijlmermeer estate, Amsterdam

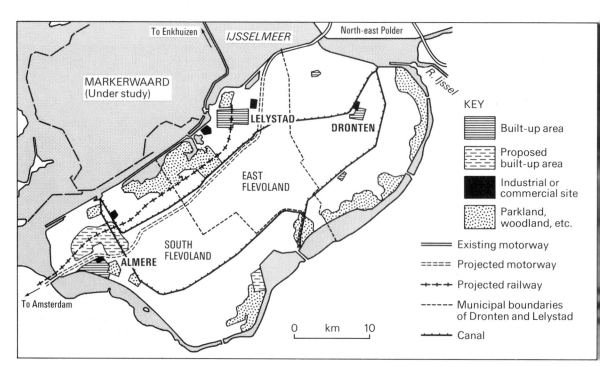

Fig. 13.12   Flevoland: new town

Plate 13.15   Zoetermeer new town in the Netherlands

Plate 13.16   Almere new town, South Flevoland

RECLAIMING LAND FOR URBAN DEVELOPMENT

Before World War 2, the Zuyder Zee was sealed off by a huge dyke, leaving behind a lake, the Ijssel Meer, much of which has since been reclaimed (Fig. 13.11). The original intention was to provide more farming land to feed the dense population of the Netherlands. In the case of the more recent reclamation of the East and South Flevoland polders, however, (Fig. 13.12), the intention is less to provide new farming land, and more to provide land for new towns and recreational development, and protect the threatened 'green heart'. The first new town, Lelystad (Fig. 13.12) had a population of 35 000 in 1979 and is intended to reach 70 000 eventually. The most recent development, shown on Plate 13.16, is at Almere, which had a population of 4200 in 1979 and is intended to reach 74 000. Motorway links are now complete, and a railway is planned (Fig. 13.12), from Amsterdam to Almere and Lelystad. The waters left between Flevoland and the mainland are intended particularly for recreational use. Notice a yachting marina being developed at Almere on Plate 13.16. Notice too how a line of canals as well as a road pattern has been created, so that the residential areas have ready access to the water, so much enjoyed by Dutch people.

Exercises

6. (a) Outline the problems faced by West Berlin in not being physically part of West Germany.
   (b) Contrast the post-war growth of Berlin under capitalist and communist systems.
7. What different ideas about urban residential planning are shown on Plates 13.14, 13.15 and 13.16?
8. (a) With reference to the sections on Antwerp and Randstad Holland, outline the causes of urbanisation in Belgium and the Netherlands.
   (b) What are the main problems caused by this urbanisation?
9. Refer to the table below, which shows how the working population of the Netherlands was employed in three different years.

Activity	Percentage employed		
	1947	*1960*	*1971*
Agriculture	18.9	10.6	6.2
Manufacturing	37.9	42.2	38.7
Services (tertiary activities)	43.2	47.1	55.1

(a) Describe how the percentages employed in these three main areas of activity changed between 1947 and 1971.
(b) With reference to the Netherlands' sections of Chapter 10 and this chapter, try to explain the changes, and the effects these have had on the landscape.

SECTION E: The Developing World
14 World Population and Urbanisation

WORLD POPULATION

World Population Growth

In the early nineteenth century, the world's population reached one billion (1000 000 000). Before that time, growth had been relatively slow (Fig. 14.1). After it, growth became increasingly rapid. The 2 billion mark was reached in the 1930s, the 3 billion in 1960 and the 4 billion about 1980. It is projected that by the year 2000 the total will have reached 6 billion.

The increasing rate of growth has not been even over the world. During the nineteenth century, the industrial countries grew rapidly. The twentieth century has seen a phenomenal increase in the so-called developing countries of the world: the poorer nations of Asia, Africa and Latin America. The world map (Fig.14.2) of fairly recent growth rates shows that most of the countries of Latin America north of Uruguay, Argentina and Chile had over 2% annual growth rates and some, such as Mexico, Panama, Ecuador and Venezuala, had over 3%. This means a country with 100 million people, if this average was kept up, would

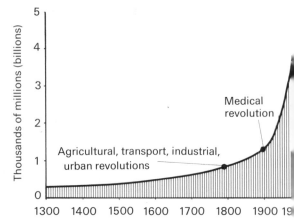

Fig. 14.1 Growth of world population 1300–1980

have 3 million more a year, or 30 million more a decade, to feed. Similar growth rates were present over most of Africa and southern and South-east Asia, where countries such as Algeria, Libya, Ivory Coast, Zimbabwe, Malagasy and Syria, Iraq and Pakistan had

Fig. 14.2 World population growth rates 1970–5, by country

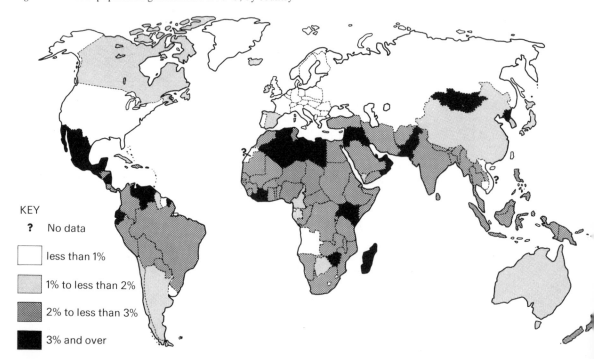

KEY

? No data

less than 1%

1% to less than 2%

2% to less than 3%

3% and over

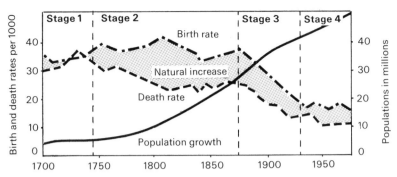

Fig. 14.3 The demographic transition in England and Wales

over 3%. By contrast, the majority of countries with less than 1% growth rates were in the developed world, as in the USA, Britain and most of Western Europe, and in the developed communist world of Eastern Europe and the USSR.

The Demographic Transition

As Fig. 14.3 suggests, overall population growth or natural increase depends upon the balance between birth and death rates. Population does not grow where the two are in balance. Fig. 14.3 indicates that over the centuries, population change has tended to pass through a series of stages, known as the *demographic transition*, illustrated here for England and Wales.

Stage 1. Birth and death rates *fluctuate*, at a *high level*. Both are at about 35 per 1000 population. Population growth is small.

Stage 2. Birth rates remain high, at about 35 per 1000, while the death rate declines rapidly, from 30 to just over 20 per 1000 population. In this *early stage of expansion*, population increase is rapid.

Stage 3. Birth rates decline, from 35 to 20 per 1000 in the example given here, with further decline in the

death rate. This is the *late stage of expansion*, and population growth remains high.

Stage 4. Birth and death rates *fluctuate*, at a *low level*. The birth rate in Englnd and Wales has come down to about 16 per thousand and the death rate to about 12 per thousand. but there are variations with some periods of increase and others of decrease in births, as in England and Wales in the 1960s and 1970s. Overall population growth is slow.

In the developing world, a similar demographic transition appears to be taking place. But the timing of the transition has been different, with most developing countries still in stage 2 or 3.

Age Structure

The age structure of the population varies greatly at different stages of the demographic transition. Fig. 14.4 shows England and Wales in stage 2 in 1871, with a balanced population pyramid, with most of the people in the more youthful age groups and least among the older. In 1971, however, in stage 4 of the transition, the 'pyramid' is top-heavy, with relatively large numbers of old people and less than would be expected of young people.

Fig. 14.4 England and Wales 1871 and 1971: age and sex structure of population

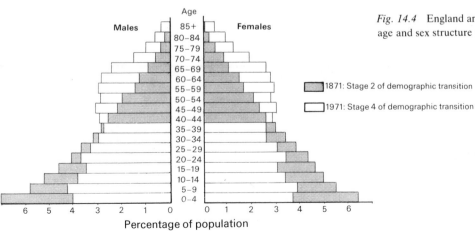

1871: Stage 2 of demographic transition

1971: Stage 4 of demographic transition

193

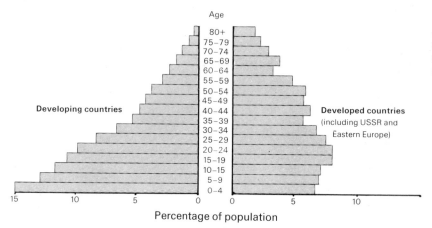

Age

Developing countries

Developed countries
(including USSR and
Eastern Europe)

80+
75–79
70–74
65–69
60–64
55–59
50–54
45–49
40–44
35–39
30–34
25–29
20–24
15–19
10–15
5–9
0–4

Percentage of population

Fig. 14.5 Population distribution by age (1980) in developing and developed countries

Fig. 14.5 shows the different average population distributions by age in the developed and the developing world. The right hand side is just like that of England and Wales in 1971, while the left hand side, showing the developing countries, is more like England and Wales in 1871, at stage 2 of the demographic transition.

Factors Influencing Population Change and Variation in the Developed World

In the nineteenth century, as we have seen, birth rates were high and death rates were declining quickly in the developed countries, giving rapid population increase. The high birth rates were influenced by the concentration of people in towns as a result of the industrial revolution (Fig. 14.1). Many of these people were in youthful age groups, and increasing marriage rates were followed by large numbers of births. At a later date, the medical revolution (Fig. 14.1), which included the discovery of new drugs, improvements in hygiene and antiseptic surgery, caused a rapid decrease in the death rate.

Before 1870, large famiies were the rule in the developed world. From the late nineteenth century, however, birth control techniques were increasingly applied. The average size of family was reduced in England and Wales from about seven in the 1850s, to just over two in the 1950s. The result of this was a much slower rate of population growth.

India: a Developing Country with a High Growth Rate

REASONS FOR THE HIGH GROWTH RATE

India's high growth rate is supported by a huge population of nearly 650 million, who take advantage of the monsoon climate and widespread alluvial soils (see Chapter 8) to grow the vast quantities of grains, particularly rice, required to feed this population. Large families persist. Parents still feel they must have many children to make up for losses through the high death rate in infancy, and to help with work in the fields, the home and the village community. There are no old age pensions available, and surviving children are expected to support their parents when they grow too old for work. Education is of low cost and does not last long. At the same time, there have been medical improvements which have increased life expectancy. More people therefore live into middle and old age. This increases the problem of supporting aging parents.

PROBLEMS CAUSED BY THE HIGH GROWTH RATE

The continual increase in the size of India's population has resulted in severe over-crowding in villages and towns, with people living in poor hygienic conditions. Facilities for sewage disposal are minimal, and under severe strain in the great cities (Plate 14.1). Where families are poor, there is insufficient food to go round and malnutrition results (see Chapter 15). If all the children survive, there is not enough land for them in the village area. Holdings are already too fragmented. A certain number drift from the countryside into the towns (see pages 202–3). But here there is not enough work to go round, and unemployment is severe. Neither is there sufficient housing, which leads to large numbers of people sleeping on the streets, as in Calcutta and Bombay (Chapter 8). The increasing numbers of children who survive infancy puts a great strain on the educational system, and many grow up illiterate.

Plate 14.1 Open drains in an Indian city

SOLUTIONS

(1) *Family planning* is one of the most important, and many developing countries are now encouraging their people to have fewer children. In India, 24% of the age group which can produce children were in 1977 practising some form of contraception or had been sterilised. The birth rate decreased by 19% between 1960 and 1977 (although this does not of course mean a drop in population, if death rates are decreasing even faster). There has been less success in Moslem countries. Probably only 6% of Pakistan's relevant population were practising birth control in 1977, and the birth rate had only declined by 8.2% between 1960 and 1977.

(2) Family planning can only succeed where there are *improvements in health* and in *farming practices*, whereby village people can be sure that more children will survive, and that there will be less need for child labour in the fields.

(3) It is also more likely to succeed where it is introduced gradually, with the cooperation of the people. There has been much resistance, in India for example, to enforced programmes of sterilisation. Private initiatives, linked with broader medical services, have tended to be more successful, convincing the women in particular that it is in their interests not to have too many children, educating them through personal discussion into the use of birth control techniques.

(4) Birth control on a vast scale is an expensive process, and financial support is needed from the countries of the developed world.

PEOPLE ON THE MOVE: MIGRATION

So far we have considered only natural changes in the population, resulting from changes in birth and death rates. Population change in particular areas can, however, be caused by movements of people. Population movement is known as *migration*. *Immigrants* are people moving into an area, therefore helping to increase its population. *Emigrants* are people moving out of an area, helping to decrease its population.

Types of Migration

Migration is a complicated process. It takes place, for example, on different time scales:

(*a*) *daily*: for example, *commuters* travelling to work in large urban centres, increasing vastly the daytime population;

(*b*) *seasonal*: for example, *nomads* moving with the seasons in search of pastures; *pilgrims* flocking to holy cities at particular times of the year;

(*c*) *semi-permanent*: for example, *migrant labour*, such as guestworkers in West German cities (Chapter 13), who stay for long periods of time but intend in the majority of cases to return home eventually;

(*d*) *permanent*: that is, migration for life. This can be *voluntary* or *forced* migration. It can also be *external*: between countries; or *internal*: within a country.

External Migration

Voluntary migration occurs where people choose to move themselves, usually in response to two sets of factors. The first are *push factors*, persuading them to move away from their place of origin. The second are *pull factors*, beckoning them to live in a new area. Plate 14.2 shows a nineteenth-century cartoon, in which poverty-stricken people were encouraged to leave Britain ('Here') in the hope of finding a richer life abroad, perhaps in North America ('There').

Large numbers of European emigrants have crossed the Atlantic, particularly in the nineteenth and twentieth centuries, as Fig. 14.6 illustrates. Thirty-three million people left Europe for the USA between 1820

Plate 14.2
A nineteenth-century emigration cartoon

HERE AND THERE;

OR, EMIGRATION A REMEDY.

and 1950. Among the main groups of migrants were poor Irish, Italians and East European Jews. Many settled in New York, where segregated immigrant districts, or ghettoes, arose (see Chapter 16).

Fig. 14.6 shows other important routes taken by migrants. Among these were Indian workers, seeking employment in the plantations of East Africa, South Africa (sugar in Natal) and South-east Asia (rubber), and Chinese, who also sought jobs in South-east Asian cities, often as traders and shopkeepers.

While much of this migration was voluntary in the sense that people chose to move, it also contained a forced element in that sheer poverty and threat of famine made it necessary to leave. Another reason for

Fig. 14.6 Main world migration routes from the eighteenth to the twentieth century

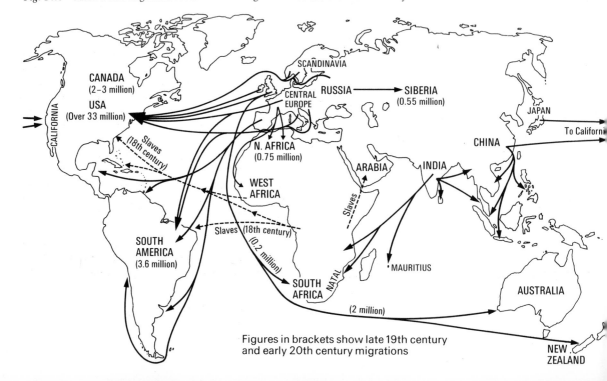

movement was the 'pull' of new worlds. Both governments and individuals saw the overseas opportunities presented in the ages of exploration. The process of *colonisation* resulted. This dated back to the sixteenth century, in the case of British, Spanish and Portuguese in the Americas, for example, and expanded greatly in the nineteenth century, the great age of the colonisation of Africa, and also of European settlement in Australia and New Zealand. Similarly, the Russians were continuing their expansion into Siberia (Fig. 14.6).

By the twentieth century, there were few lands left to open up. The process of *decolonisation* became more important, and in some cases a reverse movement developed. In the late 1950s and early 1960s, for example, immigrants from 'new commonwealth' countries, particularly the West Indies, India and Pakistan, came to Britain to look for jobs, having been pushed out by unemployment and poverty at home. Before long the British govenment checked such immigration, on the grounds that it would create social tensions and unemployment.

Internal Migration

Internal migration can be of various types: from village to village; village to town; town to town; or town to village. But the most characteristic type is rural to urban. The process is sometimes a *stepped* one, with the migrant moving first from a remote farm to a local market town, before ending up in a large city. Most migration is *short distance*, people from the countryside moving to the nearest town. But the *size of places* is also significant, and the capital city, with its wide range of job opportunities and 'bright lights', is particularly likely to attract people from further away.

Fig. 14.7 illustrates some important internal migration routes in the USA in the period following the great depression of the 1920s and 1930s. Many poverty-stricken farmers moved out of the Dust Bowl states, where soil erosion had destroyed their livelihood, to seek new opportunities elsewhere, especially in California. Coloured workers from the 'deep south' tried to find jobs in northern cities, as in the car industry of the Detroit area (see Chapter 11), and in the commercial centres of the north-eastern coast.

Forced Migration

This can be external or internal, but common to both is the fact that people are driven out forcibly, or under threat of force, by oppressive governments or groups of people. The following types can be identified:

(1) *Forced labour*, which has included:

(*a*) the *slave trade*, as a result of which large numbers of African black people were transported against their will and under appalling conditions to the plantations of South America, the West Indies, and the southern states of the USA, during the eighteenth and early nineteenth centuries;

(*b*) the use of *prisoners of war* or *political prisoners* or *criminals* to undertake work away from their homes, under prison or concentration camp conditions. The worst examples of this have been by the Nazis in central Europe in the 1930s and early 1940s, and by the communist government of the USSR, particularly in the time of Stalin, from the 1920s to the early 1950s.

(2) *Refugees*. These are people forced to move as a result of religious, political or racial persecution; or as a result of war and its aftermath. The most dramatic twentieth-century example has been the persecution of the Jews under Nazi controlled governments. Of 5.5 million Jews in Europe, no more than 1.25 million remained in 1945. Many had fled, and many more wished to leave Europe at the end of World War 2, particularly for Palestine, which was to be the promised land of the Jews (Chaper 5). But the establishment of Israel led in turn to the problem of Palestinian Arab refugees. Plate 14.3 shows a temporary camp in the Lebanon in 1952. Plate 14.4 shows a much more permanent refugee settlement in Jordan in 1980. The refugee problem here remains a source of conflict, which erupted again in 1982 in Lebanon.

Fig. 14.7   Internal migration in the USA in the inter-war years

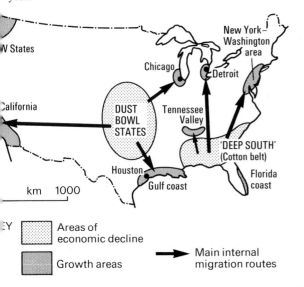

Plate 14.3   A Palestinian refugee camp in the Lebanon, 1952

Plate 14.4   A Palestinian refugee settlement in Jordan, 1980

The human misery associated with World War 2 has easily been equalled or surpassed by warfare in Vietnam, which lasted for thirty years from the late 1940s. In 1884, Vietnam became part of French Indo-China. In 1945, the communist leader, Ho Chi-Minh, declared Vietnam independent. A guerrilla warfare followed until 1954, when the French were defeated at Dien Bien Phu (Fig. 14.8). The country was divided into North Vietnam (communist) and South Vietnam (non-communist).

War broke out between the two in the late 1950s and lasted until the mid-1970s. The Americans poured in troops, over half a million at one stage, to support the anti-communist government. North Vietnamese guerrillas (the Vietcong) infiltrated the south overland (the Ho Chi-Minh trail) and by sea (Fig. 14.8). They then invaded directly (the Tet offensive). The unpopularity of the war with the people of the USA led to American troops being pulled out in 1972, but bombing of the north continued until the South Vietnamese government collapsed in 1975.

Vast numbers of refugees were created by this lengthy war. 900 000 left North Vietnam for the south after partiton in 1954. It is estimated there were 2 million refugees in Vietnam in 1967. Plate 14.5 shows refugees fleeing in terror during a bombardment of Da Nang (Fig. 14.8). Many had to leave North Vietnamese towns during American bombing. Since 1975, there have been many more Vietnamese refugees (the 'boat people'), fleeing the communist government and moving to places such as Hong Kong.

198

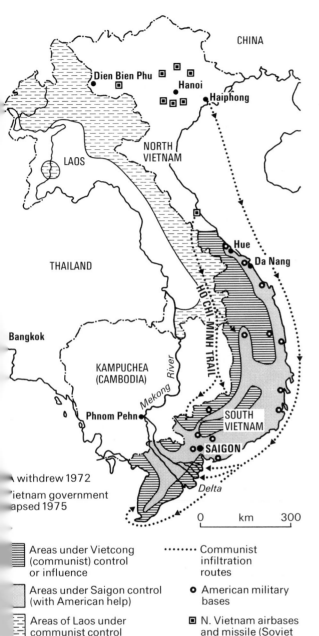

CHINA

Dien Bien Phu ◉ ◉
● Hanoi
◉ ◉ Haiphong

NORTH
VIETNAM

LAOS ⊕

THAILAND

Bangkok

KAMPUCHEA
(CAMBODIA)

Mekong River

Phnom Pehn ●

HO CHI MINH TRAIL

Hue
Da Nang

SOUTH
VIETNAM

SAIGON

Delta

0   km   300

America withdrew 1972
S. Vietnam government
collapsed 1975

▤ Areas under Vietcong
(communist) control
or influence

▥ Areas under Saigon control
(with American help)

▤ Areas of Laos under
communist control
or influence

········ Communist
infiltration
routes

◉ American military
bases

◉ N. Vietnam airbases
and missile (Soviet
supplied) sites

Fig. 14.8 The geography of the Vietnam War

Exercises

1. Refer to Fig. 14.2, a map of world population growth.
   (a) With reference to areas with an annual growth rate of over 2%, (i) describe their distribution; (ii) name one country of this type and explain its high rate of population growth; (iii) outline the problems created by rapid population growth; (iv) describe attempts being made to find solutions.
   (b) With reference to areas with an annual growth rate of less than 1%, name one country within these areas, and explain its low rate of increase and the problems this poses.
2. Refer to Plate 14.1. What features on this photograph suggest this is likely to be an area of low life expectancy?
3. Refer to Figs. 14.3, 14.4 and 14.5.
   (a) Explain the term demographic transition.
   (b) Explain and give examples of:
   (i) low but fluctuating population levels (high birth/death rates) at stage 1; (ii) rapid population increase at stage 2; (iii) a slowing down of but still considerable population increase at stage 3; (iv) high but fluctuating population levels at stage 4.
   (c) Outline how the demographic transition has varied in its timing and its intensity between developed and developing countries.
   (d) Indicate the relationships between stage in the demographic transition and the age structure of the population.
4. (a) Explain, with the help of examples, the importance of push and pull factors in migration.
   (b) Describe some of the human problems which are associated with (i) voluntary (ii) forced migration.
5. Refer to Fig. 14.9. Trace the map into your exercise book and read the details carefully. In the light of the information given, and ideas developed through the study of this chapter, draw arrows of varying thickness according to the key given, to show the likely importance of different migration routes along the lines marked (a) to (h). Briefly justify your choice of arrow in each case.
6. Refer to Plates 14.3 and 14.4, and outline the similarities and differences shown between the two Palestinian refugee settlements.

Plate 14.5 Refugees fleeing from Da Nang, Vietnam

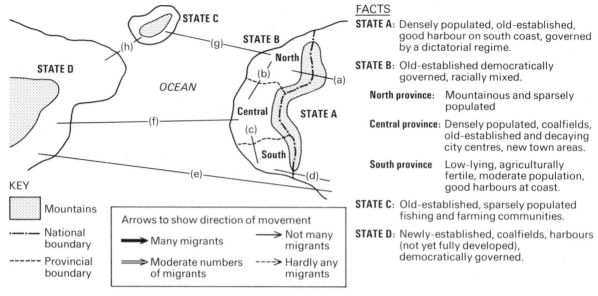

FACTS

STATE A: Densely populated, old-established, good harbour on south coast, governed by a dictatorial regime.

STATE B: Old-established democratically governed, racially mixed.

   North province: Mountainous and sparsely populated

   Central province: Densely populated, coalfields, old-established and decaying city centres, new town areas.

   South province Low-lying, agriculturally fertile, moderate population, good harbours at coast.

STATE C: Old-established, sparsely populated fishing and farming communities.

STATE D: Newly-established, coalfields, harbours (not yet fully developed), democratically governed.

KEY

Mountains

—·—·— National boundary

------ Provincial boundary

Arrows to show direction of movement

➡ Many migrants → Not many migrants

⇒ Moderate numbers of migrants ----→ Hardly any migrants

Fig. 14.9 Migration simulation

Fig. 14.10 World urban population as a percentage of the total, 1980

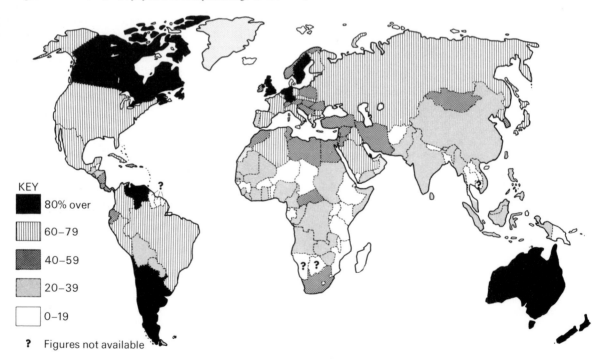

KEY

80% over

60–79

40–59

20–39

0–19

? Figures not available

The World's 'Million Cities'

Fig. 14.10 shows that the world's most *urbanised* areas, those with the largest percentage of the population in towns and cities are in the developed world, in countries such as the United Kingdom, West Germany, Sweden, Canada, Australia and New Zealand, and also in some of the less poor South American countries, namely Uruguay, Chile, Argentina and Venezuela. But developing countries have been catching up rapidly in the urbanisation process. Only 6% of the population of the developing world was living in towns of over 20 000 in 1920. This had grown to 15% in 1960 and over 20% in 1980.

One of the most striking features of urbanisation is not so much the growth of towns and cities, but of *large* towns and cities, many of which, as Fig. 14.11 indicates, now have over one million inhabitants. Some of the world's great capital cities are now of vast size. Mexico City has a population of about 12 million people, rivalling Tokyo as the world's largest city. Calcutta and Sao Paulo each have 7 million and Bombay and Cairo 6 million. If metropolitan areas as a whole are included, there are now more than twenty cities in the world with over 5 million people. As Fig. 14.11 shows, the largest proportion of 'million cities' are to be found in Western Europe, the USA, in Eastern Europe, India, China and Japan, and round the coastal fringes of Latin America.

The 'Rank-size' Rule

In some cases these 'million cities' dominate the life of the country. Thus Lima in Peru has a population of 3.3 million, and the next largest town has only 300 000. It has been suggested that in the ideal state the sizes of towns would be ranked in a proportionate relation, with no one or two cities dominant. Thus, assuming the largest city had a population of 600 000, the second largest would be half that size (300 000); the

Fig. 14.11   World cities of over one million population (late 1970s)

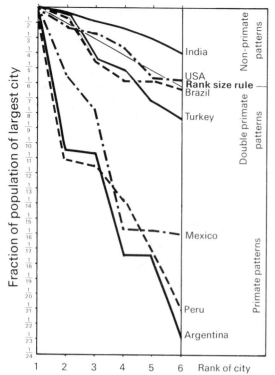

Fig. 14.12 Rank size of cities

Graph labels — y-axis: **Fraction of population of largest city** (values from $\frac{1}{2}$ down to $\frac{1}{24}$); x-axis: 1 2 3 4 5 6 **Rank of city**. Curves labelled: India, USA, Brazil, Turkey, Mexico, Peru, Argentina. Regions labelled: **Non-primate patterns**, **Rank size rule**, **Double primate patterns**, **Primate patterns**.

third largest one-third (200 000); the fourth largest one-quarter (150 000); the fifth largest one-fifth (120 000); and the sixth largest one-sixth (100 000). This gives a straight-line relation on a graph (Fig. 14.12).

This rarely happens in reality, although, as Fig. 14.12 suggests, India and the USA approach this pattern. India has nine 'million cities', four with over 3 million, and two with over 5 million. This type of pattern is known as *non-primate*. In the developing world in particular, *primate* patterns (one dominant city) are more common. Mexico, Peru and Argentina (Fig. 14.12) are examples.

An alternative pattern is the *double primate*, where two very large cities dominate. Examples include Brazil (Sao Paulo and Rio de Janeiro); Egypt (Cairo and Alexandria) and Turkey (Istanbul and Ankara). In a double primate pattern, the two largest cities are usually the capital and the main seaport or commercial centre. In the single primate pattern, the great city is usually also the capital and/or the major seaport. Primate patterns are of course also found in the developed world. Denmark, for example, has a primate pattern, Copenhagen dominating its economic life, while Spain is of double primate type, with Madrid and Barcelona its two major cities.

Problems of Urbanisation in Developing Countries: South America

Rapid urbanisation in general, and primate patterns in particular, cause great problems for developing countries. The immense influx of people from poor rural areas has led to three major groups of problems: economic, social and cultural.

(1) *Economic problems* are largely to do with the *employment* situation. A ladder of opportunity appears to beckon to the rural migrant, who on arrival in the city will seek out people known to him, probably because they came from the same village. These will not help him for long, and he quickly has to accept a casual job, say as a garden boy, in the catering trade, or as a labourer in the construction industry. A woman might be able to get domestic work or take in laundry. If unsuccessful, some might turn to trading or prostitution. If successful, a major aim is to set up a small business, such as making cheap furniture from packing cases, or as odd-job car repairers, such as those in Chimbote, Peru, on Plate 14.6. Success depends on hard work, thrift, and often patronage (personal links with influential people) and luck. If the migrant is successful, the family may save enough money to gain an education for its children. For the few, this might lead to apprenticeships and other qualifications. In the second generation this can mean jobs as skilled workers or salaried posts in the city's offices.

(2) *Social problems* are mainly to do with housing. Just as the employment market cannot cope with the flood of in-migrants, the housing is even less adequate to provide for a never-ending increase of people. *Shanty towns* have grown all round developing world cities to try to meet the problem. These are *uncontrolled* or *spontaneous* settlements in the first place built

Plate 14.6 Odd-job car repairers in Chimbote, Peru

up illegally by *squatters* on land they do not own. In 1959, 9% of Lima's population was in shanty towns or *barriadas*. This had grown to 36% in 1969, meaning that approximately one million people were living in the barriadas, often in homes made up from sacking and corrugated iron (Plate 14.7).

It must be stressed, however, that these barriadas are not necessarily permanent. Once built, the squatters resist the attempts of the local authority to turn them out. When they feel secure, and have saved a little money from employment, they seek to build more durable homes, of brick and concrete rather than cardboard, wood and corrugated iron. When this happens, the areas are known as *pueblos jovenes* (young towns), which are scattered round Lima (Fig. 14.13), often mixed in with the continuing barriadas. When the settlement is established, it may be upgraded by the local authority, who might supply water and other services. Plate 14.8 shows the Rimac valley between Callao and Lima, whose CBD can be seen in the background, where the process of converting squalid barriadas into a more permanent 'young town', with brick built walls, is well under way.

The change from the barriada to the 'pueblo joven' is therefore a sign of progress. Despite the appalling over-crowding, poor sanitation, and fire hazards, shanty towns are often seen by their inhabitants as 'slums of hope', in that there is the chance that the family lot will be improved, at least in the next generation. The size of the problem is so enormous, however, that probably this can only be true for a minority.

(3) *Cultural problems*. It is argued that access to the 'bright lights' of the city introduces the migrant to new sets of values. In the shop windows can be seen expensive consumer goods which he or she cannot afford, adding to the frustrations of urban life. It is also said that contacts with friends and relatives in the countryside are broken. The towns draw in young people from the rural areas who believe towns are the only place to be. It is difficult to get people to move the other way, and the rural areas find themselves short of able-bodied workers, doctors and teachers.

Advantages of Urbanisation

(1) As we have seen, although shanty towns are desperate places in which to live, they are seen by many inhabitants as places in which there is some opportunity for family advancement. No such prospect is seen for those remaining in rural areas.

(2) Urban development usually stimulates the economy of a country. It provides a market for agricultural produce and encourages the change-over from subsistence farming to commercial agriculture.

Plate 14.7 Barriadas, Lima

Fig. 14.13 Land-use zones of Lima

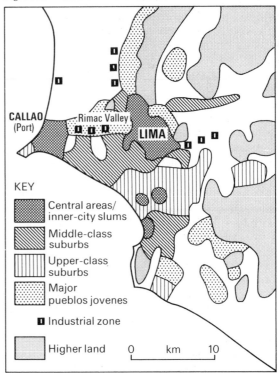

203

Plate 14.8 The conversion of barriadas to pueblos jovenes in Lima

(3) Although urban employment is often casual and poorly paid, it may bring in more income than could be obtained by staying in the countryside.

(4) Similarly, while shanty town services may be very poor, they are often better than those found in the villages. As we have seen, when shanty towns become legalised, the local authority often brings in some support services, such as roads and street stand-pipes supplying water.

(5) In some countries, the emergence of large cities has brought, it is argued, an element of national unity, breaking down the barriers between different traditional tribal groups.

Urbanisation and Apartheid: Soweto

Plate 14.9 is a photograph of migrant black workers arriving in Johannesburg. Fig. 14.14 shows the coun-

tries of origin of most of the workers: Malawi, Moçambique, Lesotho, Botswana, Zambia and Swaziland. A large proportion of the workers are males, who are forced by economic necessity to leave their families to earn money which they can send back home to support them. Many are destined for the gold mines of the Witwatersrand conurbation, of which Johannesburg is the largest urban centre (Fig. 14.15). This is the most important gold mining region in the world. South Africa produces about 70% of the non-communist world's gold.

The South African mining industry is dependent on black labour; it employs nine blacks for every one white, almost always in unskilled poorly paid jobs. There are about 400 000 black workers in gold mining, and four of the largest mines each employ over 15 000 blacks. Many of the migrant workers are single men who are housed in hostels. A typical hostel for unmarried black workers in a mine compound is shown in

Plate 14.9   Migrant workers arriving in Johannesburg

Plate 14.10. Notice that sleeping, cooking and clothes-drying quarters are all in the same room, with a coal stove in the centre, and lockers (which are not shown).

Most black workers are of course South African. They live in separate townships from the whites. The largest in the Johannesburg area is Soweto, containing over a million people (See Plate 14.12 and Fig. 14.15). Most of the housing consists of small one-storey four-roomed houses with white corrugated roofs. There are no bathrooms. Toilets are built in the yards behind the houses.

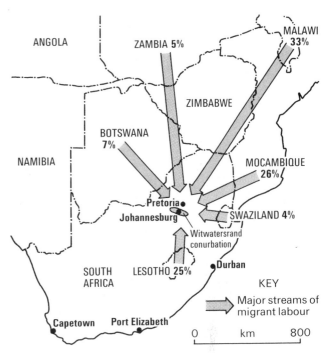

Fig. 14.14   Foreign migrant labour in South Africa

Of the South African population, 71% is black, 17% is white, 9% coloured (of mixed race) and about 3% Asian. Political power is in the hands of the white minority, made up of former British and Dutch (Afri-kaans-speaking) settlers. The average income per head of whites is approximately fourteen times that of

Plate 14.10   The inside of a South African mine compound hostel for unmarried blacks

Fig. 14.15   Witwatersrand conurbation

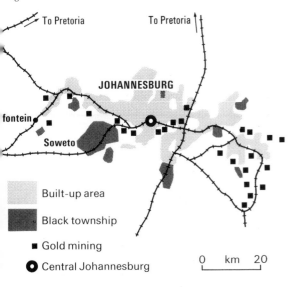

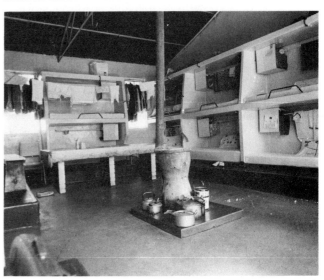

205

blacks so the whites have a very much higher standard of living. The white rulers have established a policy of separate development, or *apartheid*, for whites and non-whites. In rural areas the black population is increasingly being concentrated in small semi-independent *homelands* such as the Transkei (Plates 14.11 and 2.7*b*). These are set up by the South African government, usually in agriculturally poor areas. The Transkei was established in 1976, Bophutatswana in 1978, Venda in 1980 and Ciskei in 1981. In urban areas the blacks are forced into residentially segregated *townships* such as Soweto (Plate 14.12). From such townships many blacks commute to work in Johannesburg city centre. Plate 14.13 shows Randfontein station on one of the commuter lines of the Witwatersrand conurbation (Fig. 14.15). Note that non-whites have to travel on separate trains. Discrimination against non-whites is applied in a wide range of activities. As a result there is segregation in restaurants, schools and cultural and sporting activities. Job and education opportunities are very poor for blacks. Mixed marriages are forbidden, and whites do not work under blacks. There are strict pass laws for blacks, who have to carry identity booklets stamped with permission to work in a particular place.

Apartheid is also an economic system, based on cheap black labour, which enables South African goods to be sold at low cost to the European Community. Much of this cheap labour supply is migrant labour, also advantageous to the white factory owners in that workers can be brought in or sent home as circumstances dictate. As the migrant workers live in hostels this reduces the cost of building new residential areas to house them.

The South African policy of apartheid has been greatly criticised by other countries. What justification can be given for it? The case for apartheid is put here by a former South African Minister of Bantu affairs:

'Our policy is based on the facts... of the separateness and the diversity of the various Bantu [black] nations in South Africa as separate national entities set in separate courses to separate destinies. The Bantu in the white areas are here for the work we have to offer them and which they also need... .They are not here to anchor themselves... the Bantu has always been subject to restrictions, not because we regard him as an inferior being... [but because] we regard him as being present in another man's country.... In the final instance our work is directed at eventual geographical partition.'

Plate 14.11 Rural landscape in the Transkei 'homeland'

Plate 14.12 The South African township of Soweto

Plate 14.13 Apartheid and the commuter: Randfontein station, Witwatersrand

But apartheid creates tremendous problems in South Africa. It hinders rural development in that wives and old people in black communities are left to work the land. The system breaks up black family life and creates problems such as excessive drinking in the all male hostels in the city. It also prevents blacks from acquiring skills. It has built up bitter resentment among the non-white population, and caused political and social unrest, often resulting in violence. It needs sustaining by force. Opponents of apartheid argue strongly that apartheid corrupts the lives of both white and non-white groups, in different ways.

'The migrant labour system is based upon the premise that a human being can be broken into two parts: a "labour unit" working in town, separated from the other part, a man, with parents and wife and children, with hopes and aspirations.'

Exercises

| | Population (millions) | | | | | |
	1940	%	1960	%	1976	%
Urban	12.9	31.2	32.0	45.1	78.2	63.5
Rural	28.3	68.8	39.0	54.9	44.9	36.5
Total	41.2	100	71.0	100	123.1	100

6. Study the table above, which gives data on population change in Brazil:
   (a) Describe the changes occurring between 1940 and 1975 in respect of (i) total, (ii) the balance of urban and rural, population.
   (b) What have been the main causes of the change in rural and urban population in countries such as Brazil?

7. (a) What do you understand by the term urbanisation?
   (b) Describe, with reference to examples, different patterns of urbanisation in developing countries.
   (c) Outline the advantages and disadvantages to developing countries of primate and non-primate patterns of urbanisation.

8. Refer to Fig. 14.10.
   (a) Describe the patterns of urbanisation shown in (i) countries of the developed world (ii) countries of the developing world.
   (b) Choose a country from each of the above, and outline the problems and opportunities provided by rapid urbanisation.

9. (a) With reference to South America, outline the sequence of stages by which shanty towns and then 'young towns' (pueblos jovenes) develop.
   (b) Examine the extent to which the shanty towns can be seen on the one hand as 'slums of despair', and on the other as 'slums of hope'.

10. Refer to Plates 2.7b, 14.11 and 14.12. Describe the different landscapes and mention the problems that are likely to be experienced in living in them.

Fig. 15.1 Gross national product per head of population, 1979

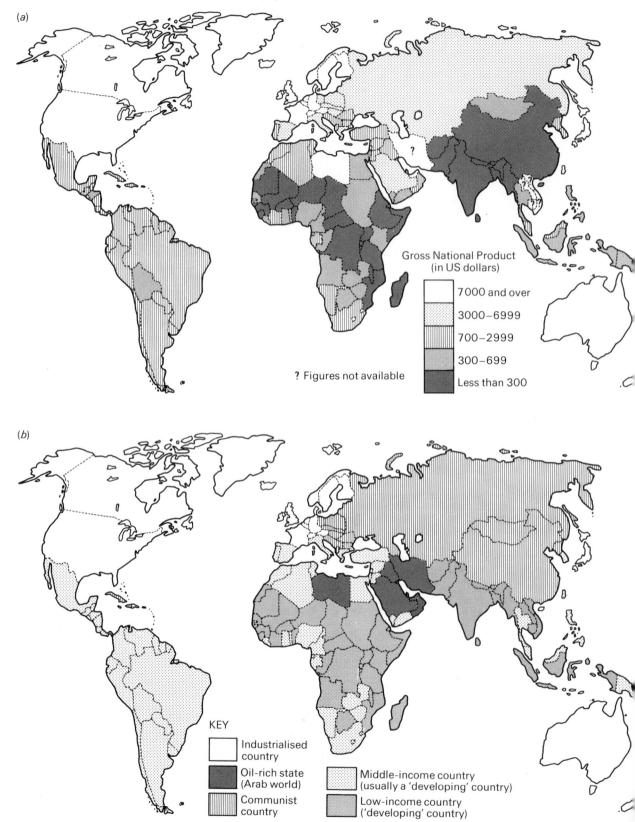

(a)

Gross National Product
(in US dollars)

7000 and over

3000–6999

700–2999

300–699

Less than 300

? Figures not available

(b)

KEY

Industrialised
country

Oil-rich state
(Arab world)

Communist
country

Middle-income country
(usually a 'developing' country)

Low-income country
('developing' country)

15 World Poverty

WHAT IS A DEVELOPING COUNTRY?

Broadly speaking, the world's countries are divided into rich and poor. The former make up the industrialised countries of the *developed world*, and are mostly in the temperate latitudes of the northern and, in the case of Australia and New Zealand, southern hemispheres; while the latter consist mainly of agriculture-based economies of the *developing world*, and are mostly in tropical latitudes. There is, however, no sharp break between the two. For example, the better off (or middle-income) countries of the developing world merge with the less well off countries of the developed world (Fig.15.1). In addition, some very rich people live in developing countries, where the gap between rich and poor may be much greater than in developed countries. Similarly, developed countries contain many poor people. The terms 'rich' and 'poor' are therefore rough averages describing countries.

A *developing country* is one with the following characteristics.

(1) Most of the people earn a living by primary production, chiefly agriculture. The staple foods are provided by subsistence farming which usually yields an inadequate and poorly balanced diet.

(2) Most of the people are extremely poor and cannot afford the facilities which the inhabitants of the developed world regard as basic necessities: decent housing and sanitation, efficient medical services and educational provision.

(3) Because of the lack of such facilities, disease and illiteracy are normal. Infantile mortality rates are high.

(4) Even so, high birth rates maintain rapid rates of population increase. A large percentage of the population is below fifteen years of age, which leads to strains on educational facilities.

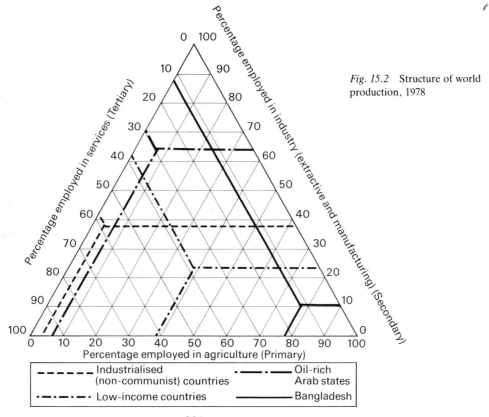

Fig. 15.2 Structure of world production, 1978

209

THE ECONOMIC BASE

Economic activities can be divided into *primary* (e.g. agriculture and fishing), *secondary* (e.g. manufacturing industry) and *tertiary* (e.g. services). The wealth generated by manufacturing industry and services is much greater than that which can be gained from concentration on primary products. Countries with the highest percentages employed in primary activities are generally the poorest countries. These are mostly in the developing world. As the triangular graph (Fig. 15.2) indicates, low-income countries on average have nearly 40% of the population engaged in agriculture, as against less than 5% in industrialised non-communist countries. In Bangladesh, almost 80% of the people are employed in primary production, and little over 10% in each of manufacturing and services. In some cases, otherwise barren countries have become rich very quickly as the result of finds of energy or mineral resources. The oil-rich Arab states, for example, have about the same percentage as industrialised countries in primary production, over 60% in industry (much of it extractive industry and processing of the material extracted, in this case oil), and 30% in services.

MEASURING WORLD POVERTY

Two ways of measuring world poverty are suggested here, the gross national product, and the physical quality of life index.

Gross National Product (GNP)

The GNP refers to the income of a country: the total value of goods and services produced by the economy over a period of time, usually one year. It is normally measured per head of population (per capita) in US dollars($).

(1) *Countries with a low GNP* (say less than $700 per capita) (Fig. 15.1), are confined to the developing world. They are mostly in Africa and south and South-east Asia. They include all the Sahel countries of Africa (see Chapter 6); the Indian sub-continent and all South-east Asian countries apart from Singapore and Malaysia.

Low-income countries are often those with population numbers too great for home agriculture to feed adequately. The situation is in many cases made worse by natural and human-made hazards. In East Africa, for example, the Sahel drought and warfare have caused famine and a major refugee problem in Somalia. Similarly, in Vietnam and Kampuchea, long

periods of war have destroyed harvests and agricultural land, which has ruined the economy and resulted in a low GNP. Where industry exists it is often on a small scale, producing a local livelihood but not generating enough wealth to allow the country to pay for all the imports it needs, for example.

(2) *Middle-income countries of the developing world* (with per capita GNPs of over $700) (Fig. 15.1), are mainly in Latin America, North Africa and the Middle East, and a few states of the western side of Africa. These also have quite considerable numbers in primary production, though generally less than 50%, but many have the advantage of additional resources, in mineral wealth and/or plantation agriculture. Nigeria, Malaysia and Venezuela are cases in point.

(3) *Countries with a high GNP* (say $3000 per capita and over), are in four main groups: the western or 'occidental' capitalist world, of Western Europe, the USA and Canada, and Australia and New Zealand; certain communist countries, in Eastern Europe and also the USSR; some oil-rich Arab states, including Libya, Saudi Arabia and Kuwait; Japan and, to a lesser extent, Hong Kong and Singapore, in the oriental world.

These countries have usually a small percentage of population engaged in primary production, while manufacturing is increasingly productive and capital intensive. Here too are highly developed tertiary activities, which foster trade and extend employment opportunities. The balance of advantages differs between the groups. The USA and Canada are self-supporting in primary products, and industrially and commercially advanced, while Japan, the most technologically advanced of all in manufacturing, has to import energy supplies, raw materials and food. The rich Arab states depend on their oil supplies for their high GNPs.

The Physical Quality of Life Index (PQLI)
(Fig. 15.3)

World GNPs range between $80 per capita in Bhutan and $17 100 in Kuwait. The discrepancy shown, however, is a distorted one, for most Bhutanese are subsistence farmers and their products do not enter the market economy, which is all that GNP measures. It does not assess the actual well-being of people. One way of doing this is to combine information on rates of life expectancy, infantile mortality and literacy. On these combined figures countries can be rated from best (100) to worst (0). Thus 100% illiteracy would rate as 0. The highest infantile mortality rate in the world (237 per thousand in 1978 in Afghanistan) would rate as 0. The lowest life expectancy (40 in 1979 in Ethiopia) would also rate 0. In contrast, the highest (76 in 1979 in Hong Kong, Japan and Sweden) would rate 100. Each of the measures would then be scaled between 0 and 100 according to the country's ranking. When the average of the three is worked out 77 is regarded as a satisfactory overall level.

As Fig. 15.3 indicates, when compared with Fig. 15.1, many countries come out similarly on both measures. The contrasts between rich and poor worlds remain. But there are some interesting differences. For example, Saudi Arabia, with a high GNP, had a PQLI of only 29, while Iran, although it had nine times the GNP per capita of India, had the same PQLI index (40). By contrast, Costa Rica, with a GNP only in the middle-income group, had a PQLI of 85.

The PQLI therefore exposes inequalities that the GNP does not. One of these is the fact that some of the oil-rich states (Kuwait is an exception) have not translated their great wealth into improved medical and educational facilities, especially for women. As we shall see, infantile mortality rates are surprisingly high and literacy rates surprisingly low in these countries. On the other hand Costa Rica, although not a rich country, has encouraged development in these fields.

HEALTH

Problems of poverty are usually linked with those of health. Poverty is associated with poor health and disease, and wealth with good health. Health is one of the major indices of the physical quality of life. There are a number of ways of measuring levels of health.

Life expectancy

This has improved in all countries since 1900. At that time, life expectancy in the developed countries averaged about 50 years, and in the developing about 23 years. In 1970, life expectancy in developed countries had reached over 70 years, and in developing over 50 years. In 1979, the figures were 57 years for low-income developing countries; 61 for middle-income; 72 for communist European states and the USSR; and 74 for the capitalist developed world. The lowest figures were for the African states south of the Sahara, averaging about 47 years, and for south Asia about 49 years.

Fig. 15.3 World physical quality of life map

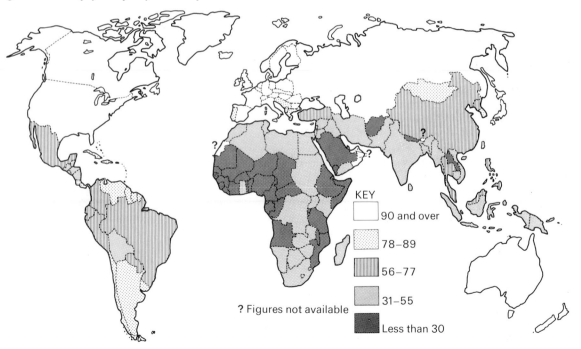

KEY

| | 90 and over |
| 78–89 |
| 56–77 |
| 31–55 |

? Figures not available

Less than 30

211

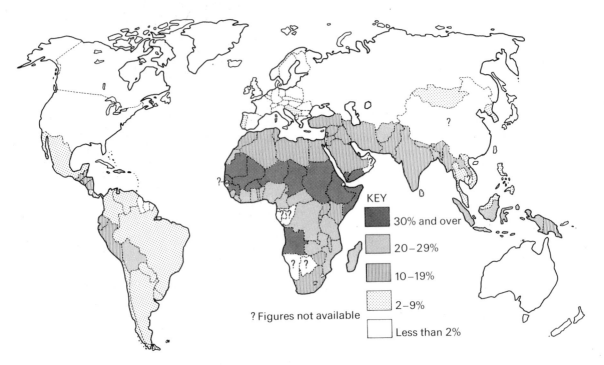

Fig. 15.4 World infant (aged 1–4) mortality rate, 1979

KEY

30% and over

20–29%

10–19%

2–9%

Less than 2%

? Figures not available

HIGH INFANTILE MORTALITY

One of the reasons for low life expectancy arises out of the frighteningly high infant mortality statistics for many developing countries (Fig. 15.4). The Yemen states and African countries south of the Sahara, for example, have rates of over 30% and in some cases over 40%, meaning that three or four children out of ten die in infancy. One reason for this is the lack of medical care. In the Sahel countries there is usually only one physician for over 50 000 people, as against one for under 700 in most European countries. Another reason for this high mortality is the menial position of women, especially in many Arab states. In the Sudan, for example, in the late 1970s only 10% of deliveries were supervised by qualified doctors, whereas in Sri Lanka most deliveries are supervised and infant mortality is only about 5%.

HIGH LIFE EXPECTANCY

One of the striking features since the 1960s has been how developing countries are catching up on developed countries in life expectancy. A number of middle-income developing countries now have life expectancies averaging over 70 years. High life expect-

ancy poses economic and social problems for all countries, but especially for poorer ones. Larger numbers of old people require expensive services and, if they are not looked after by families, pensions. An aging work-force tends to be less active and efficient. The decline in the proportion of young people leads to less demand for schools and teachers. Younger people have to produce more to provide services for the old. Increasing life expectancy also leads to an increased tendency to the diseases of aging, such as cancer and heart disease (Table 15.1).

Table 15.1 Causes of death in developed and developing countries

Causes	Percentage of deaths	
	Developed country	Developing country
Infectious/parasitic diseases	10.8	43.7
Cancer	15.2	3.7
Heart	32.2	14.8
Others	41.8	37.8
Total	100	100

Diet

An adequate diet is a vital component of good health. The poverty of developing countries leads to inadequate diets which in turn cause *malnutrition*. The diets are frequently deficient in *calories*. Each person needs about 2450 calories per day to maintain good health. The average intake in developing countries is about 2000, as against 3600 in the developed world. The diets are also deficient in *proteins*. The intake of proteins varies from an average of 50 grams (g) per person per day in developing to 110 g in developed countries. The intake of *animal protein* is even more variable: from 76 g per person per day in developed to only 8 g in some developing countries.

The typical diet in developing countries is very *monotonous*, dependent on a small number of *staple foods*, which include *grains* such as rice, wheat, millet, maize; *tropical roots* such as manioc and cassava; *vegetables* such as beans; and in some cases *fruits* such as bananas. Such monotonous diets are poorly balanced, and lead to protein and vitamin deficiencies. Among the dietary deficiency diseases are *kwashiorkor* (protein deficiency), and *marasmus* (calorie deficiency). Plate 15.1 shows a baby in a Dacca (Bangladesh) nutrition unit suffering from severe marasmus. Both diseases reduce resistance to infection and both directly and indirectly result in high infantile mortality. They also cause physical and mental retardation among those who survive.

WAYS OF IMPROVING DIETS

(1) In some cases food supplies become so inadequate that *famines* result. These are caused by natural hazards such as drought and tropical cyclones, or human activities such as war, and they lead to people crowding into refugee camps. In these circumstances the only solution is to harness massive *international aid*, from official and voluntary organisations (see page 218).

(2) In the medium term, an important means of improving diet is through *school feeding*. Plate 15.2 shows children in Thailand having their normal diet of rice and vegetables supplemented by high-protein supplements, made through the processing of local vegetables, such as soya beans. This provides one nourishing meal a day.

(3) In the long term, an important policy must be to reduce the number of mouths to feed, through *promoting family planning*.

(4) Equally important is *improving the quantity, quality and variety of foods* produced. Increased quantity

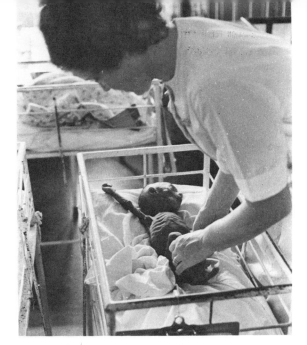

Plate 15.1 A baby suffering from marasmus, in a Dacca nutrition unit

Plate 15.2 Children's diet enrichment, Thailand

can be achieved by extending farming areas and/or increasing yields through the application of irrigation water and fertilisers. Improved yields can also arise through the use of insecticides, eradicating pests such as, for example, the swarms of locusts which on occasions devastate large areas of cropland in countries such as Ethiopia (Plate 15.3). Improved quality can be gained by using better varieties of seed, which may also be linked with better yields. Variety can be enhanced by the education of village communities in the

213

need to produce a dietary balance from the cropland. For example, proteins can be obtained from certain vegetable crops such as soya beans.

Infectious Diseases

The low life expectancies of low-income developing countries are largely the result of diseases which have in many cases been eliminated in developed countries (Table 15.1). The most widespread are *intestinal and diarrhoeal diseases*, such as dysentery and cholera, transmitted by human faeces, inadequate sanitation and polluted water supplies. Plate 15.4 shows boys in a Sahel country using water for washing and drinking, regardless of whether it is clean or polluted. *Airborne diseases*, such as influenza, smallpox and measles, are spread by inhaling germs from infected persons. *Vector-borne diseases*, such as malaria, sleeping sickness and river blindness, are carried by insects. Some are *endemic* (normally present) in particular areas, for example river blindness (Plate 15.5) in the Niger basin in West Africa.

The Economic Costs of Poor Health

Poor health reduces capacity for work, which lowers productivity and incomes. Similarly, children cannot benefit from their education if they come to school half-starved. Additionally, a large expense is involved in treating vast numbers of sick and undernourished people.

Plate 15.3   Swarm of locusts, Ethiopia

Plate 15.4   Children drinking and washing in a West African stream

Plate 15.5   Adults suffering from river blindness in the Sahel

Improvements

In the early 1980s, the United Nations established an 'International Water Decade', indicating the importance of *improved water supplies* in promoting world health. The need is to separate supplies used for drinking from those used for washing and for sewage disposal. Plate 15.6 shows women of the Sahel who have

214

Plate 15.6 Women in the Sahel carrying water from the nearest river

Plate 15.7 Making a new concrete well in the Sahel

walked several kilometres to the nearest river to collect the water they need. Much nearer and safer supplies could be obtained by digging wells into underlying water-bearing strata, and lining them with concrete as shown on Plate 15.7, again in a Sahel country. Also helpful are the cheap forms of portable latrines designed for rural use. In some cases, after suitable treatment, the sewage is accumulated in sludge troughs, and can then be applied on the fields as a natural fertiliser.

Improved vaccines are now having much success in lowering the incidence of diseases such as smallpox, leprosy and malaria. Unfortunately, disease-resistant strains in insects and viruses are developing, and the World Health Organisation is finding it very difficult to eradicate many diseases.

Primary health care is another important means of improving health, especially in rural areas. As it is impractical to supply fully trained doctors in remote districts, increasing use is being made of *health promoters*, who are trained in the basic skills of diagnosing straightforward illnesses, and prescribing the right medicines. Plates 15.8 and 15.9 show Señora Laura, a health promoter in the Chimborazo area of Ecuador, crossing difficult country on foot to help a peasant mother with a sick child on a remote farm. Such primary health care can only be completely successful if it is connected to a full health system, whereby health promoters can refer more seriously ill patients to clinics and hospitals in the towns.

Plate 15.9 A health promoter giving help on a remote Ecuador farm

Plate 15.8 A health promoter going on her rounds in Ecuador

EDUCATION

Provision and Uptake

As we have seen, educational opportunity is an important element in the physical quality of life index. One of the problems of rapid population growth is the large number of juveniles which results. Almost all of Africa, South and South-east Asia, and much of Latin America have over 50% of the population aged eighteen years and less. This puts immense strains on educational resources.

Education is something of a luxury for many children of the developing world. While literacy rates approach 100% in most developed countries, they are well under 50% in most low-income developing countries. Fig. 15.5 indicates how the position varies between different parts of the developing world in different sectors of education: primary, secondary and higher (tertiary) education. The positive feature is that in all cases there has been some improvement in the 1960–75 period, even in the most backward area, Africa south of the Sahara. But even in the best cases, in Latin America (male and female), and the Middle East and North Africa (male only), more than 20% of the population is still not enrolled at primary school. In Africa south of the Sahara, only 50% of the male population was enrolled at primary level.

The position at secondary level is much worse. Only Latin America, North Africa and the Middle East averaged over 50% enrolment among males, and among females only Latin America. The higher-education sector is even less provided for, with only Latin America touching 20% enrolment (for males) in 1975. The higher the level of education, the more expensive it is to provide, beyond the means of low-income developing countries.

The problems are a result on the one hand of the expense of providing educational facilities, and on the other the attitudes of parents towards provision. In many countries this varies between boys and girls. Note on Fig. 15.5 the disadvantaged position of girls. Apart from primary provision in Latin America, girls in all areas and at all educational levels are shown to have poorer educational opportunities than boys.

Quality of Provision

Apart from the amount of provision made, there is also the problem of the quality of provision. This is often very primitive. Plate 15.10 shows a bush school in Uganda, with an earth floor, walls made of little more than twigs, and supporting a thatched roof. The

Fig. 15.5 School enrolment ratios in the developing regions of the world, 1960–75

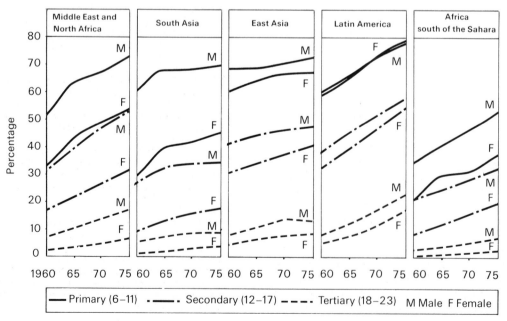

216

Plate 15.10   A bush school in Uganda

Plate 15.11   A Nigerian school classroom

provision of Plate 15.11, in Nigeria, is more permanent, but the facilities are still meagre, with overcrowded classrooms separated by a thin partition.

Education, health, poverty and general economic development are closely connected. Thus lack of dietary knowledge is caused in part by poverty and in turn leads to malnutrition and low productivity. Similarly, lack of technical knowledge is associated with backward agriculture, low yields, again leading to inadequate feeding. Lack of knowledge of birth control techniques means high birth rates and in turn continuing poverty and health problems.

Problems and Improvements

(1) Cost of provision of education is the main problem since some sort of building is usually needed, even in tropical climates where classes can often be held out of doors with very little equipment. In addition, teachers and administrators have to be paid, and sometimes school transport laid on.

(2) Many countries have widely scattered population, making it difficult to locate schools within travelling distance of rural children. A possible solution is to establish correspondence courses to serve remote areas. Another is to provide boarding establishments.

(3) It is argued that the better off who seek education at secondary and tertiary level should be made to pay for it, with a scholarship system provided to allow poor but able children to continue at school. This would leave more money to ensure universal provision at primary level.

(4) Some also argue that the best investment for the future for any country is to improve the education of girls which, as Fig. 15.5 indicated, is mostly way behind that of boys. It is pointed out that where women have been well educated, marriage takes place later;

this and increased knowledge of family planning reduces birth rates; in consequence, families are smaller and fewer children die in infancy; family well-being is improved by knowledge of how to provide more nutritious food; while the better educational qualifications mean a greater capacity to add to the family income. There are, however, strong prejudices against the education of girls, especially beyond primary level, in many countries.

Exercises

1. Refer to Fig. 15.1a.
   (a) Describe and explain the distribution of countries with a GNP of (i) less than $700 (ii) $3000 or more per annum.
   (b) Why is GNP not an entirely satisfactory index of poverty?
   (c) Outline the similarities and differences in the distributions in Fig. 15.1a and the physical quality of life map (Fig. 15.3).
2. Refer to Fig. 15.4.
   (a) Describe the distribution of countries with infantile mortality rates of (i) 30% and over; (ii) 10–29%; (iii) less than 10%.
   (b) Explain the reasons for the differences shown.
   (c) Outline the problems caused by (i) high infant mortality; (ii) high life expectancy.
3. (a) What are the essentials of a healthy diet?
   (b) What are the principle causes of disease in low-income countries of the developing world?
   (c) Discuss three ways in which overseas aid can help to combat disease.
4. Refer to Fig. 15.5.
   (a) Describe how educational provision varies in the different parts of the world shown in respect of (i) age (ii) sex.
   (b) What are the arguments which would suggest that making equally good provision for girls as boys is more important for a developing country, than increasing the chances of students going on to a free higher education?

North – South: the Brandt Report

In 1980, the Brandt Report, *North – South: a Programme for survival* was published. Its message was that the survival of humankind will depend on improved cooperation between the countries of 'the North': the developed world; and 'the South': the developing world. The main suggestions of the report include the following:

(1) there must be an emergency programme to help the world's low-income developing countries, including assistance with water and soil management, health care and industrial development;

(2) there must be an end to mass hunger and malnutrition, through help with agricultural research, irrigation, fertilisers and the development of fisheries;

(3) there should be more international support for family planning programmes;

(4) the funds and skills being poured into arms development should be channelled into peaceful uses;

(5) world trade should be geared to encouraging the developing world to have a greater part in the processing, distribution and marketing of their own commodities, to increase income;

(6) a shift away from over-dependence on non-renewable energy resources such as oil is required;

(7) international regulations are needed for the sharing of technology and control over the activities of multi-national corporations;

(8) the flow of overseas aid should be enlarged, with an international 'income tax' to spread wealth from rich to poor countries;

(9) the United Nations system needs strengthening;

(10) more attention needs to be paid to educating the public and especially the young about the importance of international cooperation.

The Positive Side: International Aid

What the Brandt Report is advocating is a large-scale extension of developments already taking place, through help given to developing countries by official and voluntary organisations.

Among the official international organisations are the United Nations *Food and Agricultural Organisation* (FAO, with its headquarters in Rome); the *World Bank* (headquarters in Washington and Paris); the *United Nations Educational, Scientific and Cultural Organisation* (UNESCO, headquarters in Paris); the *United Nations Children's Fund* (UNICEF, headquarters in New York); and the *World Health Organisation* (WHO, whose Geneva headquarters is shown on Plate 15.12).

Vast numbers of voluntary organisations exist to promote overseas aid. These include, in the United Kingdom:

Centre for World Development Education, which aims to increase knowledge of world development and developing countries;

Christian Aid, the official development and relief agency of the British Council of Churches;

Oxfam, which raises large funds for relief and development projects;

Population Concern, which concentrates on raising funds for family planning and to spread demographic information;

Save the Children Fund, which raises relief and development funds for the welfare of children;

Voluntary Service Overseas, which recruits volunteers to work on projects for the alleviation of poverty in the developing world;

War on Want, which spreads information on the causes of poverty and the role of aid and development, and supports district projects.

In times of emergency, such as the famines in recent years in Somalia, these organisations join together in sending aid. Apart from these national organisations, there are of course many local ones.

Plate 15.12 The World Health Organisation headquarters in Geneva

The Negative Side: Unequal Terms of Trade

The countries of 'the North' rely on those of 'the South' for a wide range of foodstuffs and raw materials, such as coffee, cocoa, tea, bananas, jute, rubber and tropical hardwoods. Some of the countries of 'the South' are heavily reliant on one or two items in their export trade. Copper, for example, makes up over 90% of Zambia's exports, and sugar over 90% of those of Mauritius. It is very risky for any country to rely on one product for its foreign income. In the case of agricultural products, for example, bad weather or disease can reduce output causing the loss of vital export earnings.

In addition, the prices of primary products tend to fluctuate widely. For example, by selling 10 lbs of tea in 1970 Sri Lanka could buy 2.6 bushels of wheat. In 1974, it took the sale of 13.5 lbs of tea to buy that amount of wheat. Tea prices remained fairly constant from 1958 to 1974, but this meant a fall in the *real* price, as the costs of other commodities rose. Similarly, sugar prices shot up to over $1000 per tonne in 1974, but were down to less than $200 per tonne in 1976 and 1977. These variations are particularly damaging to countries relying on one or two exports.

Another serious blow has been the increase in the cost of oil since 1973 (see Chapter 5). It was $2.6 a barrel in that year, and had risen to $13.6 in 1978, $20 in 1979, and $34 by the end of 1980. The rise has had a particularly bad effect on the low-income developing countries which need to import oil. In the early 1950s, for example, less than 10% of India's import bill was for petroleum and petroleum products. By 1975 this had risen to a crippling 26%.

Another disadvantage to developing countries is that the trading linkages date back to colonial times. In India, for example, the British set up tea plantations in such areas as Assam (Plate 15.13), based on cheap local labour. Tea remains one of the cheapest drinks we have. We can make it for less than 1 p per cup. But workers on the Assam tea plantations earn only about £13 per month. The development of plantations in such areas has had the advantages of providing employment, possibly better wages than the local average, and also overseas earnings for the country concerned. But it has also reduced the amount of land available for producing food crops.

Plate 15.13 An Assam tea garden in 1880

Like other world trades, that of tea is controlled by *multi-national corporations*. These are enormously powerful. The Mitsubishi corporation, based in Japan, has an annual revenue 1½ times greater than the combined GNPs of the thirty-one least developed countries of the world. These corporations use extremely sophisticated computerised marketing procedures, and work the world's commodity markets to their own advantage. Their purpose is to maximise profits, and not to help the producers, who are in a sense their opponents. In deciding prices, therefore, the buyers usually hold the stronger hand, and the developing countries often receive less than they should, and often less than they need, for their produce. Only the oil-producing countries, which joined together to form OPEC (Oil Producing and Exporting Countries) in 1973, have overcome the dominance of multi-national corporations. A rapid increase in the price of oil resulted.

BANGLADESH: A STUDY IN MULTIPLE DEPRIVATION

As we have seen, the developing world can be divided into middle-income and low-income countries. Many of the latter are desperately poor, suffering from multiple deprivation. One such country is Bangladesh, whose GNP is $90 per capita. Only Bhutan is lower than this in the world rankings. Bangladesh became independent in 1971, before which it was East Pakistan. Its population in 1980 was 89 million, and the population density 588/km^2. Over 82% of its population is engaged in primary production. Its short history has been marked by never-ending food shortages and at times by famine, with starving children dying in their thousands. The country has suffered both natural and human-made hazards.

Natural Hazards

FLOODS

The Ganges, Brahmaputra and Meghna rivers meet to form a huge delta at the head of the Bay of Bengal (Fig. 15.6). After the monsoon rains, these rivers flood in late summer and autumn. Plate 15.14 shows flood scenes in the capital city, Dacca, which lies on

Fig. 15.6 Bangladesh

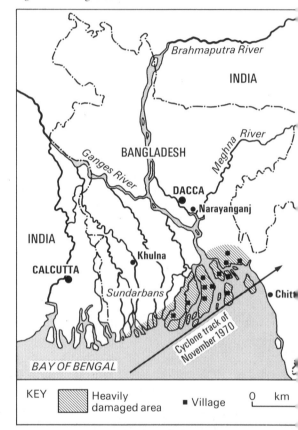

Plate 15.14 A flooded street in Dacca, 1974

one of the distributaries of the delta (Fig. 15.6). The floods are vital to the country's agriculture, as they lay down silts which constantly renew soil fertility and allow as many as three crops of rice per year to be grown. Agriculture has therefore to adapt itself to the 'amphibious environment' of the delta. In some years, however, as in 1971, when over one-third of the country was under water, the floods are particularly serious and cause great damage, loss of life, and economic expense.

CYCLONES

As we saw in Fig. 9.2, the Bay of Bengal lies in one of the major zones of tropical storm activity, and the main direction of these storms is towards the low-lying delta region of Bangladesh. In November 1970, when the country was still East Pakistan, one of the worst natural disasters of the twentieth century struck. Violent winds hit the Sundarbans area, an environment of forests, swamps and *levées* and rice fields. Roads, railways and bridges were destroyed and villages, such as that on Plate 15.15, torn apart. Even worse was the storm surge or tidal wave which followed, up to 9 m high, which drowned vast numbers of people. In all,

500 000 people lost their lives and 3.3 million were affected in the area shaded on Fig. 15.6. The economic cost for such a poor country was appalling.

Human Hazards

WAR

Worse was to follow. At about the same time, civil war against West Pakistan broke out. A military government had exercised brutal control over the East Pakistanis, pressing for independence. When West Pakistani troops came in, millions of East Pakistani refugees fled into neighbouring parts of India. India, with serious problems of its own, was determined not to accept these refugees. It went to war against West Pakistan, defeated its forces, and occupied Dacca. The Indians recognised an independent Bangladesh. Nine months of war had devastated the country, with bridges and ferries destroyed, and ports mined. Ten million refugees trecked back into Bangladesh, and 30 million displaced persons needed rehousing. Disease was brought back by the refugees, who had been crowded together in insanitary surroundings, and this and famine increased the death toll.

Plate 15.15 Cyclone damage in a village on the Ganges delta, 1970

Plate 15.16   A boy carrying jute, Bangladesh

ECONOMIC HAZARDS

As is the case with other low-income countries, Bangladesh depends on one cash crop, jute (Plate 15.16), and one subsistence crop, rice. Jute production has been seriously affected by political events. When Pakistan and India were separated in 1947, the main jute factories were in the Calcutta area of India (Fig. 15.6), while the main jute-growing areas were in East Pakistan. India then increased its jute growing, while jute manufacturing was expanded in the Dacca – Narayanganj area of East Pakistan (Fig. 15.6). Thus East Pakistan, later Bangladesh, continued to rely too much on one product (Table 15.2). Jute and jute products now make up over 90% of the volume of exports and two-thirds of export earnings.

Another problem is that Bangladesh would prefer to

Plate 15.17   Domestic manufacture of jute matting, Bangladesh

Table 15.2   Bangladesh trade: Import and exports, 1980

Imports	$million	Exports	$million
Capital goods	462	Jute goods	294
Other raw materials	360	Raw jute	169
Food grains (esp. wheat)	236	Leather	57
Other consumer goods	160	Fish	50
Fertiliser	151	Tea	39
Crude petroleum	148	Others	62
Cotton	100	Total	671
Others	243		
Total	1860		

export more jute products and less raw jute. This is because jute products would bring in extra earnings and provide jobs at home. Plate 15.17 shows the manufacture of jute matting in a small-scale domestic concern, so typical of industry of Bangladesh. However, when jute products are sent to such areas as the EEC, they have to face higher tariffs than raw jute, which makes them less economic to export. In addition, synthetic substitutes, for carpet backing, for example, have reduced the demand for jute.

As Table 15.2 shows, the money Bangladesh earns by its exports does not nearly meet the bill for imports. There is a negative balance of $1189 million. The difference between earnings and expenditure is met by foreign aid, which totalled $1600 million in 1979.

DISEASE AND ILLITERACY

Bangladesh is one of the four countries in the world still affected by smallpox. Malaria, intestinal diseases and malnutrition are widespread. The life expectancy is 49 years for men and 47 for women. Only half the population had access to safe water in 1975 while the daily calorie intake per capita is only 90% of what is required. The adult literacy rate in 1976 was 26%, ranging from over 30% for males to less than 20% for females; and from over 40% in urban areas to less than 25% in rural areas.

Table 15.3   Aid from World Bank to Bangladesh 1980/1

Purpose of aid	Amount ($million)
(1) Agricultural credit	40
(2) Irrigation and drainage	18
(3) Development finance	50
(4) Energy	85
(5) Industry	35
(6) Transportation	25
(7) Others	81
Total	334

Aid

Bangladesh is therefore high on the list of 'suitable cases for treatment' by international aid organisations. Table 15.3 shows the aid given by the World Bank in 1980/1. The items on the table can be summarised as follows:

(1) *agricultural credit* for installing tube wells, grain storage facilities, and the like, to improve agricultural incomes;

(2) *irrigation and drainage grant*, to increase agricultural acreage and yields, and improve domestic water supply;

(3) *development finance*, to assist government investment in export and import substitution industries (saving money on imports);

(4) *energy grant*, to promote development of the country's natural gas supplies and reduce dependence on imported oil;

(5) *industry grant*, to improve productivity and raise the level of employment in small-scale cottage industries, e.g. handicrafts;

(6) *transportation grant*, particularly to improve harbour facilities at the main port, Chittagong (Fig. 15.6);

(7) *others*, which include grants for foreign exchange for buying imports, providing technical assistance for development projects, and the like.

Exercises

6. Refer to Table 15.2.

    (*a*) Describe the main features of the import and export trade of Bangladesh.

    (*b*) Why does the country need to import (i) capital goods (ii) food grains, cotton and fertilisers; (iii) crude petroleum?

    (*c*) What are the problems associated with the nature of the export trade?

    (*d*) In what ways are these problems typical of the trade of developing countries, and why is this so?

7. Refer to Tables 15.4 and 15.5.

    (*a*) What do Table 15.4 (*a*) and (*b*) tell you about the pattern of provision of overseas aid from the developed world?

    (*b*) What do Table 15.5 (*a*) and (*b*) tell you about the distribution of the recipients and the types of projects supported by such organisations as the World Bank?

    (*c*) Choose two types of aid shown on Table 15.5 (*b*) and, with reference to one country or area, show how this aid has been used and say what the likely benefit it will be.

8. Refer to Plate 15.13.

    (*a*) Name three different types of people represented.

    (*b*) Discuss the possible relationships between these groups, economically and socially.

9. Discuss the evidence provided by Plates 15.1, 15.14, 15.15 and by information in the text which suggests that Bangladesh is a country suffering from multiple deprivation.

10. Discuss ways in which in the present day the developed world is hindering development in the developing world.

Table 15.4   Providers of overseas aid

(*a*) *Official Assistance to developing countries as percentage of GNP, 1979*

Oil-rich Arab states	2.8
Norway/Sweden/Finland	0.3
EEC countries	0.2
Japan	0.1
USA/Canada	0.08
Australia/New Zealand	0.05

(*b*) *Percentage provided of total subscriptions to the World Bank, 1980/1*

EEC countries	37.9
USA/Canada	36.1
Japan	12.0
Norway/Sweden/Finland	5.2
Oil-rich Arab states	3.9
Australia/New Zealand	2.25

Table 15.5   Projects approved by World Bank: area and type, 1980/1

(*a*) *Areas approved for projects*

Areas	Percentage of funds allotted
Latin America/Caribbean	25.7
Southern Asia	20.6
S. Europe, Middle East and north Africa	19.8
E. Asia and Pacific	19.2
W. Africa	7.6
E. Africa	7.1

(*b*) *Types of projects approved*

Type	Amount ($million)
Agriculture and rural development	3763.00
Eduation	735.30
Energy and power	1982.50
Industry	885.50
Transportation	1062.80
Water supply and sewerage	534.60
Others	3327.30
Total	12291.00

SECTION F: Conclusion
16 Planet Earth: Problems and Prospects

In a number of chapters in this text, attention has been drawn to the unequal and wasteful ways in which human kind has used the resources provided by planet earth. In this concluding section, a summary will be made of the various ways in which human beings have polluted their environment, squandered its natural resources, and threatened their own future, and the policies being put forward in the attempt to remedy these problems.

POLLUTING THE ENVIRONMENT

Pollution of the Waters

LAKES AND RIVERS

Riverside and lakeside locations have always attracted settlements and manufacturing industries, for accessible water supply, for disposal of sewage and industrial effluent, and for the cheap transport of raw materials and finished products. The disposal of effluent and sewage, however, lowers the oxygen content of the water and, when this has gone beyond a certain limit, life in the river dies (Plate 16.1). As we have seen (Fig. 12.6), the Rhine is one of the most polluted rivers in Europe, with many large towns, chemical works and other industrial users of water along its banks.

Plate 16.1   Dead fish in a polluted West European river

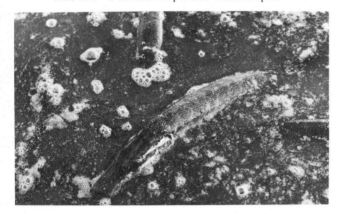

SEAS AND OCEANS

Not only are fish affected by the chemical changes brought by excessive waste disposal; people are affected as well. The disposal of mercury effluent from a chemical works at Minamata on the Kyushu coast of Japan killed both fish stocks and caused the so-called Minamata disease, which attacks the nervous system in human beings, causing mental deficiency and death in the worst cases.

One of the worst dangers at sea today is the movement of huge tankers, each of which can carry hundreds of thousands of tonnes of crude petroleum. Such ships are difficult to manoeuvre, and disastrous wrecks have occurred off the coasts of Western Europe. The *Amoco Cadiz*, which ran aground off Brittany in 1978, did untold damage: its oil polluted beaches, ruining the tourist trade, damaging inshore fishing grounds, and killing off millions of birds. Plate 16.2 shows a helpless cormorant, its winds clogged as a result of an oil spill off the coast of Cornwall.

Solutions to the problem are difficult in that the industrial concerns which are responsible for polluting the waters are powerful, and remedies are usually expensive, or even impractical. How can a chemical works do without a water supply and a means of disposing of effluent? There has, however, been some success in reducing pollution. For example, fish, including even salmon, can now be found in the Thames. But, at sea, it is difficult to prevent or to check oil spillages. Many take place deliberately and secretly at night, when skippers 'clear the tanks'.

Plate 16.2   A helpless cormorant, a result of oil pollution in Cornwall

Plate 16.3   Nineteenth-century type of industrial landscape, Stoke-on-Trent

Pollution of the Land

Severe pollution of the land has been the result of industrialisation and urbanisation. The landscape of nineteenth-century Britain was ripped apart by the growth of extractive and manufacturing industry. Plate 16.3 shows a typical scene in the Potteries, where the ground was worked for clay for the kilns which can be seen in the background. Smoke from the chimneys of factories and terraced houses polluted the atmosphere. This situation has been much improved by the filling in of clay pits, the grassing over and levelling of coal tips, and the imposition of smoke control zones.

Another type of land pollution reflects the activities of consumer society. Great urban populations, especially wealthy ones, produce huge quantities of waste. An increasing percentage of this waste is made up of plastic packaging and metals which do not decompose. Areas popular with tourists suffer from discarded litter. Plate 16.4 shows a West German forest area which has been used as a refuse tip, disfiguring the landscape and creating a health hazard. In the developed world, official refuse tips are increasingly being reclaimed to provide recreational or even building land. In the developing world, they are often scavenged by poorer people for what they may find. An important means of conserving materials such as metals, glass and paper is *recycling*. This includes, for example, collecting old newspapers and bottles, and reprocessing them for later use.

Land pollution also occurs in rural areas. Chemicals are sprayed on crops to kill off weeds and insects and increase yields. Such chemicals are in effect poisons. One much-used chemical, DDT, does not break down easily and becomes concentrated in organisms such as predatory birds and fish at the end of the food chain. There is a great deal of concern at the long-term impact of artificially fertilised foods on the human diet.

Plate 16.4   A refuse tip in a West German forest

225

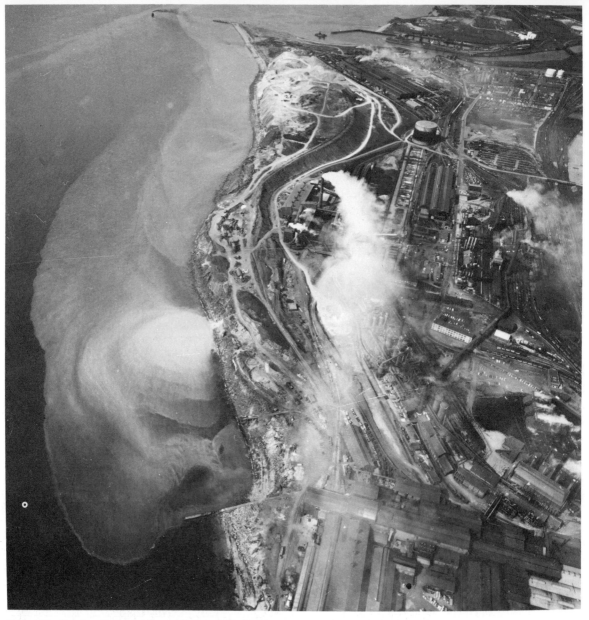

Plate 16.5   Sulphur dioxide and sea pollution at Workington

Pollution of the Air

SMOKE

Plate 16.5 shows a former steel plant at Workington that was managing to pollute land, water and air at the same time. Factory and domestic chimneys give off sulphur dioxide. In winter conditions, especially where there is an inversion of temperature (that is, the higher layer in the atmosphere is at a higher temperature than the ground layer) the smoke can rise only as far as the inversion, then it spreads out and is trapped in the ground layer. Under sunny conditions, this produces *smog*, which blankets out the ground layers even while it is sunny above. This is a serious health hazard, particularly to old people with bronchial complaints. In some countries, however, such as Britain, the imposition of smoke control zones has considerably improved the situation, and serious smogs are a thing of the past.

Such is not the case in Los Angeles, however, where the main problem comes from car exhaust fumes. Fog is a natural phenomenon in the Los Angeles area, as a result of the cool offshore Californian current, and the physical nature of the site of the city – a bay of low-land, surrounded by higher land (Fig. 16.1) which causes the ponding of cold air, and temperature inversions. In addition, this is not a particularly windy area, which makes it more difficult for the fog to disperse.

Unfortunately this fog readily turns into a *photo-chemical smog*. Plate 16.6 shows the downtown sky-scrapers of Los Angeles blanketed on the eighth day of one of the city's worst smog attacks, in 1979. The photo-chemical smog is foul-smelling, and causes severe eye irritation, coughing, fatigue and occasionally death. It is caused by the high incidence of sunlight which, in combination with foggy conditions, acts upon the hydro-carbons and nitric oxides of exhaust fumes. Los Angeles residents on average experience eye irritation on nearly ten times as many days as the next worst American city. In fact 50% of its population experiences such irritation on 115 days every year. The chief culprit is the car exhaust. Los Angeles is the city of the car, criss-crossed by major freeways (Fig. 16.1) which bring thousands of vehicles into the city every day (Plate 16.7). The smog is therefore a daytime phenomenon. Most nights and early mornings are crystal clear. The public health authorities careful-

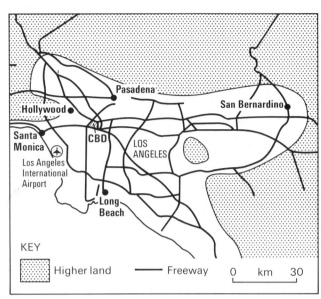

Fig. 16.1 The Los Angeles freeway system

ly monitor such pollution, and if it passes a certain level they have the authority to close down factories and even bring traffic to a standstill.

Plate 16.6 Photo-chemical smog, Los Angeles

Plate 16.7   Dense traffic on a Los Angeles freeway

major problem of the developed world in particular. It can cause serious inconvenience to residents in certain areas, such as those living near elevated motorways. Noise from the kind of heavy traffic shown on Plate 16.7 is at about 85 dB, and can reach 100. Residents in the vicinity of airports have even worse problems to face if their homes are affected by the noise 'corridors' which lie in the direction of the airport runways. As a result, there are restrictions on night-time use of major urban airports such as London's Heathrow.

Pollution through War

No activity damages the area it affects more than modern warfare. As we saw on Plate 13.10, even traditional bombing can devastate vast areas of cities. In the Vietnam War, it is calculated that 25 million bomb craters were created. Equally or even more serious than these is the use of chemical warfare. In Vietnam, for example, the Americans sprayed a chemical defoliant, 245-T, from the air (Plate 16.9), to force North Vietnamese troops out of the forests where they were hiding. Over 2.2 million hectares of forest and cropland were destroyed by this means. The reduction in crops led to malnutrition. The chemical used is known to cause terrible skin injuries and diarrhoea, as well as possibly cancer, miscarriages and mental deformity.

Plate 16.9   Chemical defoliation of a forest in Vietnam

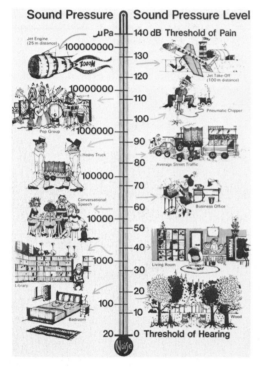

Plate 16.8   Measurement of noise pollution: decibel levels

NOISE

Plate 16.8 shows two scales by which noise can be measured, of which the most popular is decibels (dB). It indicates that a 1 dB sound can scarcely be heard, while anything over 100 can be distinctly unpleasant. Continuous noise at over 85 dB can damage hearing, as can occasional noise at over 135 dB. A jet take-off has a decibel level of over 120. Noise pollution is a

The most serious current threat to the future of human kind is that of thermo-nuclear warfare. World War 2 was brought to an end by the use of the first atomic bombs to be dropped on cities: Hiroshima and Nagasaki in Japan. Of Hiroshima's 343 000 population, 66 000 were killed and 69 000 injured. Two-thirds of the city's structures were destroyed or severely damaged. As well as the people burned to death in the fireball, there have been after-affects of the cancer-producing radio-activity released by the bomb, which have caused many more deaths. Plate 16.10 is of the shell of one of Hiroshima's pre-war buildings, the Industrial Promotion Hall, with the memorial cenotaph behind and the peace memorial building in the background. The atomic bomb devastated an area of about 10 km², an area equivalent of the centre of one of the world's great cities. A thermo-nuclear bomb can destroy a whole conurbation.

CONSERVING RESOURCES

Agricultural Land

Agricultural land has supported the progress of human kind throughout its civilised history. In the past century in particular, agricultural land has been needlessly destroyed.

Plate 16.10   Hiroshima memorials

SOIL EROSION

This has been caused by unwise methods of *cropping*, such as growing the same crops year by year, ploughing downslope, and planting crops annually in areas too dry for arable farming. Plate 16.11 is a photograph of soil erosion in northern Greece, caused by deforestation and over-grazing. Instead of seeping slowly into the soil, rainwater runs off quickly. As a result, it washes the top-soil downslope: *sheet erosion*; or collects in rills which are enlarged to become gullies: *gully erosion*. Both types are illustrated on the photograph.

In the Dust Bowl states of the USA (Fig. 14.7), ploughing of land in periods of drought led to serious *wind erosion*, the removal of top-soil, and the laying waste of large areas of land. As we have seen in Chapter 6, this *desertification* process has taken place on an even more disastrous scale in the Sahel countries, as a result of drought and over-grazing. Another cause of wind erosion is the removal of trees, which act as windbreaks.

Plate 16.11   Soil erosion in Macedonia

Plate 16.12 Soil conservation in Iraq

Conserving Soils

Methods of safeguarding agricultural land from erosion have been well known for a long time. One is the *rotation of crops*, whereby different crops are planted over a four-year period or more, each taking different nutrients out of the soil, and some, such as legumes, putting nutrients back in. Another method is *contour ploughing*, in which the plough follows the contours. The furrows therefore run across the slope of the land, and gullying is prevented. A similar method is *terracing*, which, as we saw in Chapter 8, has been practised extensively in the loess plateau of China to prevent the serious gullying experienced there. Plate 16.12 illustrates soil conservation measures in Iraq. Here severely eroded land is being reclaimed by planting wattle fences, arranged in terraced form, with the soil behind being grassed. Stones have been placed to plug the gully at the bottom of the slope, to prevent further downwash. Plate 16.13 shows *afforestation* taking place in the drought stricken landscape of Upper Volta, one of the Sahel countries. This is a long-term but vital measure needed in the restoration of the landscape, to form windbreaks to prevent further erosion.

INCREASING AGRICULTURAL YIELDS

We noted in Chapter 15 that one means of achieving greater yields lies in the extension of the area of agricultural land. Drainage (as of the Zuyder Zee in Chapter 10) and irrigation (as in the Negev Desert in Chapter 5) are two important methods.

The 'green revolution' has sought to increase yields through the evolution of better seeds. At one time it was thought that this would solve the world's food problems. But it has been found to be effective only among better-off farmers, for it means buying more costly seeds, fertilisers and improving irrigation in drier areas. It has not helped the poorer farmers of countries such as India. Also, the green revolution has promoted further planting of more profitable crops like wheat and rice, and this has unfortunately led to a decrease in lentils, peas and beans, all of which are important sources of protein in the Indian diet.

Conserving the Forests

We observed the dangers of over-exploitation of forest resources in Chapters 3 and 7, noting that it is much easier to replace relatively quickly the softwood coniferous forests, with their stands of similar trees, than the slower growing tropical hardwoods, with their rich variety of different plants.

Plate 16.13 Replanting trees in Upper Volta, Sahel

Conserving Wildlife

The consumer societies of developed countries, whether seeking food, clothing or merely recreation, have caused the massive destruction of wildlife all over the world, on land and sea. Among the many endangered species are the blue whale, the Polar bear, the Asiatic cheetah, the Indian tiger, the American alligator and the North American wood bison. Shooting the Indian tiger was outlawed in 1970. The stripping of jungle for firewood and building material, and illegal hunting, led to fears that the tiger would become extinct. It is now protected in nine forest reserves. The North American bison in 1500 spread over most of the grasslands of the USA and Canada. By 1880 (Fig. 16.2) its territory had been reduced to two small areas. At one time there were over fifty million bison. These had been decimated to about 500 in 1890 as a result of the opening up of the west by railways, and the desire to use the open range for cattle farming.

Fig. 16.2 The reduction of the territory of the North American bison

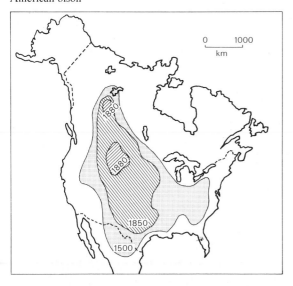

While the developed world is largely at fault in demanding furs and skins apart from food, and hunting as a means of recreation, the people of the developing world are only too ready, understandably, to adopt illegal methods to supply the demand. On the conservation side, zoos and wildlife parks are being used for breeding and thus the conservation of endangered species.

Conserving the Oceans

We noted in Chapter 8 that the main fishing nations of the world are Japan and the USSR, followed by China and Peru. Not able to supply their needs from home waters, Japan and the USSR especially have overfished vast areas of the world's oceans, putting stocks at risk. This is no new phenomenon. Within historic times, for example, herrings have been driven out of the Baltic Sea and the North Sea in turn. In recent years they have had to be protected off Scottish waters.

Various solutions have been offered in the attempt to conserve the world's fisheries.

(1) *Restrictive measures* have been suggested, such as imposing *fishing limits*, allowing only home fleets to fish inside such limits. This principle has been successfully employed by Iceland, a small country heavily dependent on its fish stocks. Other measures are to *control the size of fish nets*, to ensure that fish live to maturity before they are caught; and also the *size of the fish catch*, by giving each country and each of its fishing vessels a quota. Both of these measures are difficult to enforce, and there is much illegal fishing.

(2) More *positive measures* include the *seeking out of types of fish formerly little used*, and therefore plentiful. One of these is the *blue whiting*, found off the west coasts of Ireland and Scotland, and known to be very palatable, Another is the *krill*, a small shrimp-like sea creature, the food of the whale. Decimation of whale stocks has resulted in an immense growth of the stocks of krill in Antarctic waters. This has been made into krill paste as a human food, and it could also be useful as a fertiliser and as animal feed, rich in protein.

The extension of *fish farming* is another possibility. This already takes place on a large scale, often in enclosed, shallow, warm coastal lagoons, as in Hong Kong, Malaysia and Indonesia. In Western European countries, large numbers of rainbow trout are produced in this way.

In future, there may be a need to utilise the ocean's vast stock of *plankton*, the main food of many sea creatures. While this is unappetising as a human food, it could indirectly enhance food stocks by forming the basis of animal feed.

Conserving Minerals and Fuel Supplies

Minerals and fossil fuels are examples of *non-renewable resources*, which cannot be replaced, though they can often be substituted, sometimes at much extra cost. At the present rate of use, the following will be used up by the years given:

tin, lead, zinc and copper by A.D. 2000
petroleum and natural gas by A.D. 2010
bauxite and manganese by A.D. 2250
nickel, iron and chromium by A.D. 2500
coal by A.D. 4000

There are various ways of delaying, or even avoiding, the exhaustion of these resources.

(1) *Slower rate of use*: in the case of oil, one advantage of the OPEC imposition of much higher prices (Chapter 5) has been that the countries importing this oil have seen the need to use it more wisely. The USA, for example, is conserving oil through using less extravagant cars.

(2) *Finding new sources of existing minerals and fuels*, as has happened, for example, with the discovery of oil in inaccessible areas such as northern Alaska and the floor of the North Sea. Similarly rich manganese nodules and other mineral resources have been found on ocean floors.

(3) *New methods of extraction* are required to utilise ocean floor deposits, and also to make use of low-grade ores, previously uneconomic to extract, but profitable when prices rise, as happens when scarcity sets in.

(4) *Finding substitute sources* has already taken place as part of general technological change. Plastic is increasingly used rather than tin for storing food. Nuclear fuel and, to a lesser extent, the tides, solar energy and the wind, have been used on a limited scale in place of the 'fossil fuels': coal and oil.

Scenic Resources

The caption on the building on Plate 16.14 reads: 'The reconciliation of technology and nature'. It is an arguable point whether the stunning scenery of the Bernese Oberland in Switzerland is improved by these human-made objects: whether the building is really in harmony with the surroundings. It is true that from a distance the building would look puny in this majestic setting. Millions of people find recreation and refreshment in beautiful surroundings, however, and it is inevitable that even remote places, whether in the mountains, in forests or at the coast are going to be exploited by people. The danger to the environment is increasingly being recognised by the setting up of National Parks and other official agencies to protect areas of outstanding natural beauty. A similar conservationist approach is taking place in historic towns, to prevent the destruction of buildings of great cultural interest.

Plate 16.14 Human intervention in the Bernese Oberland

CITIES IN CRISIS

The stress in Chapters 14 and 15 has been on the problems of the developing world. The quality of life in these countries is related to the serious problems of over-population, of food shortages, poor health and educational facilities. In the developed world, and especially in its great cities, patterns of modern living have not only accelerated the depletion of natural resources, but also led to great social and psychological strains. Certain metropolitan areas are in a state of crisis. Two of these are considered here: Tokyo and New York, one from the oriental and one from the occidental world, and both the main commercial centres and largest cities of extremely wealthy countries.

Plate 16.15 The Ginza, Tokyo's main shopping street

Tokyo

Fig. 16.3 shows Tokyo's metropolitan area, the size of a large conurbation, with 27 million inhabitants, sprawling round the shores of Tokyo Bay. Like other major Japanese cities, it is confined between the mountain mass of the interior and a highly indented coast (Fig. 8.7). It suffers alarmingly from congestion: the sheer weight of vast numbers of people. Plate 16.15 is a view of the Ginza, Tokyo's main shopping street, during a period when vehicle access is prohibited to allow space for pedestrians. In the rush hours, crowding is even greater, especially at stations, where 'pushers' are employed to pack people onto trains. Housing is equally congested, as can be seen in the foreground of Plate 16.16. Central areas of the city house as many as 30 000 people per square kilometre. Floor space per person is very small by western standards, even for well-to-do people. The conurbation has over 80 000 factories and about 3.5 million cars. An elaborate and expensive urban motorway system (Plates 8.12 and 16.17) only in part relieves traffic congestion. Railways have to tunnel not only through the mountain areas of Japan, but also the buildings in great cities. They run on elevated sections past densely packed office blocks (Plate 16.17). The lack of flat land makes urban expansion difficult. Reclamation of land has been a help (Fig. 16.3), but this and the associated pumping have resulted in land subsidence.

Pollution of the atmosphere is great (Plate 16.16), both through urban traffic and the heavy industries round Tokyo Bay, which also pollute the coastal waters. Sewage facilities are poor, with only 52% of homes connected to the mains sewage system. Garbage is dumped on offshore islands. There has been a marked improvement in the control of pollution in the 1970s. Even so, Japan has had to pay a heavy social price for its economic miracle (see Chapter 8).

Fig. 16.3 Tokyo's metropolitan area

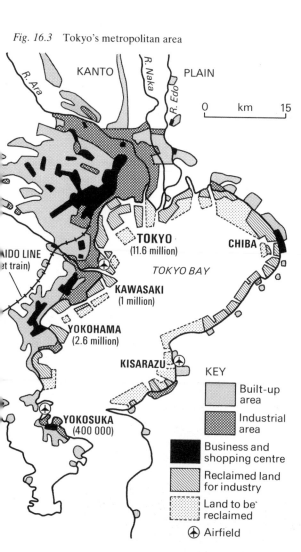

KANTO PLAIN

R. Ara
R. Naka
R. Edo

0   km   15

TOKYO (11.6 million)
CHIBA
TOKYO BAY
KAWASAKI (1 million)
YOKOHAMA (2.6 million)
KISARAZU
YOKOSUKA (400 000)

IDO LINE
et train)

KEY
Built-up area
Industrial area
Business and shopping centre
Reclaimed land for industry
Land to be reclaimed
✈ Airfield

233

Plate 16.16   Congestion and pollution in Tokyo

Plate 16.17   Railways and motorways beside office blocks in Tokyo

Tokyo also faces the natural hazard of lying on the circum-Pacific earthquake belt, at the edge of the Pacific Plate (Chapter 1). The Kanto earthquake of 1923 destroyed Tokyo and Yokohama and killed 150 000 people. While many modern shops and office blocks are built to withstand another great earthquake, this is not true of housing. Tokyo's economic prosperity may seem fragile if great natural forces hit it again.

New York

New York is the largest element in an enormous urban sprawl of population along the north-eastern seaboard of the USA, stretching from Boston to Washington, containing 43 million people. To such an urban sprawl, made up not just of cities but of conurbations, joining, the term *megalopolis* has been applied (Fig. 16.4).

Over 16 million people live round the mouth of the Hudson river (Fig. 16.5), the most congested area being Manhattan Island (Plate 16.18). One reason why urban sprawl has reached such an extreme stage in the

Fig. 16.4 Megalopolis, USA

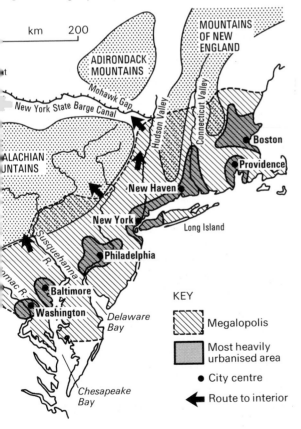

KEY

Megalopolis

Most heavily urbanised area

● City centre

◀ Route to interior

Fig. 16.5 Central New York

KEY
1960–75 period

Black population

Puerto Rican population

CBD (Skyscraper landscape)

M Midtown **D** Downtown

Garment industry

Port area

USA has been the success of the automobile, and an advanced motorway system in which large amounts of freight are carried by road transport. Manufacturing and warehousing, as well as retail units, have been dispersed to estates on the edge of cities, as central locations have become more expensive. Unlike office blocks, which can use little land by building upwards (see Plate 16.18), many industrial and service buildings require a lot of ground space, which is too costly in the centres of cities such as New York. The motor car has also allowed professional and office workers to

Plate 16.18   Manhattan

Plate 16.19   East side, Manhattan: office blocks and tenements

live far away from their work, causing suburbanisation and extensive commuting.

One consequence has been the occurrence of tremendous congestion in city centres. The problem in New York is so great that it has the lowest car ownership of any of the great cities of the USA. The huge office blocks of downtown and midtown Manhattan (Plate 16.18 and Fig. 16.5) accommodate a great many workers, who must rely on the commuter rail and underground system, with its terminals reached by tunnels under the Hudson and East Rivers.

THE SOCIAL PROBLEMS OF NEW YORK

New York illustrates well some of the serious social consequences that have followed the unchecked growth of megalopolis. Note how in Plate 16.19 of the south-east part of Manhattan, with Brooklyn beyond, prosperity and disadvantage lie side by side, with affluent hotels and office blocks, and high-density tenements, old and new, in close proximity.

New York was the main point of entry for European migrants in the nineteenth and early twentieth centuries (see Chapter 14), and Manhattan and neighbouring parts of the Bronx and Brooklyn were the main quarters for immigrant residence during this period. Many worked in small-scale manufacturing industries, such as the garment industry (Fig. 16.5), for very low wages.

Fig.16.5 indicates the concentration of later influxes of population into New York, chiefly black people, originally from the southern states, and more recently Puerto Ricans, coming in from the Caribbean. These inhabit some of the most deprived parts of the city, such as Manhattan, Brooklyn and the Bronx. Plate 16.20 shows the decayed property of one of these areas, probably in a Puerto Rican district, with maps of Latin America painted on the playground wall.

Plate 16.20   Slum property in Harlem

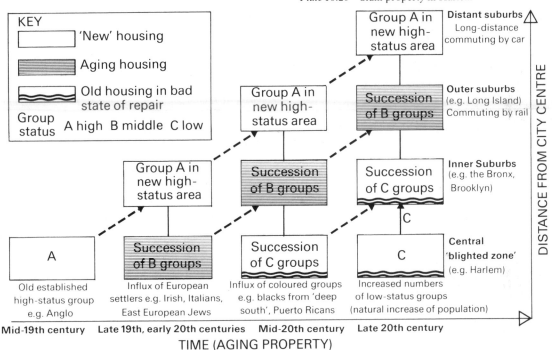

Fig. 16.6   Residential change in New York, 1850–1980

New York illustrates well how residential changes take place over time, with once quite prosperous property decaying as a result and being taken over by later and often poorer in-coming groups. The process is shown diagrammatically on Fig. 16.6.

(1) In the first stage, residential areas of Manhattan were of good quality, inhabited by well-off or at least comfortable white groups, often of West European origin.

(2) From the mid-nineteenth century, there was a large influx of poorer European groups, including Irish, Italians and East European Jews. This 'invasion' tended to drive the higher-status European groups to new residential areas, such as the Bronx. Their residences in Manhattan were taken over by the poorer Europeans.

(3) These new groups established themselves and improved their status. There was a later influx of coloured people, including blacks from the 'deep south', and then Puerto Ricans. A 'knock-on' effect resulted, with earlier groups in turn being pushed outwards. Italians and other European settlers moved out to areas such as the Bronx, as Harlem increasingly became a coloured quarter. Well-to-do residents moved to outer

237

suburbs, as on Long Island, and commuted to work.

(4) As more coloured people have come in, they have spread to inner suburbs in the Bronx and over large areas of Brooklyn. Other groups have moved even further out, and there is now a great deal of long-distance commuting.

The multi-racial character of New York, and particularly the fact that the different racial groups are residentially segregated, with some living comfortably in affluent suburbs and others in over-crowded conditions in city centre tenements (Plates 16.19 and 20), has created tremendous social tension. This often spills over into violence. In 1972 New York was at the top of the 'crime league' of United States cities for murders (19.1 per 100 000 population) and for robberies (877.4 per 100 000 population). It continues to be a violent city. As well-to-do people have moved out into the suburbs often beyond the metropolitan area (the 'white flight' as it is sometimes called), central areas are left with more than their fair share of poverty. While commercially New York is an exceptionally wealthy city, it has not been able to provide enough public resources to improve conditions in its slum areas. So social unrest continues, and the gap between rich and poor remains wide.

FUTURE PROSPECTS

Above humankind hang two dark clouds, both threatening to rain destruction on large portions of the human race and its habitat. One is the prospect of *worldwide famine*, resulting from what seems an unending increase in world population, which at present rates of increase could reach six billion by A.D. 2000. It is essential to the future well-being of the whole earth that the developed world takes more seriously its obligations to the developing, not only because this is morally right, but because in the long run it will benefit all. This means not only giving a larger percentage of GNPs in aid (see Table 15.4), but also boosting trade and ensuring that developing coutries achieve fair prices for their produce. This will of course put up prices in developed countries.

The threat of famine affects most directly the developing world. The developed world fears more directly the threat of *thermo-nuclear war*, possibly accompanied by chemical and/or biological warfare. The peace of the world is at present maintained by the so-called 'balance of terror'. Some hold this to have been successful, in view of the fact that there has been no war on a world-wide scale since 1945. Those who campaign for nuclear disarmament, however, point out that the risk of storing nuclear weapons is too great, and some appalling mistake might unleash a thermo-nuclear war. They argue that even domination by another power would be more tolerable than this. Additionally, the 'balance of terror' means that both capitalist and communist powers spend large amounts of money on the armaments. As the Brandt Report (page 218) has pointed out, less should be spent on preparation for war and more on peaceful purposes, especially giving more help to the developing world.

Underlying these great issues, one about human rights and the other about human conflict, are geographical patterns and geographical factors. But these alone tell only part of the story. The developing world is partly as it is because of the facts of geography. This is true to a lesser extent of the developed world, although there more favoured environments mean that human systems exercise greater influence than, for example, climatic systems. In developed countries the working of the world's two major political systems, capitalism and communism, has a bigger impact on the quality of life than physical differences. One of the ideas behind this book is that it is important to think about and debate the great world issues, and that it is important that this thinking should be based on information that is as accurate, balanced and up-to-date as practicable. It is not enough to study the facts of geography, however. Geography we know is about the planet earth. But if it is to be a geography relevant to our needs it has to be seen not only in terms of physical and economic activities, but also in terms of social, political and moral attitudes. Do you see the peoples you have studied as different from (and perhaps inferior to) yourself? Do you think more highly of the things people have in common – the need to earn a living; to enjoy good health; to be educated; and to experience warm personal and social relationships – rather than the things which divide them?

Index